The geology of the northern North Sea

BRITISH GEOLOGICAL SURVEY

United Kingdom Offshore Regional Report

The geology of the northern North Sea

H Johnson, P C Richards, D Long and C C Graham

LONDON HMSO 1993

Production of this report was funded by the Department of
Energy (now incorporated into the Department of Trade and
Industry) and the Natural Environment Research Council

The coastline used on many maps and diagrams in this book is
based on Ordnance Survey mapping

Bibliographic reference

JOHNSON, H, RICHARDS, P C, LONG, D, and GRAHAM, C C.
1993.   *United Kingdom offshore regional report: the geology of the
northern North Sea.*   (London: HMSO for the British
Geological Survey.)

Printed in the United Kingdom for HMSO
Dd 292040   C20   3/94   531/3   12521

ISBN 0 11 884497 0

Contents

FIGURES

vii

Foreword

The northern North Sea region is extremely important to the economy of the United Kingdom (UK) because most the Nation's oil is found within it. As a result, it has been the subject of intensive study by the oil industry. The oil province is centred around the Viking Graben and East Shetland Basin, which have been important depocentres since Permian times, and were particularly important areas of rifting in the Late Jurassic. Since then, thermal sag has led to the accumulation of thick late Mesozoic and Cenozoic sediments, which have encroached on to the adjacent East Shetland Platform.

This report, based largely on the work of the British Geological Survey (funded by the Department of Energy and the Department of Education and Science), describes the geology of the UK sector of the northern North Sea from 58°N to just north of 62°N. All aspects of offshore geology are described, from the deep structure to the sea-bed sediments and economic geology. A regional mapping programme of much of the UK Continental Shelf has resulted in the production of geological and geophysical maps at a scale of 1:250 000; the maps immediately relevant to the northern North Sea area are shown inside the back cover of this report. Interpretations of confidential oil-company data from which generalised information has been abstracted are included. Much company data from the area are now released in line with licensing arrangements, thereby providing an important body of information.

For the past 20 years the area has been a very important part of Britain's resource base and a major contributor to the Nation's wealth. As a result of a vigorous and successful exploration programme, proven and probable hydrocarbon reserves have been maintained. But if that resource base is to be maintained well into the future, then it is essential that the rate of success of exploration and exploitation continues. Whilst this depends on many things including the price of oil, the tax regime, and technological developments, it is also dependent on new ideas. This publication provides many new ideas and should also prove to be an important stimulus for new ideas in the future, on which to base the exploration successes of the twenty first century.

Peter J Cook, DSc
Director
British Geological Survey
March 1993

ACKNOWLEDGEMENTS

Responsibilities of individual authors in the production of this report are as follows:

H Johnson — Structure, Pre-Permian, Upper Cretaceous, Tertiary

P C Richards — Permo-Triassic, Jurassic, Lower Cretaceous, economic geology (hydrocarbons)

D Long — Introduction, Quaternary, nonhydrocarbon economic geology, and compilation of the report

C C Graham — Sea-bed sediments

The Offshore Regional Report Series is co-ordinated by the Marine Geology Group, and is edited by D Evans with A G Stevenson.

In addition to the work of the authors, the report draws heavily upon the knowledge, expertise and support of other BGS staff, not only within the marine sphere, but also from the Land Survey and specialists in the fields of sedimentology, biostratigraphy, cartography and publication. Their contribution has been fundamental to production of the report. In particular, the following provided critical comment: K Hitchen, D W Holliday, S Holloway, R Holmes, F May, J B Riding, A C Skinner and G Warrington.

The following companies are gratefully thanked for their permission to use their unreleased data in this report:

Arco British Ltd for the seismic section in Figure 16

BP Exploration for the seismic sections in figures 14, 15 and 17, and for use of data from wells 211/11-4 and 210/15-4

GECO Exploration Company Ltd for the seismic section in Figure 12

Haliburton Geophysical Services for the seismic section in Figure 27

Occidental Petroleum (Caledonia) Limited (now EE Caledonian Limited) for use of data from well 16/12-7.

Western Geophysical for the seismic sections in figures 18 and 21.

Additionally, the British Petroleum Company plc. is thanked for providing the photograph of the Magnus Platform on the front cover.

Figure 1
Location map of
the report area
showing licence
blocks, released
commercial wells,
oilfields, BGS
shallow boreholes,
and simplified
bathymetry.

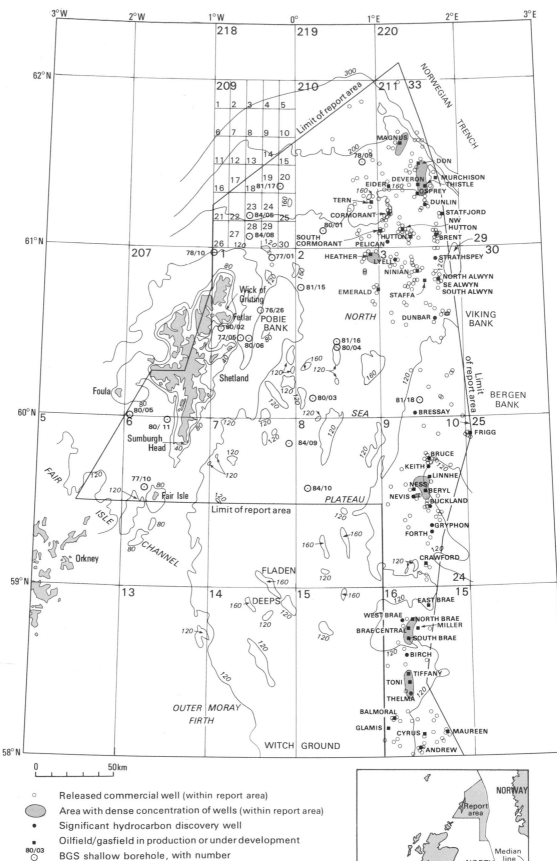

0   50km

○ Released commercial well (within report area)

⬮ Area with dense concentration of wells (within report area)

● Significant hydrocarbon discovery well

■ Oilfield/gasfield in production or under development

80/03
○ BGS shallow borehole, with number

120 Bathymetry, contour interval 40m.

Note: The commercial wells are numbered by
quadrant (eg 209) followed by the
block number (eg 209/4), and in
sequential order of drilling within
that block (eg 209/4-1 etc).
Quadrant numbers on the Norwegian
Continental Shelf are shown in red.

1 Introduction

This report area forms the northernmost part of the North Sea, and covers an irregularly shaped area between 58°N and about 62°N (Figure 1). The western boundary is an irregular line extending broadly north-eastwards through Shetland, whereas the eastern boundary is coincident with the United Kingdom (UK)/Norway median line. The area therefore includes the eastern coast of Shetland, as well as the island of Fair Isle, and covers an area of approximately 50 000 km².

The hills on the islands of Shetland are rounded and generally do not rise to more than 200 m above OD, and the land is deeply penetrated by inlets of the sea, known locally as voes. The islands are made up of rocks deformed or emplaced during the Caledonian orogeny. The basement is overlain locally by Devonian rocks (Figure 2). Inland exposure is poor due to thin Quaternary cover and the development of Holocene peat, but rocks are exposed at the coast, where there are high cliffs.

Offshore, the physiography is much smoother. Around the coasts of Shetland there is no sign of a wave-cut platform at the foot of the cliffs; rather, the cliffs plunge steeply to a water depth of about 80 m (Figure 1). The extensive close proximity to the coast of relatively deep water is unique in the UK. Beyond this nearshore zone, across the western part of the East Shetland Platform, bedrock occurs at or within a few metres of the sea bed. The sea then deepens northwards and eastwards across the North Sea Plateau. Beyond this plateau, the shelfbreak lies just outside the northern limit of the report area, and the western slope of the Norwegian Trench occurs in its north-eastern corner. Banks or topographic highs such as Pobie Bank, Viking Bank and Bergen Bank are generally restricted to a zone of 80 to 100 m water depth (Figure 1). Sea-floor depressions occur locally to about 160 m depth; these include several small basins east of Pobie Bank as well as the eastern edge of the much larger Witch Ground Basin.

The report area can be divided into two main structural parts; the East Shetland Platform, and the surrounding basins including the Viking Graben (see Figures 5 and 10). The Viking Graben and East Shetland Basin have been the sites of extensive Permo-Triassic to Quaternary sedimentation. The East Shetland Platform, although comprising thick Devonian rocks on basement, has a more limited cover of post-Carboniferous deposits. The northern North Sea is an important part of the North Sea oil province, and includes several major UK oilfields such as Cormorant, Brent, Magnus (see front cover), Ninian and Brae, and part of the Frigg Gasfield (Figure 1). Several major fields also occur in the Norwegian sector to the east.

The earliest reported geological interpretation of material from the northern North Sea was during the 19th century, when arctic, littoral shells were dredged from the sea bed at a depth of 165 m off Shetland (Tylor, 1869). These were interpreted as representing times of greatly reduced sea level during a glacial episode. Further random dredgings gave only glimpses of the Quaternary geology beneath the northern North Sea; Miocene shallow-water limestone dredged from the sides of the Fladen Deeps just south of the report area (Figure 1) indicated the existence of rocks offshore that had no equivalents on the adjacent land (Newton, 1916). Before these findings, the belief was that the Caledonian rocks of Scotland continued, close to the sea bed, north-eastwards to Norway (Suess, 1906).

Not until 1968, with the publication of the British Geological Survey (BGS) aeromagnetic maps covering Shetland and Orkney (see inside back cover), and another for the Norwegian Sea (Avery et al., 1968), was there an attempt to interpret the geology east of Shetland. Flinn (1969) suggested that the very smooth, negative magnetic anomalies are the result of a thick pile of Devonian and younger sediments extending eastwards from close to the Shetland coastline.

A major expansion in offshore geological knowledge began in the early 1970s from investigations by the hydrocarbon industry. Although oil and gas prospects had long been noted in sediments of Carboniferous to Tertiary age on land around the North Sea, it was not until the large Groningen Gasfield of The Netherlands was discovered in 1959 that interest turned to the North Sea itself. Commercial success in the southern North Sea led companies to expand their interests northwards to the more hostile environment of the central and northern North Sea. The first licence blocks within the report area were issued in 1965 as part of the second round of UK licensing, and hydrocarbons were first found by Total in early 1971 in well 3/25-1. The first major discovery in the northern North Sea was made at what was to become the Brent Oilfield, when Shell/Esso well 211/29-1 found oil in Jurassic sandstones in June 1971. Since that time, over 800 exploration and appraisal wells have been drilled, and by the end of 1990 there were 27 oilfields and one gasfield in production, and a further 6 under development (Department of Energy, 1991). The area has become the most important oil-producing province on the UK Continental Shelf.

Work to elucidate the geology of both the basin and platform areas was undertaken by BGS as part of a national programme to produce reconnaissance geological and geophysical maps of the UK Continental Shelf (Fannin, 1989; see inside back cover). The mapping programme has provided much input into this report, as have extensive commercial exploration data interpreted by BGS on behalf of the Department of Energy. The commercial data used are confined to those released by the Department of Energy prior to January 1991, or released by oil companies earlier than required by statute. Also, because of the area's economic importance, many studies have been published in the literature.

GEOLOGICAL SUMMARY

Shetland is formed largely of sedimentary rocks which were metamorphosed, and intruded by a wide variety of igneous bodies, during the Caledonian orogeny and earlier; its islands form a link between portions of the Caledonian fold belt in Norway and mainland Scotland. The remainder of the land is formed of sedimentary and volcanic rocks of Devonian age, which were emplaced during and after the final phase of the orogeny (Figure 2). Devonian rocks in different parts of the islands were laid down in a variety of environments, and suffered different tectonic stresses before being brought together by transcurrent faulting. The island of Fair Isle to the south comprises a thick sequence of sediments that may range from Early to Mid-Devonian in age. Thus, in Devonian times, an

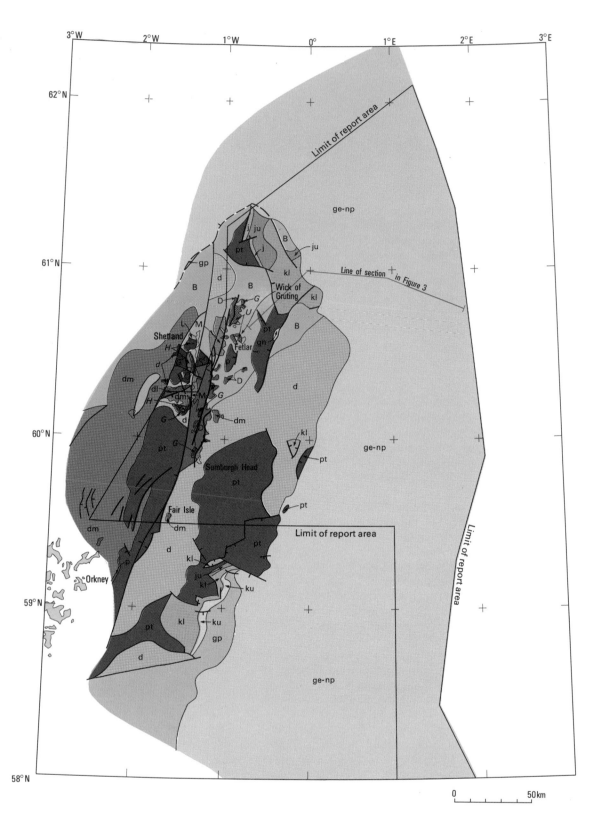

Figure 2 Solid geology of the report area. For key see Figure 3.

eroded-down Caledonian mountain chain was masked by sedimentary deposits in the region between Shetland and Norway.

In Carboniferous times, the Shetland Platform may have been a source of clastic sediments that were deposited farther south as part of the coal-measure deltas; there was only very minor deposition within the report area. Local marine sedimentation occurred during the Late Permian within the southern part of the Viking Graben, although continental deposition was more widespread and continued during Triassic times, when it was concentrated in fault-bounded basins (Figure 3) which formed due to extensional stresses as the North Sea graben began to take shape.

The Early Jurassic saw the replacement of continental conditions by a marine environment as the sea invaded from the north. The mudstone-dominated Lower Jurassic succession was overlain by the deposits of Mid-Jurassic deltas that spread from the south or south-west. The Late Jurassic was a time of marine submergence and major rifting in the Viking Graben and East Shetland Basin, as block faulting led to uplift of the rift flanks and the deposition of coarse-grained clastic sediments shed from these highs. However, the more-widespread deposition of thick, black, organic-rich shales was dominant. Submergence continued in Cretaceous times with the deposition of predominantly argillaceous lithologies. A thick Cretaceous succession accumulated in the Viking Graben,

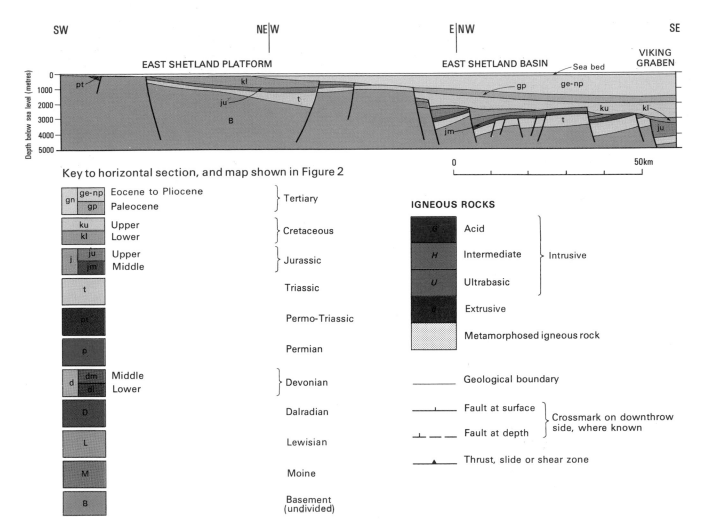

Figure 3 Cross-section across the northern North Sea. For location see Figure 2.

and a thin veneer was deposited on the peneplaned East Shetland Platform.

The opening of the north-east Atlantic Ocean during the early Tertiary led to uplift along the Atlantic margin of north-western Europe, and there was thermal-sag subsidence centred over the Viking Graben. This resulted in the deposition of over 2000 m of sediments within the graben, and onlap across the eastern half of the East Shetland Platform to develop a 'steer's head' basin geometry (Figure 3). Subsidence and sedimentation diminished towards the end of the Tertiary, but increased again during the Quaternary when glacial processes increased the supply of sediments to the area. Lower Pleistocene shallow-marine sediments are overlain by glaciomarine and glacial deposits which show evidence of significant erosive episodes. There is also a thin cover of sea-bed sediments which developed as sea level rose in the early Holocene.

2 Structure

The most important structural element of the northern North Sea is the 500 km-long, north-north-easterly trending Viking Graben, which forms part of a more-extensive North Sea rift system (Figure 4). The Viking Graben contains up to 11 000 m of Mesozoic and Cenozoic sediments (Fichler and Hospers, 1990; Hospers and Ediriweera, 1991) and, together with the East Shetland Basin (Figure 4), is a major oil province. The Viking Graben and the East Shetland Basin have been extensively explored, and a wide and contrasting range of structural interpretations has been proposed. The structure adjacent to the graben is less well known because fewer data are available.

The structural development of the northern North Sea can be understood by reconstructing the interaction of litho-spheric plates. Crystalline metamorphic basement in the region is composed of rocks compressed during the Caledonian and earlier orogenies. The Caledonian orogeny lasted from the late Cambrian to the end of the Silurian (G Rogers et al., 1989), and resulted in the suturing of the Laurentian, Baltican and Avalonian plates (Figure 4), and the formation of a three-armed belt of deformed rocks (Ziegler, 1982; Ziegler and Van Hoorn, 1989; Glennie, 1990a).

The basement over most of the UK northern North Sea consists of high-grade metamorphic rocks and some deformed plutonic rocks intruded by a number of later igneous bodies (Frost et al., 1981). Aeromagnetic data suggest that this Caledonian basement has a dominantly north-easterly to east-north-easterly trending tectonic grain, similar to that seen in both the Scottish Highlands and the Norwegian Caledonides (Johnson and Dingwall, 1981). It is very likely that basement structure has exerted some control on the subsequent development of sedimentary basins throughout the region (Threlfall, 1981; Beach, 1985; Doré and Gage, 1987), although some major basement structures, such as the Highland Boundary Fault, may have been largely inactive after Palaeozoic times (Klemperer and Hurich, 1990).

Following the Caledonian orogeny, Devonian sedimentary basins developed in the region. Reconstructions of Devonian

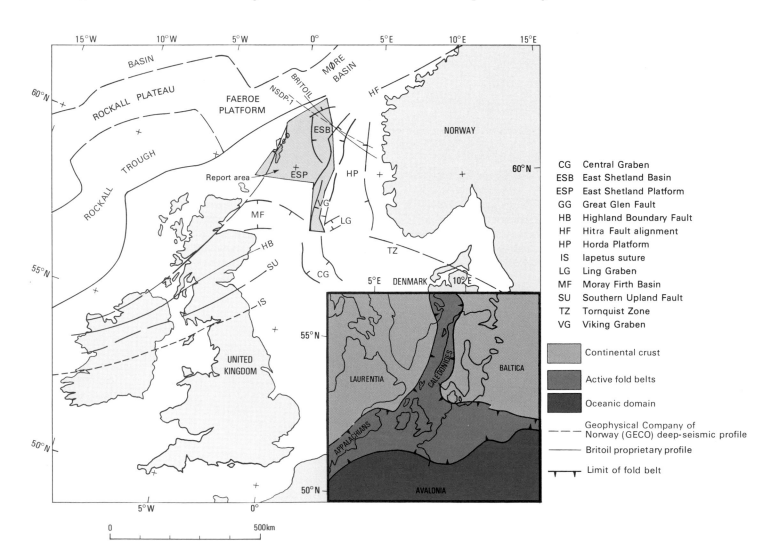

Figure 4   Regional structural-framework map showing the North Sea rift system. Modified after Doré and Gage (1987). The inset map shows a tentative late Caledonian tectonic framework of the Arctic–North Atlantic realm, simplified after Ziegler (1982).

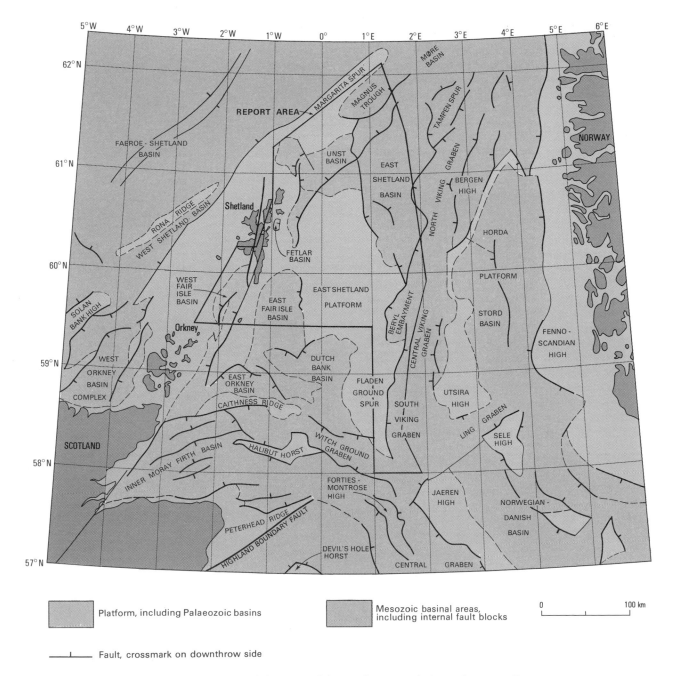

Figure 5 Simplified map of major structural elements of the northern North Sea and surrounding areas. Compiled from published BGS maps and Vollset and Doré (1984).

palaeogeography are uncertain, but the main feature in the northern North Sea region was the Orcadian Basin that extended eastwards from the Moray Firth to the western coast of Norway (Ziegler, 1982; Richards, 1990a). Over 5000 m of continental-facies Old Red Sandstone were deposited in this basin, and the fundamental control on its development may have been collapse of overthickened Caledonian continental crust by extensional tectonic processes (Beach, 1985; Norton et al., 1987), perhaps with a major strike-slip control (e.g. Turner et al., 1976; Ziegler, 1982).

According to Ziegler (1982), the northern North Sea was largely an area of nondeposition and erosion during the Carboniferous. Redbeds and a 4 m-thick black shale of Carboniferous age have, however, been recorded from the Central Viking Graben, and coal-bearing strata of Viséan and Namurian age occur in parts of the outer Moray Firth to the south of the report area (Andrews et al., 1990). Haszeldine and Russell (1987) have speculated that rifting of the Viking

Graben may have begun during the Carboniferous. Seismic data suggest that Devono-Carboniferous deposits in the outer Moray Firth are locally deformed into long-wavelength folds, and are truncated beneath Permian strata. It may be speculated that these folds relate to the Late Carboniferous Variscan orogeny in continental Europe, which marked the closure of the Proto-Tethys Ocean and the creation of the supercontinent of Pangaea. Regional studies suggest that during latest Carboniferous to Early Permian times, north-west Europe was transected by a postorogenic system of conjugate shears which reactivated older basement faults (Read, 1987; Ziegler and Van Hoorn, 1989), and that regional uplift in the North Sea at this time was accompanied by erosion of Carboniferous and Devonian strata.

In the North Sea, but mainly to the south of the report area, Early Permian subsidence formed the broad, east–west-trending Northern and Southern Permian basins (Glennie, 1990b). Gradual facies and thickness variations indicate that

5

the subsidence of these basins was dominated by regional downwarping. The narrow Viking and Central grabens are dominantly Mesozoic structures, although the age of rift initiation is debated. In general, the grabens have a northerly trend (Figures 4 and 5) that cuts across the structural grain of the Caledonian basement (Watson, 1985). Permo-Triassic strata in the northern North Sea are locally over 3000 m thick (Ziegler, 1982; Steel and Ryseth, 1990) and dominantly of continental, redbed facies. However, some Upper Permian marine limestones and evaporites were deposited in the south of the report area, and also on the Margarita Spur in the north (Figure 5).

The Mesozoic North Sea rifts are generally considered to be an integral part of a major rift system whose origin is linked to the opening of the North Atlantic Ocean. Rift-induced subsidence in the Viking Graben appears to have reached a maximum during the Late Jurassic and earliest Cretaceous, when up to 3000 m of marine sediments accumulated in the graben. Following this rifting pulse, the amount of fault-controlled subsidence across the northern North Sea decreased substantially.

Marine Cretaceous and Tertiary strata have a more widespread distribution than the Jurassic, and reach a combined thickness of over 4500 m in a basin overlying the Viking Graben (Ziegler, 1982). Paleocene uplift of northern and western Britain is related to early Tertiary crustal separation and sea-floor spreading in the North Atlantic. This uplift resulted in the influx into the basin of large amounts of clastic sediments shed from the Orkney–Shetland Platform to the west. Up to about 2500 m of Cenozoic sediments accumulated in a broadly synclinal sag basin centred over the Mesozoic rifts (Day et al., 1981; Nielsen et al., 1986; Klemperer and White, 1989).

BASIN-DEVELOPMENT MODELS AND THE DEEP STRUCTURE OF THE NORTHERN NORTH SEA

The absence of a significant gravity low over the large thickness of relatively low-density sedimentary deposits in the North Sea grabens led Donato and Tully (1981) to infer isostatic equilibrium, with thinned crust and a raised Mohorovičić discontinuity (Moho) beneath the graben axes. The mechanism by which continental lithosphere is thinned to produce sedimentary basins has been the subject of debate.

Early models for the evolution of the North Sea rift system suggested there had been mantle-plume-generated uplift centred on the Middle Jurassic basaltic volcanic pile that lies at the intersection of the Viking Graben, the Moray Firth Basin and the Central Graben (Figures 4 and 6a). These three rifts were regarded as failed arms of a triple junction (Whiteman et al., 1975; Ziegler, 1975). Structural relief on the areally extensive rift dome at the confluence of the grabens, estimated at between 1500 and 2500 m (Ziegler and Van Hoorn, 1989), was considered responsible for major erosion of Lower Jurassic and older sequences in the central North Sea. However, according to both Leeder (1983) and Kent (1975), the domal uplift may have been of the order of only some 60 m.

McKenzie (1978) proposed that the North Sea rifts had formed by uniform stretching and thinning of the lithosphere (Figure 6b) as a result of Mesozoic horizontal extension. This stretching caused an isostatically driven, fault-controlled subsidence of the crust (rift-basin phase) due to the replacement at depth of low-density crustal material by more-dense mantle material. Instantaneous stretching in the brittle upper crust was accommodated by rigid-body fault-block rotation, whereas in the lower crust and lithospheric mantle, pure shear is assumed to have occurred by ductile flow. The thinning of the

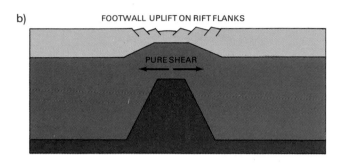

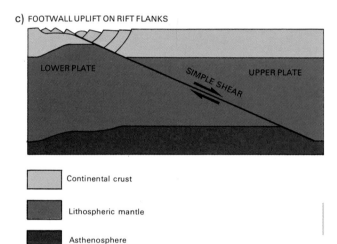

Figure 6 Rift models. (a) Mantle-plume model, e.g. Ziegler (1982). (b) Coaxial-stretching model, after McKenzie (1978). (c) Lithospheric simple-shear model, after Wernicke (1981).

lithosphere created a thermal anomaly caused by elevation of the lithospheric isotherms. Gradual, exponential decay of this anomaly was accompanied by thickening of the cooling lithosphere and further isostatically driven subsidence to produce a late Mesozoic and Cenozoic thermal-sag basin (Dewey, 1982). Modifications to the simple stretching model take into account a protracted time period for the rifting event (Jarvis and McKenzie, 1980) and nonuniform or depth-dependent stretching (e.g. Rowley and Sahagian, 1986), which may involve more-widespread stretching of the mantle lithosphere than the crust. The latter may explain uplift of early-formed rift flanks, and the regional onlap of the thermal-sag basin which produced a 'steer's-head' basin profile (Leeder, 1983).

Leeder (1983) disputed the mantle-plume model for North Sea basin development on the basis that there is no convincing evidence for kilometres of uplift of the central North Sea during the Mid-Jurassic, and because the lithospheric stretching model can account for melting in the asthenosphere and magmatism in the crust without invoking a mantle plume

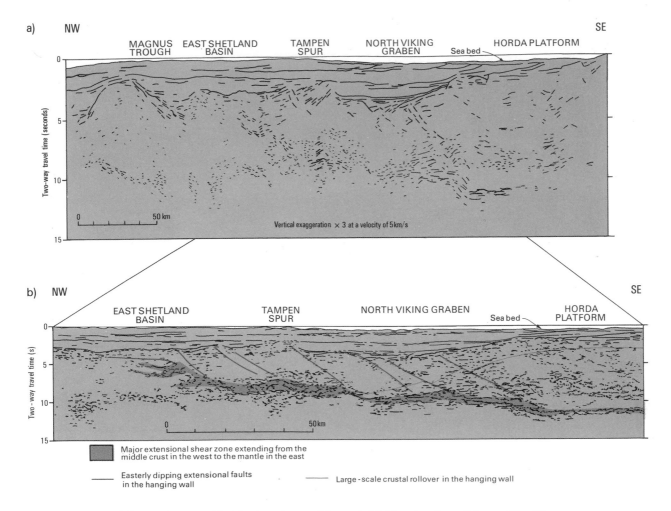

Figure 7 Britoil deep-seismic profile. For location see Figure 4. (a) Line drawing of the profile. After Beach et al. (1987). (b) Interpretation of the central part of the profile. After Beach (1986).

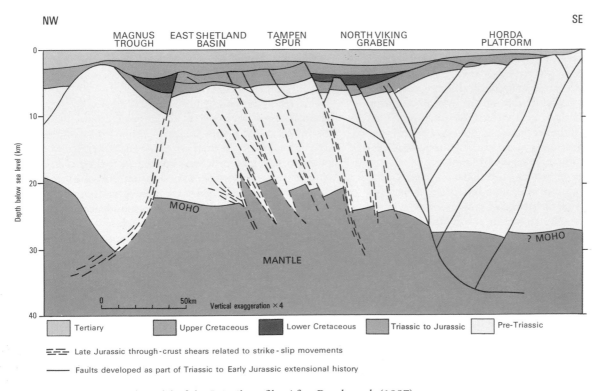

Figure 8 A geological model of the Britoil profile. After Beach et al. (1987).

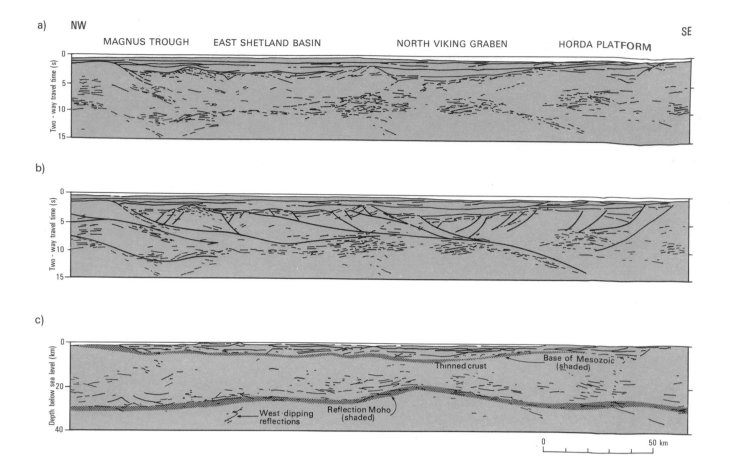

Figure 9 Deep-seismic profile NSDP line 1. For location see Figure 4. (a) Line drawing of principal reflections on the profile. After Gibbs (1987b). (b) Interpretation of (a) with faults shown as continuous lines. After Gibbs (1987b). (c) Migrated and depth-converted line drawing of the profile. After Klemperer (1988).

(Dixon et al., 1981; Latin et al., 1990). According to Ziegler (1982; 1983), however, the amount of extension calculated from the restoration of fault blocks, as defined from commercial seismic-reflection profiles, is significantly less than predicted by the stretching model. In order to account for this apparent discrepancy, Ziegler (1982, 1988a) and Ziegler and Van Hoorn (1989) advocated that crustal thinning across the Viking Graben was achieved during the Mesozoic rifting stage, not only by mechanical stretching of the upper crust, but possibly also by thermally induced physio-chemical processes that affected the lower crust, causing an upward displacement of the geophysically defined Moho.

There are, however, difficulties associated with estimating regional extension from normal faults interpreted from seismic profiles. For example, seismic data commonly do not unambiguously constrain the geometry of the faults, fault blocks may deform internally, and it is possible that not all faults are imaged on seismic profiles. White (1990) suggested that well data from the East Shetland Basin (Figure 5) do sufficiently control seismic interpretation to enable an estimate of upper crustal stretching to be made from normal faulting. He concluded that there is no discrepancy between the amount of extension estimated from backstripped subsidence data, deep-seismic profiles, and normal faults, thus supporting the stretching model of McKenzie (1978).

In contrast to the stretching model, Wernicke (1981) has argued that lithospheric extension and sedimentary basin development can be accommodated by slip along low-angle (less than 30°) faults or 'detachments' which offset the Moho and penetrate to the base of the lithosphere (Figure 6c). As exten-

sion takes place, the hanging wall (upper plate) breaks up into a series of fault-bounded blocks, whereas the footwall (lower plate) remains undeformed. Beach (1986) and Gibbs (1987a; 1987b) argued that both the polarity (asymmetry) of normal faulting and the pattern of subsidence in the northern North Sea Basin indicate control primarily by motion along a low-angle lithospheric detachment.

The style of normal faulting in the northern North Sea rift system is also a controversial topic. For example, Klemperer and White (1989) and White (1990) considered that the large normal faults in the East Shetland Basin (Figure 5) are approximately planar, having rotated in the manner of the 'rotating domino' model (e.g. Morton and Black, 1975). They assumed that the lower crust can flow, thus eliminating a 'space problem'. However, from geometrical constraints, Gibbs (1984) asserted that in order to achieve large amounts of upper crustal extension as suggested by stretching models, shallow-dipping fault planes are necessary. Gibbs (1984) predicted that cross faults, not to be confused with subsequent strike-slip faults, are an integral part of the extensional system. He proposed the term 'transfer faults' for these cross faults, and suggested that both transpressional and transtensional components of faulting can occur.

Deep-reflection profiles collected in the northern North Sea generally indicate a highly reflective lower crust of variable thickness, sandwiched between an acoustically transparent upper crust and a nonreflective mantle (McGeary et al., 1987). Highly reflective intervals in the upper part of the crust correlate with well-layered sedimentary basins, and reflections commonly interpreted as fault planes are imaged

Figure 10
Generalised structural framework of the northern North Sea.

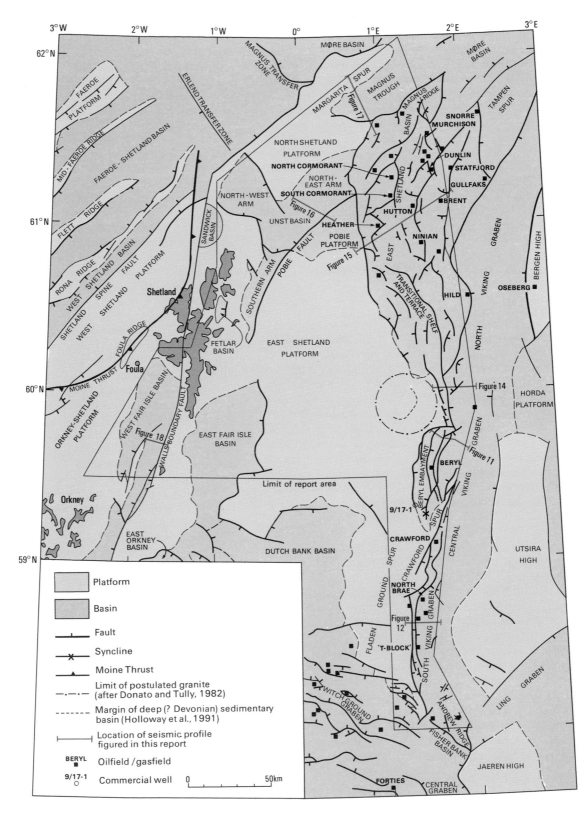

within the largely unreflective upper-crustal basement. The base of the reflective lower crust on reflection profiles generally varies around 10 s two-way travel time (TWTT), from about 20 to 30 km depth (Figures 7 and 8), and is generally considered to correspond to the refraction Moho (Barton et al., 1984; Barton, 1986).

Line drawings of migrated and depth-converted deep-reflection profiles across the East Shetland Basin and Viking Graben (Figures 7, 8 and 9) show crustal thinning (Klemperer, 1988). The thickness of prerift basement ranges from about 32 km beneath the East Shetland Platform and west-

ern Norway, to about 15 km beneath the axis of the North Viking Graben. Assuming a uniform crustal thickness prior to rifting, this indicates crustal thinning by more than 50 per cent beneath the graben (Klemperer, 1988). These results are broadly in agreement with the interpretation of both seismic-refraction (Solli, 1976) and gravity data (Donato and Tully, 1981; Zervos, 1987; Fichler and Hospers, 1990).

Dipping reflections are present in the upper mantle on all the deep-reflection profiles across the northern North Sea. Both Beach (1986) and Gibbs (1987a; 1987b) interpreted strong, easterly dipping upper mantle reflections east of the

Viking Graben as the downdip extension into the mantle of a lithospheric simple-shear detachment (Figures 7b and 9b). However, both Klemperer (1988) and Klemperer and White (1989) have shown that westerly dipping reflections are also present in the upper mantle west of the Viking Graben (Figure 9c). They argued that since the pattern of mantle reflections beneath the North Sea is broadly symmetrical, it should not be used to justify asymmetrical models for basin development. Furthermore, Klemperer and White (1989) and White (1990) suggested that the geometry of thermal subsidence can be used to test extensional models, being symmetrical for the pure-shear models and asymmetrical for simple-shear models. They concluded that the observed distribution of subsidence in the North Sea Basin is best explained by uniform stretching (Figure 6b).

EVOLUTION OF THE MAJOR STRUCTURAL ELEMENTS

Viking Graben and East Shetland Basin

The 500 km-long, narrow, north-north-easterly trending Viking Graben straddles the median line between the UK and Norwegian sectors of the northern North Sea (Figures 5 and 10). The East Shetland Platform lies to the west of the southern and central parts of the Viking Graben, but to the north, a broad, intermediate fault terrace, the East Shetland Basin, separates the North Viking Graben from the East Shetland Platform. In the extreme south of the report area, the Viking Graben terminates in a structurally complex region at its intersection with the Central Graben, the Moray Firth Basin and the Ling Graben. To the east of the Viking Graben, in the Norwegian sector, are the partly fault-bounded Utsira High, Bergen High and Horda Platform (Vollset and Doré, 1984).

The Viking Graben and East Shetland Basin are predominantly Mesozoic structural features, and contain thick accumulations (up to 11 000 m) of Triassic to Quaternary sediment. In general, the Viking Graben has an asymmetric, half-graben geometry, with the larger faults and thicker synrift deposits developed along its western margin. The age of rift initiation of the Viking Graben is the subject of debate; it may be pre-Permian (Haszeldine and Russell, 1987; Steel and Ryseth, 1990), but the consensus seems to favour two main phases of rifting: during the Late Permian or earliest Triassic, and the Late Jurassic. Nevertheless, opinions vary on the relative amounts of crustal stretching in each phase (Giltner, 1987; Badley et al., 1988; Marsden et al., 1990; White, 1990). The structural evolution of the Viking Graben and East Shetland Basin is considered below in a series of time intervals.

PERMO-TRIASSIC

Glennie (1990a) postulated an Early Permian initiation of the Viking and Central grabens because of the close proximity of lower Rotliegend volcanic rocks to the Central Graben, and the presence of Upper Permian salt within the South Viking Graben. About 200 m of Zechstein halites were penetrated in the southern Beryl Embayment on the western margin of the Central Viking Graben in well 9/17-1 (Figure 10), the most northerly halite sequence known in the UK North Sea. Ziegler (1982) reasoned that this thick salt could be explained as a downfaulted prerift deposit, and favoured a Triassic age for graben initiation. Ziegler (1982) and Steel and Ryseth (1990) noted that there are considerable thickness variations of Triassic strata in the East Shetland Basin, and considered it unlikely that such variations reflect a pre-Triassic basement

topography. They suggested that intra-Triassic faulting, and possibly block rotation (rifting), was a more likely cause. Ziegler (1982) postulated that the extremely low level of volcanic activity associated with Triassic rifts of the North Sea, and the absence of major doming, suggests that rifting was due to crustal extension rather than a response to the development of mantle plumes.

From evidence in the Oseberg Oilfield on the Bergen High to the east (Figure 10), Badley et al. (1984; 1988) recognised deeply buried and tilted fault blocks beneath an unconformity at the base of the Triassic. They described a set of northerly trending, basement-involved, down-to-the-west, rotational, normal faults, and a pre-Early Triassic, wedge-shaped, synrift unit that infills the early rift topography. This synrift unit is overlain by a Lower Triassic to Middle Jurassic sequence that thickens westwards towards the axis of the North Viking Graben, and has been interpreted as a postrift sequence related to thermal subsidence (Badley et al., 1988). According to Badley et al. (1988), the fault zones belong to a Late Permian to very Early Triassic rift phase, reactivated during Late Jurassic rifting.

On the Horda Platform (Figure 10), Steel and Ryseth (1990) described eastward-tilted, basement fault blocks overlain by a wedge-shaped sequence up to 2000 m thick that fills a rift topography. An overlying, 3000 m-thick Early Triassic to earliest Jurassic sequence of subparallel reflectors generally blankets the infilled asymmetric rifts. Steel and Ryseth (1990) noted that a lower unit of the upper sequence does thicken substantially towards some major faults, and inferred that rifting continued into Scythian times, having been initiated during the Permian or earlier. Steel and Ryseth (1990) further suggested that there are more signs of active intra-basinal faulting in the upper part of an Upper Triassic to Lower Jurassic (Rhaetian to Sinemurian) sequence, where depocentres tend broadly to occupy the site of the subsequent Viking Graben.

Badley et al. (1988) compared the decompacted thickness of ?Permian to Middle Jurassic strata overlying tilted basement on the Horda Platform, which has a maximum thickness in the range of 4000 to 6000 m, with the much thinner succession, up to 1500 m, observed in the East Shetland Basin to the west of the graben. They inferred that an asymmetric basin developed during this time, with the most active faults along its eastern margin. Steel and Ryseth (1990) tentatively envisaged a full graben north of the Horda Platform during Rhaetian to Sinemurian times, and a half-graben to the south with a western master-fault system. On the basis of the Triassic thickness variations deduced from well and seismic data, Frostick et al. (1992) postulated an Early Triassic rift phase in the Beryl Embayment, with syntectonic depositional thicknesses greatly influenced by approximately east-trending transfer faults. In contrast, Triassic strata apparently show no thickening towards the fault bounding the northern Beryl Embayment (Figure 11), and have been interpreted to be prerift deposits (Swallow, 1986).

JURASSIC

The Viking Graben and East Shetland Basin underwent major structural development during Jurassic times; these developments are considered on a geographical basis, with the Viking Graben divided into its southern, central and northern components.

South Viking Graben

The South Viking Graben lies to the south of the North Brae Oilfield (Figure 10), and is only about 50 km wide. The graben has a markedly asymmetric profile, with a generally

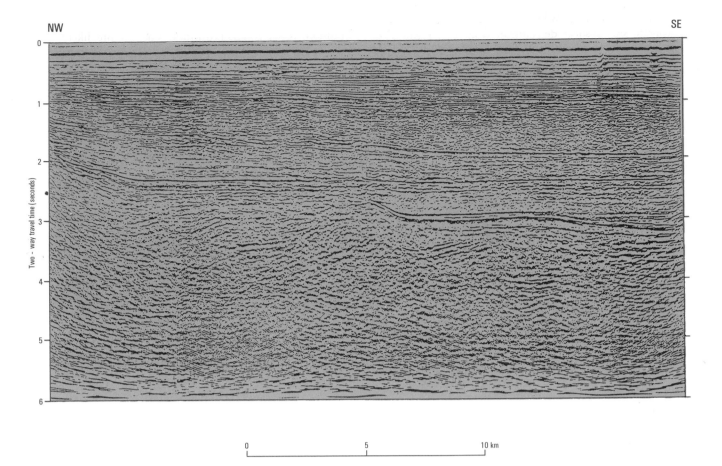

NW   SE

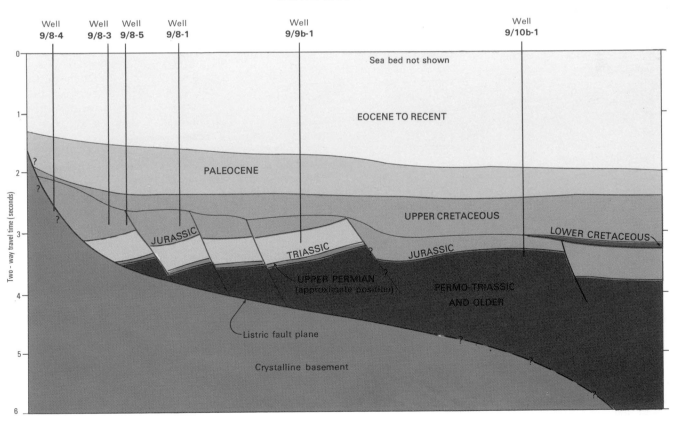

BERYL EMBAYMENT

Well
9/8-4

Well
9/8-3

Well
9/8-5

Well
9/8-1

Well
9/9b-1

Well
9/10b-1

Sea bed not shown

EOCENE TO RECENT

PALEOCENE

UPPER CRETACEOUS

LOWER CRETACEOUS

JURASSIC

TRIASSIC

JURASSIC

UPPER PERMIAN
(approximate position)

PERMO-TRIASSIC
AND OLDER

Listric fault plane

Crystalline basement

—— Accommodation fault

Figure 11   Seismic-reflection profile across the northern Beryl Embayment, with interpreted line drawing.
The wells shown lie either on the line of the section or within 2.5 km of it. For location see Figure 10. After
Swallow (1986).

11

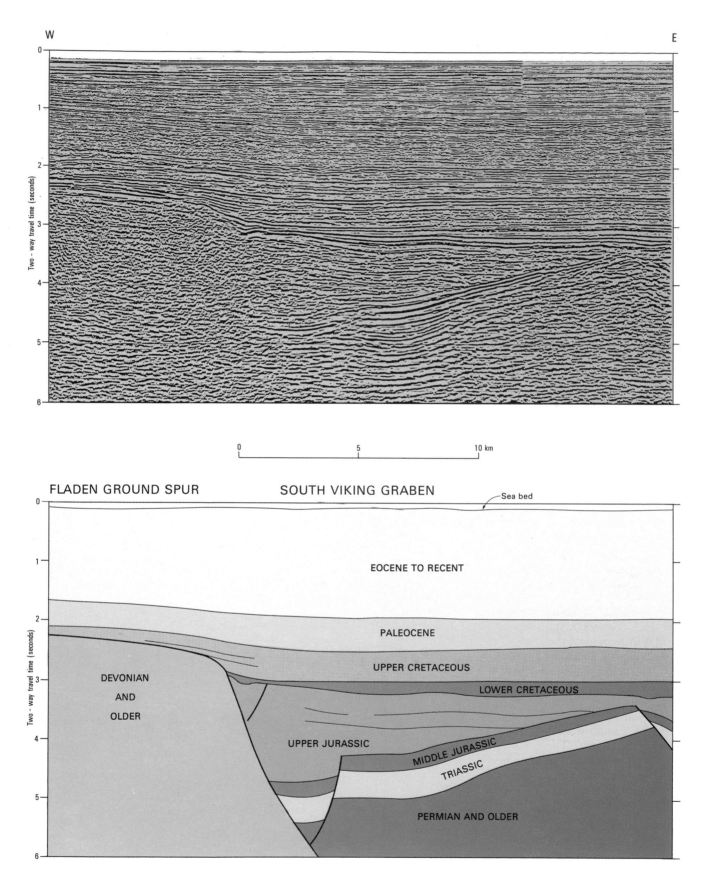

Figure 12 Seismic-reflection profile across the South Viking Graben, with interpreted line drawing. For location see Figure 10.

north-trending, rotational, basement-involved, normal fault zone forming its western boundary with the Fladen Ground Spur (Figure 12).

The Lower Jurassic is absent or patchily distributed over the South Viking Graben, perhaps as a result of broad up-warping of the central North Sea during the Early to Mid-Jurassic (Richards et al., 1988; see Chapter 5). In general, the Bajocian to Callovian succession thickens away from the graben margin towards the basin axis. This suggests that, although there was probably some local fault control on depositional thicknesses, the Middle Jurassic succession predates the main phase of extensional rifting. Significant Mid-Jurassic faulting may however have exerted penecontemporaneous control on the distribution and thickness of the volcanic rocks in the central North Sea (Woodhall and Knox, 1979).

Upper Jurassic syntectonic strata attain a maximum thickness of the order of 3000 m against the western margin of the graben, but thin markedly to the east (Figures 12 and 13). The eastern margin of the graben is less well defined, with relatively smaller faults bounding the structurally high Utsira High in the Norwegian sector. Major extensional rifting in the South Viking Graben, as recognised by major rotational normal faulting and the shedding of coarse-grained, clastic, synrift sediments from the Fladen Ground Spur, generally occurred from late Oxfordian to late Volgian times. Lithologies suggest rapid, fault-controlled subsidence that outpaced sedimentation during the late Oxfordian to earliest Kimmeridgian. The development of a markedly asymmetric graben at this time restricted deposition of coarse-grained, clastic sediments to the western margin of the basin. Locally, clastic deposition continued until earliest Cretaceous times.

The nature of the western fault margin varies along its length. In the Brae region, the fault zone is narrow and quite steeply dipping, although the occurrence of stratal rollover and antithetic accommodation faults in the hanging wall suggests that the main fault probably has a somewhat listric geometry. By contrast, in the T-Block area (Figure 10), there is a faulted terrace about 8 km wide on which the faults become systematically younger to the west, probably due to progressive footwall collapse. Generally, the total amount of fault displacement along this western margin decreases southwards.

On the Norwegian side of the South Viking Graben, Gowers (1979) described eastward-verging, asymmetric folds and associated, arcuate, listric, reverse faults. He suggested that these structures may have developed by eastward salt movement in response to rapid loading by thick wedges of Upper Jurassic strata along the western flank of the graben.

The South Viking Graben shelves to the south of about 58°15'N, where the thickness of syntectonic Upper Jurassic strata is generally less than 500 m (Figure 13). This zone lies at the confluence of several regional structural alignments (Doré and Gage, 1987), and has a complex structure. Hamar et al. (1980) recognised the north-westerly trending Andrew Ridge (Figure 10), a feature running between the Jaeren High and the southern tip of the Fladen Ground Spur, as forming the southern limit of the Viking Graben. To the south-west of the Andrew Ridge is the north-westerly trending Witch Ground Graben, a Late Jurassic to earliest Cretaceous half-graben with a south-westerly thickening wedge-shaped fill of syntectonic sediments. The similarly trending Fisher Bank Basin, a Late Jurassic half-graben, lies to the south-west of the Andrew Ridge (Figure 10). Doré and Gage (1987) postulated that the north-easterly trending Ling Graben to the east of the Andrew Ridge represents a continuation of the Highland Boundary Fault alignment (Figures 4 and 5). Furthermore, Doré and Gage (1987) speculated that the intersection of this major structural fracture zone with the west-north-westerly trending Tornquist Zone (Figure 4) provided a focus for Mid-Jurassic volcanic activity, although Klemperer and Hurich (1990) proposed from seismic evidence that the Highland Boundary Fault and Tornquist Zone were largely inactive throughout Late Palaeozoic and Mesozoic times.

Figure 13 Generalised isopachs of Upper Jurassic deposits in the Viking Graben and East Shetland Basin. Norwegian data after Pegrum and Spencer (1990).

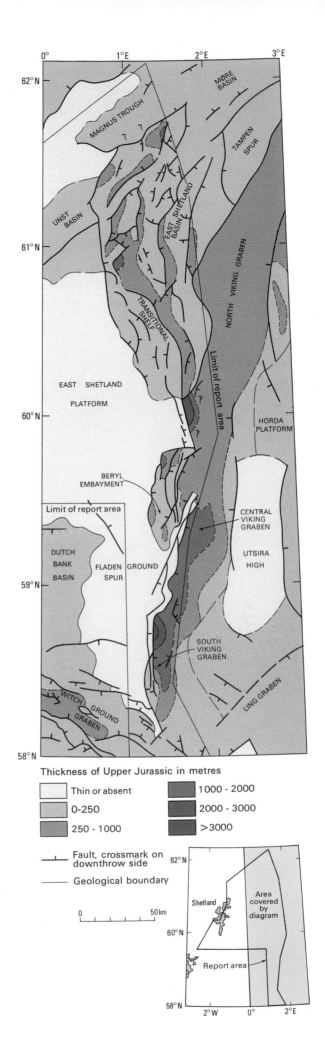

Thickness of Upper Jurassic in metres

Thin or absent	1000 – 2000
0–250	2000 – 3000
250 – 1000	>3000

Fault, crossmark on downthrow side

Geological boundary

0   50 km

The extreme south of the report area has been affected by salt diapirism that may in part have been triggered during the Late Jurassic by relatively minor transtensional faulting along the Tornquist Zone (Pegrum and Ljones, 1984). The salt diapirs form traps for oil, such as at the Maureen Oilfield, and cut the base of the Cretaceous, but do not penetrate the seismic reflector marking the top of the Chalk/Shetland Group.

To the north-west of the North Brae Oilfield, an easterly offset to the western margin of the Viking Graben marks the northern limit of the South Viking Graben (Figure 10), this east-north-easterly trending fault zone is probably a major transfer fault.

Central Viking Graben, Crawford Spur and Beryl Embayment

North of the Brae transfer fault, north-north-easterly trending normal faults form the terraced western margin of the Central Viking Graben, which extends north to about 60°N, very largely in Norwegian waters. The marginal faults become systematically younger to the west, and define the margin of the Crawford Spur, a structural high mainly consisting of Old Red Sandstone, that separates the Central Viking Graben from the Beryl Embayment to the west (Figure 10).

The Beryl Embayment is a north-north-easterly trending Mesozoic sub-basin that is defined by a westward *en-échelon* offset of the graben-bounding fault (Figure 10). A number of dominantly northerly to north-north-easterly trending normal faults transect the embayment, where they bound a complex of tilted fault blocks.

A broad, approximately 10 km-long, north-trending syncline and an associated north-easterly trending reverse fault affect Permo-Triassic strata in the southern Beryl Embayment. Frost (1987) interpreted the reverse fault and syncline as evidence for end-Mid-Jurassic (Callovian) compressional reactivation (perhaps with a component of minor strike-slip movement) of earlier-formed tensional faults that follow basement structural trends. An alternative explanation is that the Beryl Embayment is a major hanging-wall basin, and the syncline is a geometrical consequence of, and related to, the shape of an underlying low-angle, ramp-and-flat detachment surface (Gibbs, 1987c). In this extensional model, the reverse fault associated with the syncline possibly relates to transpressional transfer faulting, or to subsequent compression.

Swallow (1986) interpreted the northern part of the Beryl Embayment to overlie a south-easterly dipping, low-angle detachment fault (Figure 11). Well and seismic evidence here indicate that differential subsidence and syntectonic sedimentation began in the Early Jurassic, and reached its acme in Late Jurassic times. Rollover (reverse drag) and accommodation faults are interpreted in the hanging wall (Figure 11). The possible detachment zone dips at 10 to 15° towards the east at between 7 and 8 km depth, but removal of postrift tilting would indicate an original dip of less than 10°. Swallow (1986) postulated that the detachment zone might not be a reworked Caledonian thrust, but could be a tectonically exploited unconformity between Devonian sediments and Caledonian crystalline basement.

At the northern margin of the Beryl Embayment, its bounding fault swings to an east-north-easterly trend (Figure 10). On the basis of high magnetic anomalies and a negative residual gravity anomaly, Donato and Tully (1982) postulated that this eastward deflection of the graben margin is controlled by a Caledonian granite pluton on the eastern edge of the East Shetland Platform (Figure 10). Holloway et al. (1991) suggested that the granite may be much smaller than postulated by Donato and Tully (1982), and that a ?Devonian basin may occupy this part of the platform. The

deflection of the graben margin may indicate another transfer-fault zone.

North of the Beryl Embayment, a large northerly to north-north-westerly trending, relatively steeply dipping, rotational, normal fault separates the Central Viking Graben from the East Shetland Platform. An eastward-thinning wedge of syntectonic Upper Jurassic Humber Group strata over 2000 m thick is banked against this fault zone (Figures 13 and 14). Seismic reflections from the underlying Middle Jurassic strata dip westwards towards the major fault, and appear essentially parallel bedded on seismic profiles; they therefore predate major half-graben rifting. Jurassic and older deposits in the hanging wall are cut by rotational, westward-dipping, accommodation faults. Subsequent nonrotational Cretaceous and Tertiary faulting along the graben margin has migrated westward, thereby increasing the width of the graben.

North Viking Graben, East Shetland Basin, and Transitional Shelf and Terrace

At about 60°N, the axis of the Viking Graben swings to a north-north-easterly trend, and diverges from the edge of the East Shetland Platform, with the development of an intervening zone of Mesozoic sediments in the East Shetland Basin and in the Transitional Shelf and Terrace (Figure 10). Almost all of the North Viking Graben lies in the Norwegian sector. Seismic sections across the North Viking Graben and East Shetland Basin (Figures 7, 8, 9 and 15) commonly indicate an asymmetry in the upper crustal structure, with westerly tilted fault blocks (Beach, 1986; Gibbs, 1987a; 1987b). Nevertheless, a symmetrical graben profile was interpreted around the Norwegian Hild and Oseberg oilfields (Figure 10) by Marsden et al. (1990). Synrift Upper Jurassic deposits up to 1000 m thick (Pegrum and Spencer, 1990) are preserved on the downthrown sides of the rotational faults which bound the North Viking Graben to the west (Figure 13). The graben margin crosses to the Norwegian sector at about 60° 20'N, but at about 60° 30'N it is offset to the north-west by a major fault forming a structural nose (Figure 10 and 13) on which lies the structurally complex Hild Oilfield (Rønning et al., 1986; Rønning, 1987). From about 60° 50'N, the graben margin trends north-north-east or north-eastwards into the Norwegian sector, where it is bounded to the north by the Tampen Spur (Figure 10).

The East Shetland Basin is characterised by a series of tilted fault blocks bounded by faults on a variety of trends affecting the Jurassic sequence (Figure 10). The largest throws generally occur on the northerly trending faults that downthrow to the east, separating large, elongate, westward-tilted fault blocks about 10 to 20 km wide (Figure 15). Two prominent and economically important, subparallel, north-trending structural blocks occur; the more westerly one is marked by the location of the Ninian, Hutton, Dunlin and Murchison oilfields, whereas the eastern block contains the Brent and Statfjord oilfields (Figure 10). Easterly trending faults are important in the Brent Oilfield. The north-easterly trending faults are mainly developed in the northern part of the East Shetland Basin, where fault-block tilt direction is more variable. The north-westerly trending faults are mainly developed south of the Cormorant Oilfield (Speksnijder, 1987).

Lower and Middle Jurassic sequences in the East Shetland Basin generally thicken towards the axis of the Viking Graben (Brown et al., 1987; Richards, 1990b; see Chapter 5), although units such as the Broom Formation do show wedge-shaped depositional geometries associated with fault-controlled, intra-basinal subsidence (Brown et al., 1987). Nevertheless, because of their overall geometry, Lower to Middle Jurassic strata are generally interpreted to have been

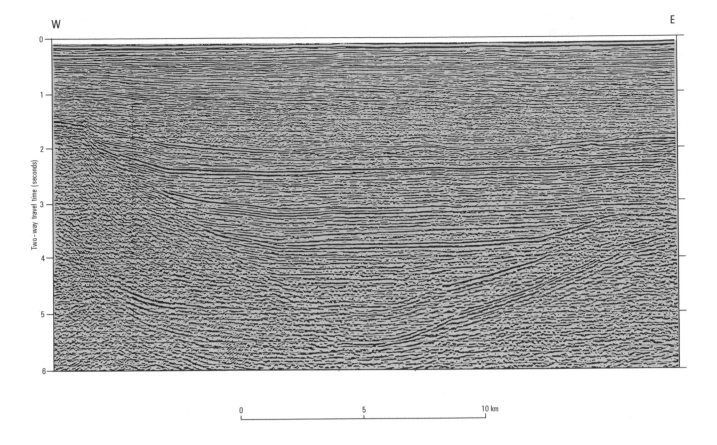

W   E

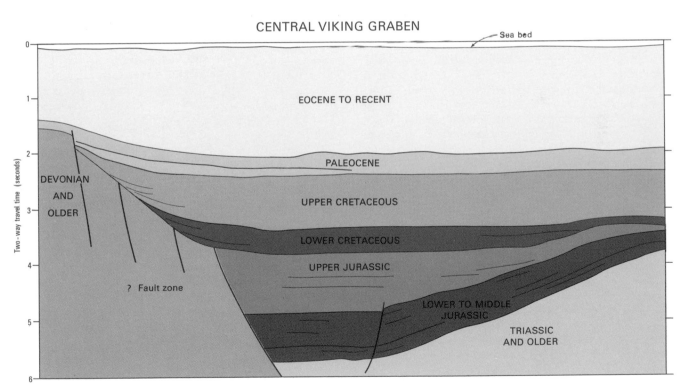

CENTRAL VIKING GRABEN   Sea bed

EOCENE TO RECENT

PALEOCENE

DEVONIAN
AND
OLDER

UPPER CRETACEOUS

LOWER CRETACEOUS

UPPER JURASSIC

? Fault zone

LOWER TO MIDDLE
JURASSIC

TRIASSIC
AND OLDER

Figure 14   Seismic-reflection profile across the Central Viking Graben, with interpreted line drawing. For location see Figure 10.

deposited during a time of relative tectonic quiescence, which Badley et al. (1988) related to a thermal subsidence phase following a ?Permo-Triassic rifting episode.

In contrast, the mainly Upper Jurassic Heather and Kimmeridge Clay formations (lower Bathonian to Ryazanian) in the East Shetland Basin generally display marked thickening towards both basin margin and intra-basinal faults (Figure 13), with divergent internal reflections commonly evident on seismic profiles (Figure 15). Substantial rotational movement on the main faults resulted in tilting of the fault blocks, and reverse drag or rollover is evident in the hanging walls of numerous major faults. Seismic-reflection data generally show onlap of the tilted Middle Jurassic Brent Group by reflections within the synrift Upper Jurassic Heather

Formation (Figure 15). Limited erosion of the Brent and Dunlin groups beneath synrift sediments occurred locally on the crests of tilted fault blocks, where early synrift sediments are in some cases absent. The most extensive erosion occurred on the fault block closest to the Viking Graben, the Brent–Statfjord Block (Figure 10).

Badley et al. (1988) recognised two stages of Late Jurassic rifting; these are represented by the Heather Formation (lower Bathonian to lower Kimmeridgian) and the Kimmeridge Clay Formation (Kimmeridgian to Ryazanian). Badley et al. (1988) inferred rotation on reactivated, basement-involved, planar faults during the first rifting stage, and suggested that evidence of reverse drag during the second stage indicates that fault planes may detach above the earlier, basement-involved faults. From geometrical considerations, Gibbs (1987a) postulated that the East Shetland Basin fault blocks detach along low-angle sole faults, stepping down from about 5 to 6 s TWTT in the west, to about 8 to 9 s TWTT in the axial part of the graben. However, according to Klemperer and White (1989), rigid-body rotation of fault- bounded crustal blocks (domino-style faulting) is more likely.

On the basis of seismic evidence, and because of the apparently anomalously large amounts of uplift and erosion experienced by major fault blocks in the Tampen Spur, Frost (1989) doubted the extensional rifting model depicted by Badley et al. (1988). Frost (1989) interpreted seismic data to show synclines in hanging-wall blocks rather than reverse-drag features, and postulated that this points to a post-Brent Group compressional event. According to Badley et al. (1989), the hanging-wall dip reversals illustrated by Frost (1989) are compaction synclines related to extensional faulting. They furthermore interpreted local uplifts experienced by fault-block crests as isostatic footwall uplift associated with that faulting. Locally, however, seismic evidence across some of the tilted fault-blocks in the East Shetland Basin is ambiguous, and reverse drag on the downthrown side of Late Jurassic faults is not ubiquitously apparent.

Hay (1978) postulated that north-easterly trending faults, which are important in the northern part of the East Shetland Basin, have a strike-slip component of movement, and are related to a reactivated Caledonide tectonic grain. He hypothesised that the resulting rotation of fault blocks about a vertical axis, as a result of the strike-slip movement, would explain observed variation in block tilt direction. Speksnijder (1987) interpreted the north-easterly and north-westerly trending faults in the East Shetland Basin as showing rapid changes in style and amount of throw along strike. These are basement-involved, steep, and locally reverse faults showing resemblance to flower structures that are known from oblique-slip fault zones. Speksnijder (1987) postulated that strike-slip movements along these basement faults had facilitated overall east–west Late Jurassic extension in the East Shetland Basin, in the manner of transfer faults (Gibbs, 1984). Furthermore, Speksnijder (1987) suggested that numerous, arcuate, listric, growth faults in the sedimentary cover around the Cormorant Oilfield sole out in a common detachment surface about 100 m above the Caledonian basement.

The amount of strike-slip movement in the northern North Sea is difficult to quantify. On the basis of an apparent discrepancy between the crustal stretching factor (ß) inter-

Figure 15 Seismic-reflection profile across the East Shetland Basin, with interpreted line drawing. For location see Figure 10.

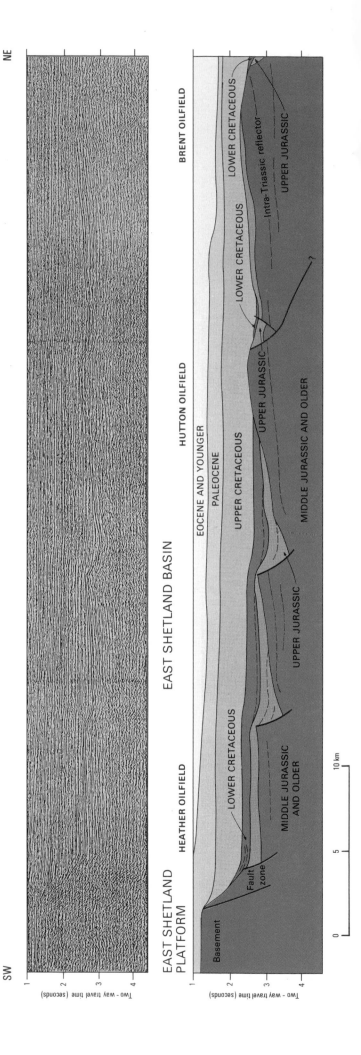

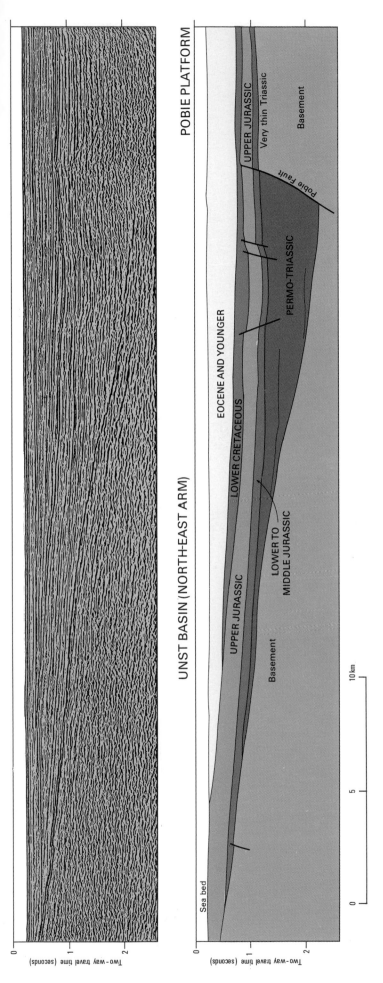

Figure 16 Seismic-reflection profile across the Unst Basin, with interpreted line drawing. For location see Figure 10.

preted from Mesozoic and Tertiary basin-centre subsidence history (ß = 3.3), and that measured from the Britoil deep-seismic profile (Figure 7) across the North Viking Graben (ß = 2.3), Beach et al. (1987) proposed a two-phase structural model. There was an initial Triassic to Early Jurassic episode of extension along a low-angle, east-dipping detachment, followed by Late Jurassic to Early Cretaceous development in a dominantly strike-slip mode (Figure 8). Beach et al. (1987) suggested that strike-slip movement occurred along moderately steeply dipping, through-crust shears with extension (and local compression) along the axis as well as across the rifts. Beach (1985) postulated that during the Jurassic, sinistral slip movement, essentially parallel to the Norwegian coast, was transferred southward into the Viking Graben. In a contrasting interpretation, Gibbs (1987b) concluded that Late Jurassic strike-slip displacement across the northern North Sea Basin used low-angle, eastward-dipping detachments that were formed in a prior extensional episode (Figure 9b).

Klemperer (1988) doubted the high stretching factor (ß = 3.3) estimated by Beach et al. (1987), because this amount of stretching is greater than that at which oceanic crust might be expected to form. Certainly large-scale basalt volcanism would be expected, but is not observed. Furthermore, Roberts et al. (1990) suggested that structural features in the North Viking Graben and East Shetland Basin, that have been interpreted to indicate a strike-slip setting (Beach, 1986; Speksnijder, 1987), can be reinterpreted as extensional structures consistent with orthogonal opening of the rifts. According to Giltner (1987) and White (1990), there is no discrepancy between northern North Sea crustal thinning estimated from total subsidence observations and deep-reflection profiles, and they favoured a uniform-extension model of basin development similar to that of Jarvis and McKenzie (1980).

The Transitional Shelf and Terrace forms a broadly lozenge-shaped, fault-bounded terrace that is structurally higher than the East Shetland Basin, but downthrown from the East Shetland Platform (Figure 10). It is underlain by Caledonian metamorphic basement and Old Red Sandstone, and has a relatively thin Mesozoic cover compared to the East Shetland Basin, up to about 500 m (Wheatley et al., 1987). Rotational, down-to-the-east, normal faults generally trend north-west to north, and stratal isopachs suggest that although faulting was locally initiated during Oxfordian to Kimmeridgian times, the main tectonic pulse occurred in the Volgian, and reached its climax in the Ryazanian (Wheatley et al., 1987).

CRETACEOUS

Over many structural highs, a significant, regional, but commonly slight, angular disconformity separates the Humber Group (Bathonian to Ryazanian) from the overlapping, dominantly argillaceous, Cromer Knoll Group (late Ryazanian to late Albian). The Cromer Knoll Group generally thins towards major faults, and compactional normal drag is common (Figures 12, 14, and 15). Badley et al. (1988) have attributed these characteristics in the North Viking Graben to a major, synchronous, basinwide change in tectonic style; they suggested that rifting, as recognised by fault-block rotation, ceased towards the end of Ryazanian times. It was followed

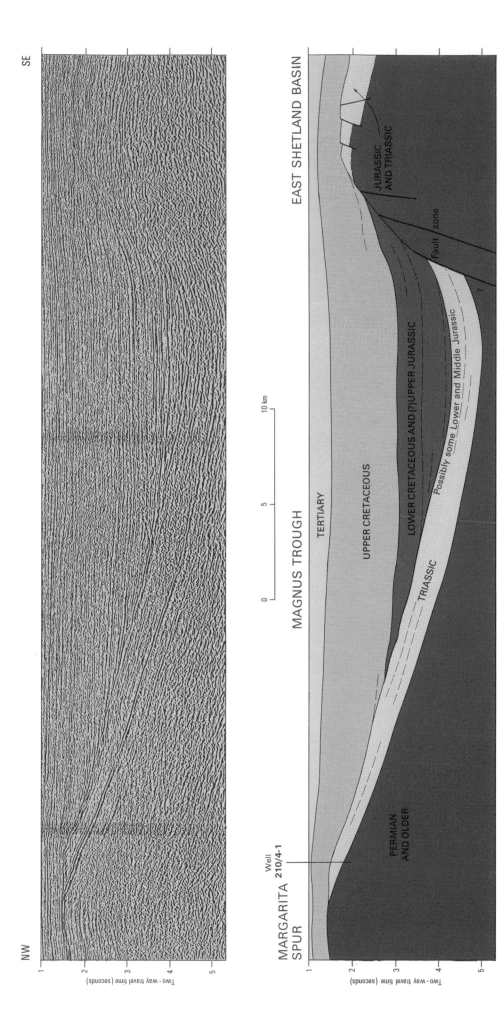

Figure 17 Seismic-reflection profile across the Magnus Trough, with interpreted line drawing. For location see Figure 10.

18

by a thermal subsidence episode during which depositional patterns were controlled by nonrotational subsidence, and footwall uplift associated with fault-blocks bounded by basement-involved, planar, normal faults (e.g. Gabrielsen, 1986). These new faults developed in the footwalls of the pre-existing fault scarps; within individual footwalls, faulting is considered to have moved progressively towards the basin margin as time passed.

Thus, Badley et al. (1988) differ from Vail and Todd (1981) and Rawson and Riley (1982) in attributing the major change from the Humber Group to the Cromer Knoll Group primarily to tectonic events in the basin, rather than to eustatic sea-level changes.

At the end of the Late Jurassic to earliest Cretaceous rifting episode, most of the Viking Graben was probably submerged, and Badley et al. (1988) postulated that only the crests of major fault blocks, such as the Brent structure, may have been emergent. Thereafter, the rift topography became progressively infilled to produce a broadly asymmetric, westerly thickening wedge (Figure 8) of Cretaceous deposits (Beach, 1986; Badley et al., 1988).

On a basinwide scale, nonrotational, fault-controlled subsidence was initially (late Ryazanian to Albian) concentrated in the axis of the Viking Graben. As time elapsed (Cenomanian to Turonian), subsidence spread progressively outwards from the graben areas, thereby broadening the main area of subsidence at a time coincident with global sea-level rise (Haq et al., 1987). By Coniacian to Maastrichtian times, most of the basin was undergoing relatively uniform thermal subsidence, and faulting was confined to the basin margin (Badley et al., 1988).

Pegrum and Ljones (1984) interpreted local reversal of normal faults on the eastern flank of the South Viking Graben late in Early Cretaceous times to be the result of sinistral transpression along west-north-westerly trending faults of the Tornquist Zone, in response to early Alpine plate impact in southern Europe. According to Gibbs (1987a), inversion of the Gullfaks structure on the Tampen Spur (Figures 7 and 10), as evidenced by Tertiary thickness changes, started at least during the Cretaceous. To the northeast of the Gullfaks structure, a compressional dome affecting Cretaceous and older rocks has been interpreted as an effect of strike-slip basement faulting (Hamar and Hjelle, 1984).

TERTIARY

The axis of the Tertiary northern North Sea Basin coincides closely with the trace of the Viking Graben, and Tertiary subsidence can be largely related to thermal cooling of the lithosphere following rifting (Thorne and Watts, 1989; Klemperer and White, 1989). However, according to Rochow (1981) and Beach et al. (1987), faults were rejuvenated along the western margin of the Viking Graben and East Shetland Basin during the Paleocene, when large volumes of clastic sediments were shed from the uplifted and eastward-tilted East Shetland Platform. No rollover of Cretaceous seismic reflections is associated with the subsidence (Rochow, 1981), and Badley et al. (1988) considered that graben subsidence was controlled by reactivated, planar, normal faults along the old rift margin.

From heavy-mineral provenance studies, Morton (1982) recognised two distinct episodes of source-area uplift and fault-controlled subsidence in the Paleocene of the northern North Sea. Initially, north to north-north-easterly trending faulting took place along the margins of the southern and central parts of the Viking Graben, and subsidence was minimal to the north and east. Subsequently, north-north-westerly trending faults were reactivated along the margin of the East Shetland Basin to the north. Morton (1982) related these distinct episodes of faulting to changes in the regional stress field associated with events in the North Atlantic prior to crustal separation between Greenland and Rockall.

Fagerland (1983) reported a complex, sinuous, but generally north-trending zone of basement-involved faults along the margin of the Utsira High on the eastern side of the South Viking Graben (Figure 10). He concluded that there had been an episode of Paleocene fault reactivation with dextral strike-slip movement along a north-north-westerly trend which may be related either to the opening of the Norwegian–Greenland Sea, or less probably, to the northernmost expression of the Alpine orogeny. Pegrum and Ljones (1984) also recognised local inversion and reverse displacements of the Paleocene sequence on the eastern flank of the South Viking Graben, and postulated a phase of late Eocene transpression on rejuvenated north-westerly trending basement-involved faults related to the Tornquist Zone.

Unst and Fetlar basins

Lying to the west of the East Shetland Basin (Figure 10), the Unst Basin is the erosional remnant of a larger, Permian to Cretaceous depocentre that overlies Old Red Sandstone and Caledonian basement. The basin contains up to 3600 m of Permo-Triassic redbeds overlain by up to about 800 m of Jurassic sediment, up to 400 m of Lower Cretaceous deposits and, in the east, up to about 500 m of Tertiary strata (Figure 16; Johns and Andrews, 1985).

The basin consists of three arms that are partly fault-bounded. The north-east arm is a half-graben bounded to the south-east by the Pobie Fault, and contains the basin's thickest sedimentary succession, about 4000 m (Figure 10). The northern part of the north-west arm is a half-graben bounded on its eastern edge by a major north-west-trending fault which Duindam and Van Hoorn (1987) regarded as an extension of the Erlend Transfer Zone (Figure 10). The southern part of the north-west arm is however fault-bounded on both sides (Figure 10). The narrow, south-westerly trending southern arm is bounded to the east by the Pobie Fault; this arm is structurally higher than both northern arms, and is separated from them by a major east–west fault (Johns and Andrews, 1985).

The structural style as interpreted by Johns and Andrews (1985) is dominated by normal faulting; relatively deep, low-angle seismic events, which dip contrary to the bedding and flatten out within basement at 3 to 3.5 s TWTT, have been interpreted as listric faults. The basin is considered to have been initiated during the Early Permian, with syndepositional movement on the basin-bounding faults occurring throughout Permo-Triassic deposition. Pull-apart extension on a north-easterly trend is believed to have been the result of sinistral strike-slip movement on the Pobie Fault, in association with similar movement on the Great Glen shear trend. The Jurassic was a time of tectonic inactivity in the Unst Basin; compressional folds in the Lower Cretaceous deposits, and minor reverse fault movement affecting Jurassic strata on north-north-west-trending faults, have been interpreted to result from minor Early Cretaceous strike-slip along the Pobie Fault. Inversion of the basin, probably from latest Cretaceous to mid-Paleocene times, and associated with the opening of the North Atlantic, resulted in major erosion, to be followed by Tertiary deposition.

In a contrasting interpretation, Beach (1985) considered that the Unst Basin is underlain by low-angle, easterly dipping detachment faults, and favoured a strike-slip mechanism of basin evolution with much greater extension along the north-east-trending part of the basin than across it.

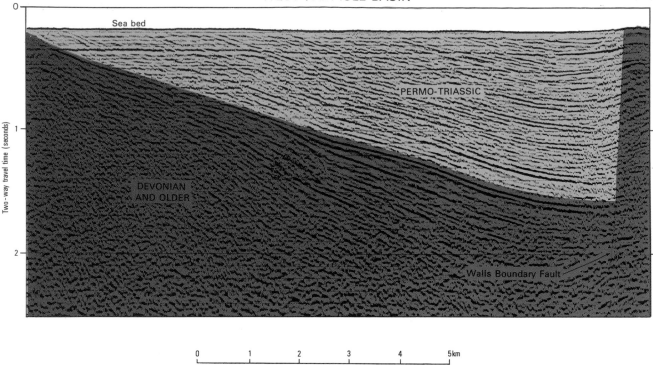

WEST FAIR ISLE BASIN

Figure 18 Interpreted seismic-reflection profile across the West Fair Isle Basin. For location see Figure 10.

The small Fetlar Basin lies to the west of the Unst Basin and adjacent to the east coast of Shetland. It is probably infilled by thin Permo-Triassic redbeds. The basin is bounded to the east by a normal fault, and is considered to represent a downfaulted remnant of a more extensive Permo-Triassic cover that once existed over the region (BGS Shetland Solid Geology sheet).

Magnus Trough

The north-easterly trending Magnus Trough lies to the north of the East Shetland Basin beyond the Magnus Ridge (Figure 10). A major, steeply dipping, normal, growth fault along its south-eastern boundary gives the trough an asymmetric, south-easterly tilted, half-graben geometry. Seismic data appear to indicate that Permian and Mesozoic strata on the downthrown side display normal drag (Figure 17). The Magnus Trough plunges to the north-east, where it merges with the Møre Basin (Nelson and Lamy, 1987); to the south-west it borders the North Shetland Platform. The Margarita Spur, a north-easterly trending, south-easterly tilted fault block that is an extension of the North Shetland Platform, forms the north-west margin to the Magnus Trough. On the Margarita Spur, Permo-Triassic redbeds overlie basement, and are unconformably overlain by onlapping Upper Cretaceous strata (Figure 17).

In the Magnus Trough, thin Zechstein limestones and anhydrites near the base of the redbed sequence provide a strong reflection on seismic profiles (Figure 17). About 1500 m of Triassic strata underlie the trough, and the lack of significant divergence of Triassic reflectors indicates that they predate the onset of major half-graben rifting in this basin. According to Nelson and Lamy (1987), a south-easterly thickening wedge of syntectonic strata up to about 5000 m thick is banked against the southern faulted margin of the trough. The age of rift initiation is unknown, but may be Late

Jurassic (Nelson and Lamy, 1987) or Early Cretaceous (De'Ath and Schuyleman, 1981). If the rifting was during the Late Jurassic, it would imply that the early Kimmeridgian Magnus Sand submarine fan of the East Shetland Basin (De'Ath and Schuyleman, 1981) was derived from the relatively small Magnus Ridge (Figure 10). Jurassic rocks have not been drilled in the trough; the upper 620 m of the syntectonic sequence are of Early Cretaceous age (Ryazanian/Valanginian to early Hauterivian), and consist predominantly of sandstones. This synrift sequence is onlapped in the south-east by about 3000 m of Lower and Upper Cretaceous mudstones, which also onlap the boundary fault zone, but do not thicken towards the fault, and presumably postdate rifting. The Upper Cretaceous deposits of the Magnus Trough onlap the Magnus Ridge and Margarita Spur, and are overlain by up to 1500 m of Tertiary strata.

According to both Roberts et al. (1990) and Duindam and Van Hoorn (1987), the major west and north-west-trending faults that bound the southern margin of the Magnus Trough and intersect with the northern flank of the Margarita Spur (Figure 10) acted as complex transfer faults between the extensional West Shetland and Møre basins. Nelson and Lamy (1987) conjectured that the Magnus Trough boundary fault soles out to the north along a detachment surface lying at about 12 to 15 km depth beneath the Margarita Spur. In contrast, Beach et al. (1987) interpreted the trough's bounding fault to be a steeply dipping, through-crustal shear, related to the Great Glen Fault lineament, that had accommodated Late Jurassic to Early Cretaceous, sinistral, strike-slip movement (Figure 8). According to Gibbs (1987a), however, eastward-dipping reflectors underlying the deepest part of the Magnus Trough do not represent a continuation of a Permian unit drilled to the north-west in well 210/4-1, but mark a major, low-angle detachment fault that links to a through-crustal detachment shear (Figure 9b). The steeply dipping marginal fault of the trough was considered by Gibbs

(1987a) to be a sidewall fault, related to the Great Glen Fault system, that accommodated sinistral oblique-slip in a transtensional pull-apart basin.

West Fair Isle Basin

This elongate, north-north-easterly trending basin extends from the east of Orkney to south-west of Shetland, and is bounded to the west by the Orkney–Shetland Platform, and to the east by the East Shetland Platform. Only the northern half of the basin lies within the report area (Figure 10). The northern half of the basin is an easterly tilted half-graben (Figure 18), with a normal component of movement on the eastern boundary fault (Johnson and Dingwall, 1981; McGeary, 1987; BGS Fair Isle Solid Geology sheet). The western margin of the basin is unfaulted, and defined by the sea-bed limit of Permo-Triassic redbeds that have been drilled in the basin (Evans et al., 1981). Flinn (1969) and Bott and Browitt (1975) first identified the basin from gravity and magnetic data, and concluded that it contains up to 2300 m of Mesozoic sediments overlying Old Red Sandstone that is probably 3000 to 5000 m thick.

Reflection-seismic data indicate that Permo-Triassic rocks attain a thickness of about 2500 m in the basin (BGS Fair Isle Solid Geology sheet), and display parallel, evenly spaced reflectors (Figure 18). There is no evidence of thickening of stratigraphical units towards the basin-bounding fault, as would be expected in an asymmetrically subsiding rift. This suggests that the basin-bounding fault is post-Triassic, and that the basin is a faulted erosional remnant of a larger area of Permo-Triassic deposition. Down-faulting probably occurred during the Late Jurassic, as in adjacent basins to the east.

The fault controlling the eastern margin of the basin is a continuation of the Walls Boundary Fault, which is the likely northern continuation of the transcurrent Great Glen Fault in Scotland (Flinn, 1961; McQuillin et al., 1982). McGeary (1987) interpreted deep-reflection profiles across the Walls Boundary Fault, both to the north and south of Shetland, to show a vertical strike-slip fault that locally offsets the Moho. In the vicinity of Fair Isle, the basin-bounding fault has an *en-échelon* offset to the west, and the distribution of a scissor-fault and a compressional, reverse-fault-bounded block suggest that dextral transcurrent movement has occurred (Johns and Andrews, 1985). However, Beach (1985) favoured a sinistral sense for Triassic to Jurassic movement on this fault, and interpreted the West Fair Isle Basin as a pull-apart basin with a much greater amount of extension subparallel to its length compared to that across its width. Gibbs (1987b) postulated that the basin is underlain by an easterly dipping, low-angle, detachment fault.

East Fair Isle Basin

Lying east of Fair Isle, and surrounded on three sides by the East Shetland Platform (Figure 10), is an outcrop of Permo-Triassic redbeds termed the East Fair Isle Basin (BGS Fair Isle Solid Geology sheet). The western boundary of the basin is erosional, but the east of the basin is bounded by a sinuous, northerly trending fault. In the south, the East Fair Isle Basin merges with the East Orkney and Dutch Bank basins, where relatively thin Jurassic, Cretaceous and Tertiary deposits overlie the Permo-Triassic (Andrews et al., 1990). The thickness of redbeds in the basin is poorly constrained, but seismic evidence indicates about 2 km of Permo-Triassic strata adjacent to its faulted eastern margin (BGS Fair Isle Solid Geology sheet).

East and North Shetland platforms, and Fladen Ground Spur

The East Shetland Platform is mainly fault-bounded, and extends from the Viking Graben and the East Shetland Basin in the east, to the West Fair Isle Basin in the west. To the north it is bordered by the Unst Basin and to the south by the Dutch Bank Basin (Figure 10). The North Shetland Platform lies to the north of the Unst Basin, and a structural ridge which extends north-eastwards from it forms the Margarita Spur (Figure 10). The Fladen Ground Spur is the southern extension of the East Shetland Platform, and separates the South Viking Graben to the east from the Witch Ground Graben to the south-west (Figure 10). The East and North Shetland platforms and Fladen Ground Spur are composed of Old Red Sandstone and Caledonian basement, overlain in the east by an eastward-thickening Tertiary sequence (Figure 3).

Permian, Triassic and Jurassic strata are generally absent across the East Shetland Platform, but are locally preserved along the margin adjacent to the Viking Graben. According to Ziegler (1982), uplift and eastward tilting of the Shetland Platform during the Late Jurassic was associated with doming of the south-west Norway–Faeroe rift zone, and the resulting erosion caused clastic sediments to be shed into the rapidly subsiding North Sea rift. Relatively thin Cretaceous deposits (Figure 12), up to about 500 m thick, cover the Fladen Ground Spur (Ziegler, 1982). Possible Cretaceous deposits are also preserved in a small graben on the western part of the East Shetland Platform north of the East Fair Isle Basin (BGS Fair Isle Solid Geology sheet), which suggests that Cretaceous strata may formerly have been more extensive.

The uplift and emergence in early Tertiary times of an area extending from the Scottish Highlands to Shetland is generally attributed to opening of the North Atlantic. This uplift resulted in substantial erosion, and large volumes of denudation products were shed eastwards and south-eastwards towards partly fault-controlled basins in the Viking Graben, Moray Firth Basin and Central Graben (Ziegler, 1975; Rochow, 1981; Knox et al., 1981). Cenozoic subsidence has formed a broad synclinal downwarp centred over the North Sea rift system, and Tertiary deposits pinch out westwards across the East Shetland Platform (Ziegler, 1982; Nielsen et al., 1986).

3 Pre-Permian

Pre-Permian rocks make up much of the East and North Shetland platforms and the Fladen Ground Spur (Figure 19), and form the foundation on which the Mesozoic rift basins developed. However, relatively little is known about them, despite numerous studies carried out on land. The pre-Permian geology of the northern North Sea may have exerted an important influence on later Mesozoic basin development (see Chapter 2).

PRE-DEVONIAN

The pre-Devonian basement underlying the northern North Sea consists of rocks metamorphosed and deformed during the Caledonian and earlier orogenic cycles, when plutonic rocks were also emplaced (Frost et al., 1981; Ziegler, 1982). These basement rocks crop out (Figure 19) on Shetland (Mykura, 1976), and at or near the sea bed both across the northern part of the East Shetland Platform and on the North Shetland Platform (BGS Shetland and Miller Solid Geology sheets). About 30 hydrocarbon wells in the northern North Sea have penetrated to this crystalline basement (Figure 19). Well and geophysical data indicate that basement rocks generally lie at less than 3000 m depth beneath most of the East Shetland Platform, but are more than 7000 m deep below the Mesozoic rift zone of the Viking Graben (Hospers and Ediriweera, 1991). Aeromagnetic data suggest a predominantly north-easterly to east-north-easterly trending tectonic grain to the basement, similar to that seen in the Scottish Highlands and Norwegian Caledonides (Johnson and Dingwall, 1981).

The Caledonian front, marked by the Moine Thrust in the north-west Scottish mainland and by slides in Shetland (Figure 19), separates the older Archaean and early Proterozoic Lewisian Complex of the Laurentian Foreland to the west, from the younger Caledonides to the east. On the Scottish mainland, Caledonian basement north of the Highland Boundary Fault is separated into two terranes by the transcurrent Great Glen Fault. The Northern Highlands terrane to the north-west, and the Grampian terrane to the south-east, have overlapping but different tectonostratigraphical histories, and may represent displaced crustal blocks juxtaposed by strike-slip accretion during the Early Palaeozoic (Glennie, 1990a; Coward, 1990).

The Northern Highlands terrane consists mainly of late Proterozoic, Moine, psammitic and pelitic schists. These metasediments were originally deposited as sands and muds, probably in shallow-marine and tidal-mudflat environments (Harris, 1983) on a basement of Lewisian gneiss. This terrane underwent extensive late Precambrian deformation at about 750 Ma and possibly about 1000 Ma, as well as Caledonian orogenesis from 470 to 420 Ma (Fettes and Harris, 1986). As a result, Lewisian rocks are locally tectonically interleaved with highly deformed Moine (Rathbone and Harris, 1980).

In contrast, the Grampian terrane displays a continuous stratigraphy from basal Moine-like rocks into Dalradian strata. These mainly experienced Grampian orogenesis at around 490 Ma, with earlier deformation at about 590 Ma (G Rogers et al., 1989). The oldest rocks in this terrane may also have experienced deformation at around 750 Ma (Piasecki and

Van Breeman, 1983). The late Precambrian Dalradian succession consists mainly of quartzites, phyllites, slates and limestones, with subordinate metavolcanics, metagreywackes and tillites (Harris, 1983; Johnson, 1983; Anderton, 1985). The lower part of the Dalradian metasedimentary succession mostly accumulated on a shallow-marine continental shelf (Anderton, 1985). However, the upper part of the Dalradian consists mainly of turbidites; this upward change to deep-water facies, as well as an increase in volcanic activity, probably reflects greater tectonic subsidence and instability, which eventually split the continental plate to form the Early Palaeozoic Iapetus Ocean (Anderton, 1985).

The Caledonian basement of Shetland is also divided into two geologically distinct parts by the north-trending Walls Boundary Fault, which is probably the northward continuation of the Great Glen Fault (Flinn, 1961). In north-west Shetland, acid orthogneisses possibly represent part of the Lewisian Complex; these are separated from cover rocks, with tectonically interleaved Lewisian gneisses, by Caledonian-front slides (Figure 19) which may predate the Moine Thrust (Flinn, 1985). The cover rocks on western Shetland include steeply dipping bands of quartzite and schist metamorphosed during the Caledonian orogeny. However, they cannot be correlated with either the Moine or Dalradian successions of mainland Scotland (Mykura, 1976; Flinn, 1985).

To the east of the Walls Boundary Fault on Shetland, Caledonian basement is made up of metamorphic and plutonic rocks. The thick, vertically to steeply dipping, north-north-easterly trending metasedimentary succession consists of four lithologically distinct units (Flinn et al., 1972). The most westerly, made up of garnet-rich psammites and gneisses, has been equated with the Moine of mainland Scotland. The other three, comprising a more varied succession of schists, psammites, quartzites, limestones, metavolcanics, turbidites and gneisses, are equated with the Dalradian. The eastern Shetland succession is cut by a number of plutonic complexes (Mykura, 1976); on Unst and Fetlar (Figure 19), the east Mainland succession is in thrust contact with an ophiolite complex which is itself broken into thrust nappes (Flinn, 1985).

Basement rocks crop out at the sea bed to the east of Shetland (BGS Shetland and Halibut Bank Solid Geology sheets), where a variety of lithologies has been recovered, including quartzite, hornblende gneiss, banded gneiss, foliated augen granite and schist. BGS borehole 81/15 (Figure 19) penetrated serpentinite veined with talc. On the North Shetland Platform, BGS borehole 81/17 recovered hornblendite which yielded a K-Ar date of 697 ±13 Ma, although the significance of this date remains unclear (Ritchie et al., 1987).

Radiometric dating of pre-Devonian rocks in commercial wells from the northern North Sea indicates a fairly consistent pattern of Caledonian metamorphic dates at around 440 to 450 Ma, which is Late Ordovician (Frost et al., 1981; Harland et al., 1990). Wells in the northern North Sea have penetrated a varied assemblage of high-grade metasedimentary rocks (Figure 19), including biotite-garnet gneiss, garnet-mica schist, talc-chlorite schist and augen gneiss (Frost et al., 1981). This is in marked contrast to the central and southern North Sea, where only low-grade Caledonian basement rocks have been encountered (Frost et al., 1981). The offshore ex-

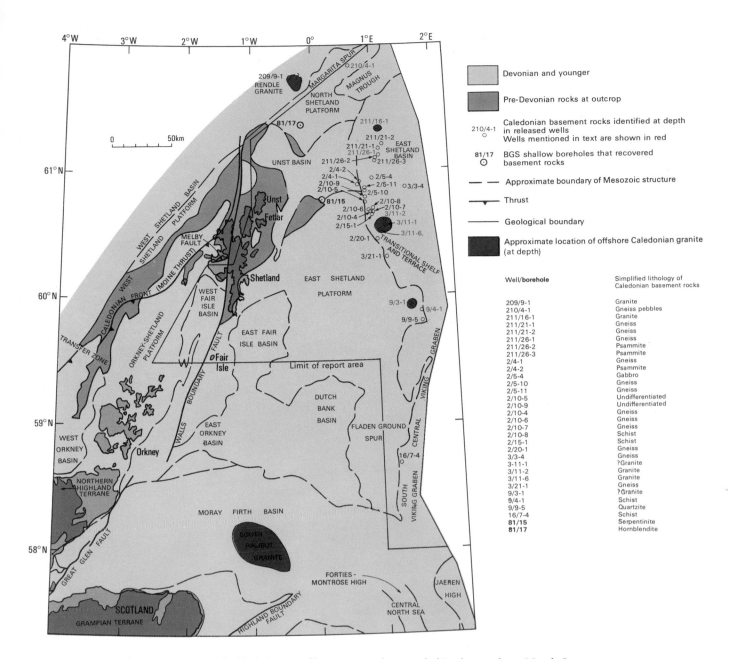

Figure 19 Distribution and simplified lithologies of basement rocks recorded in the northern North Sea and adjacent areas.

The following well/borehole lithologies are shown:

Well/borehole	Simplified lithology of Caledonian basement rocks
209/9-1	Granite
210/4-1	Gneiss pebbles
211/16-1	Granite
211/21-1	Gneiss
211/21-2	Gneiss
211/26-1	Gneiss
211/26-2	Psammite
211/26-3	Psammite
2/4-1	Gneiss
2/4-2	Psammite
2/5-4	Gabbro
2/5-10	Gneiss
2/5-11	Gneiss
2/10-5	Undifferentiated
2/10-9	Undifferentiated
2/10-4	Gneiss
2/10-6	Gneiss
2/10-7	Gneiss
2/10-8	Schist
2/15-1	Schist
2/20-1	Gneiss
3/3-4	Gneiss
3-11-1	?Granite
3/11-2	Granite
3/11-6	Granite
3/21-1	Gneiss
9/3-1	?Granite
9/4-1	Schist
9/9-5	Quartzite
16/7-4	Schist
81/15	Serpentinite
81/17	Hornblendite

Legend:
- Devonian and younger
- Pre-Devonian rocks at outcrop
- Caledonian basement rocks identified at depth in released wells. Wells mentioned in text are shown in red
- BGS shallow boreholes that recovered basement rocks
- Approximate boundary of Mesozoic structure
- Thrust
- Geological boundary
- Approximate location of offshore Caledonian granite (at depth)

tent of Caledonian metamorphic provinces is probably controlled by major faults, some of which may be extensions of structures on the Scottish mainland (Frost et al., 1981), such as the Highland Boundary Fault (Figure 5).

Biotite-gneiss pebbles in redbeds of Permian or Devonian age at the bottom of well 210/4-1 on the Margarita Spur (Figure 19) are presumed to have been derived from the local basement on the North Shetland Platform. The gneisses consist mainly of potassic feldspar and biotite with minor oligoclase, quartz and muscovite. The biotite defines a coarse, gneissose fabric, and strain features are present in all the minerals (Frost et al., 1981). The Ar-Ar age spectrum from biotite shows two main components at 442 ± 2 Ma and 248 ± 7 Ma (Frost et al., 1981). The source of the conglomerate clasts is thought to have originally crystallised during the Grampian orogeny, but the early metamorphic effects were probably totally overprinted by later Caledonian events, and the rock underwent further argon loss in Late Permian to Early Triassic times, possibly due to a tectonic or igneous event (Frost et al., 1981).

In the East Shetland Basin, well 211/26-1 (Figure 19) penetrated biotite gneiss which yielded a K-Ar whole-rock age of 430 Ma; this is probably close to the age of a retrograde Caledonian metamorphic event (Frost et al., 1981). Well 9/4-1, farther south on the eastern flank of the East Shetland Platform (Figure 19), yielded an average K-Ar age of 393 ± 7 Ma (Early Devonian — Harland et al., 1990) from hornblende-biotite schist. This may reflect the nearby occurrence of a late Caledonian pluton (Ritchie et al., 1987).

On mainland Scotland, granitic bodies were intruded into Dalradian and Moine metasedimentary rocks both at the start of uplift (c. 590 Ma — G Rogers et al., 1989), and during the main regional uplift at the waning phase of the Caledonian orogeny. The late-orogenic 'Older' granites are foliated, and were emplaced at about 470 to 460 Ma (Kneller and Aftalion, 1987), during Llanvirn to Caradoc times (Harland et al., 1990). Large, postorogenic 'Newer' granites are generally of calc-alkaline type, and were intruded during Silurian to Early Devonian times, from 435 to c.390 Ma (Brown, 1991). Caledonian plutonic complexes in east-

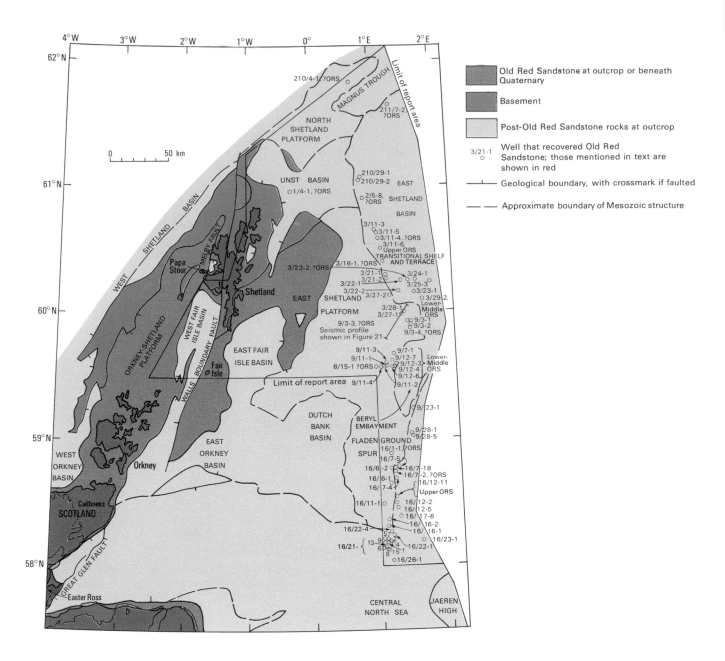

Figure 20 Distribution of Old Red Sandstone rocks in the northern North Sea and adjacent areas.

ern Shetland are of variable composition, including granite pegmatite, diorite, monzonite and granodiorite. These rocks are in places weakly foliated, indicating that they were emplaced before Caledonian tectonic activity had ceased (Mykura, 1976).

Offshore, the South Halibut Granite in the Moray Firth Basin, and the Rendle Granite north of the North Shetland Platform (Figure 19), have both yielded Caledonian radiometric ages (Hitchen and Ritchie, 1987; Andrews et al., 1990). A number of wells in the northern North Sea area have terminated in granitic rocks, and the positions of granite plutons may have influenced the development of lateral offsets of the Viking Graben margin. On the basis of magnetic and gravity anomalies and the recovery of granitic material in well 9/3-1, Donato and Tully (1982) postulated that a granite batholith 40 km in diameter offsets the western flank of the Central Viking Graben (Figure 10). However, seismic data (see Figure 21) indicate that much of the geophysical anomaly coincides with a sedimentary basin, although a small granite pluton surrounded by metamorphic rocks may be centred on well 9/3-1 (Holloway et al., 1991).

Granitic rocks were penetrated in three wells on the Transitional Shelf and Terrace (Figure 19). In well 3/11-1, the crystalline basement is reported to be a cataclastic granitic rock which is too deformed to determine whether it was originally a true granite or a granitic gneiss. The material is coarse grained, and consists mainly of quartz, plagioclase and microcline with minor muscovite, biotite and secondary chlorite (Frost et al., 1981). Well 3/11-2 penetrated red, microcrystalline granite with a granophyric texture. The main constituent minerals are pink feldspar and clear to red quartz, with muscovite, biotite and minor tourmaline. The coarse-grained granite in well 3/11-6 is dark orange, and consists mainly of orthoclase feldspar and quartz with minor biotite; a Mid-Devonian age is assigned to this granite on the oil-company log.

On a structural ridge in the East Shetland Basin, well 211/16-1 (Figure 19) penetrated a slightly weathered and deformed, pinkish grey microgranite. The microgranite consists of quartz, oligoclase, microcline and perthite, with traces of biotite and muscovite (Frost et al., 1981). Other granites probably remain to be found on the East Shetland Platform and near the margin of the Viking Graben.

OLD RED SANDSTONE

As a result of the closure of the Early Palaeozoic (Iapetus) Ocean, a large continental mass was formed at the close of the Caledonian orogeny in the North Atlantic region (Ziegler, 1988b). Following the waning of Caledonian orogenic events, uplift and crustal extension gave rise to the formation of fault-controlled graben and half-graben basins (D A Rogers et al., 1989), and subsequently to the formation of the Orcadian Basin, a major area of internal continental drainage (Norton et al., 1987) in which Old Red Sandstone (ORS) sediments were deposited.

The Orcadian Basin may have extended eastwards some 600 km from the north-east coast of Scotland to the western coast of Norway, covering much of the report area (Ziegler, 1982). Seismic profiles suggest that terrigenous and lacustrine sedimentary deposits in the basin are up to 6000 m thick. Although predominantly of Devonian age, deposition of ORS facies in northern Britain may have begun during Silurian times (Marshall, 1991) and locally persisted into Early Carboniferous times (Paterson and Hall, 1986). In places, sedimentation was accompanied by volcanism of mainly tholeiitic and calc-alkaline type, which was probably associated with emplacement of the 'Newer' Caledonian granites.

Palaeomagnetic evidence indicates that during the Devonian, northern Britain occupied a low-latitude position in the southern hemisphere (Tarling, 1985), in which the climate was probably warm to hot, and generally semiarid (Allen, 1979). A gradual change to a wetter, equatorial climate took place in Early Carboniferous times due to the northward drift of the ORS continent (Tarling, 1985). In the Moray Firth Basin, fluvial systems that deposited ORS redbeds possibly drained southwards into fluviodeltaic and shallow-marine areas represented by coal-bearing Early Carboniferous strata (Richards, 1990a).

The tectonic development of the Orcadian Basin may have been controlled by complex extensional reactivation along easterly dipping Caledonian thrusts during the collapse of the Caledonian orogen (Beach, 1985; Norton et al., 1987), and by transcurrent motion roughly parallel to the Caledonian grain (Watson, 1985; Coward, 1990). However, the amount of syndepositional fault movement is the subject of debate, and according to D A Rogers et al. (1989) and Thirlwall (1989), most of the wrench motion on the Great Glen Fault took place prior to deposition of the ORS.

The preserved thickness of the ORS is a result of the combination of Orcadian Basin development and the amount of post-Devonian erosion. In most of the wells that penetrated Caledonian basement in the northern North Sea (Figure 19), ORS rocks are absent; this may be largely the result of erosion on uplifted fault blocks. The thickness of ORS can be especially difficult to determine where it is overlain by Permo-Triassic redbeds. In the Unst Basin, well 1/4-1 (Figure 20) terminated in about 1000 m of redbeds; the upper 400 m of this succession have yielded palynoflora indicating a Late Permian age, but a Devonian age cannot be ruled out for the lowermost 375 m of sandy conglomerates with varied igneous and metamorphic clasts (Johns and Andrews, 1985). Commonly, however, ORS deposits can be differentiated from Permo-Triassic redbeds on the basis of both their higher density and their higher average sonic velocity.

Seismic-reflection data are useful in defining the preserved remnants of offshore Devonian basins beneath parts of the northern North Sea, but the structure, thickness and extent of the ORS beneath the Viking Graben, East Shetland Basin and Magnus Trough are generally not resolved. On the East Shetland Platform adjacent to the Central Viking Graben (Figure 20), seismic data indicate a synclinally folded basin (Figure 21) that contains about 6000 m of pre-Jurassic strata which, from regional considerations, are most likely to be of Devonian age (Holloway et al., 1991). Gravity, magnetic and

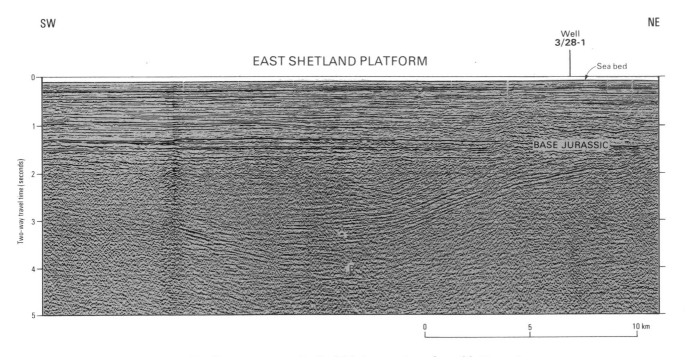

Figure 21   Seismic-reflection profile illustrating a synclinally folded succession of possible Devonian age on the East Shetland Platform. After Holloway et al. (1991). Either event A or event B may mark the base of the Devonian rocks. For location see Figure 20.

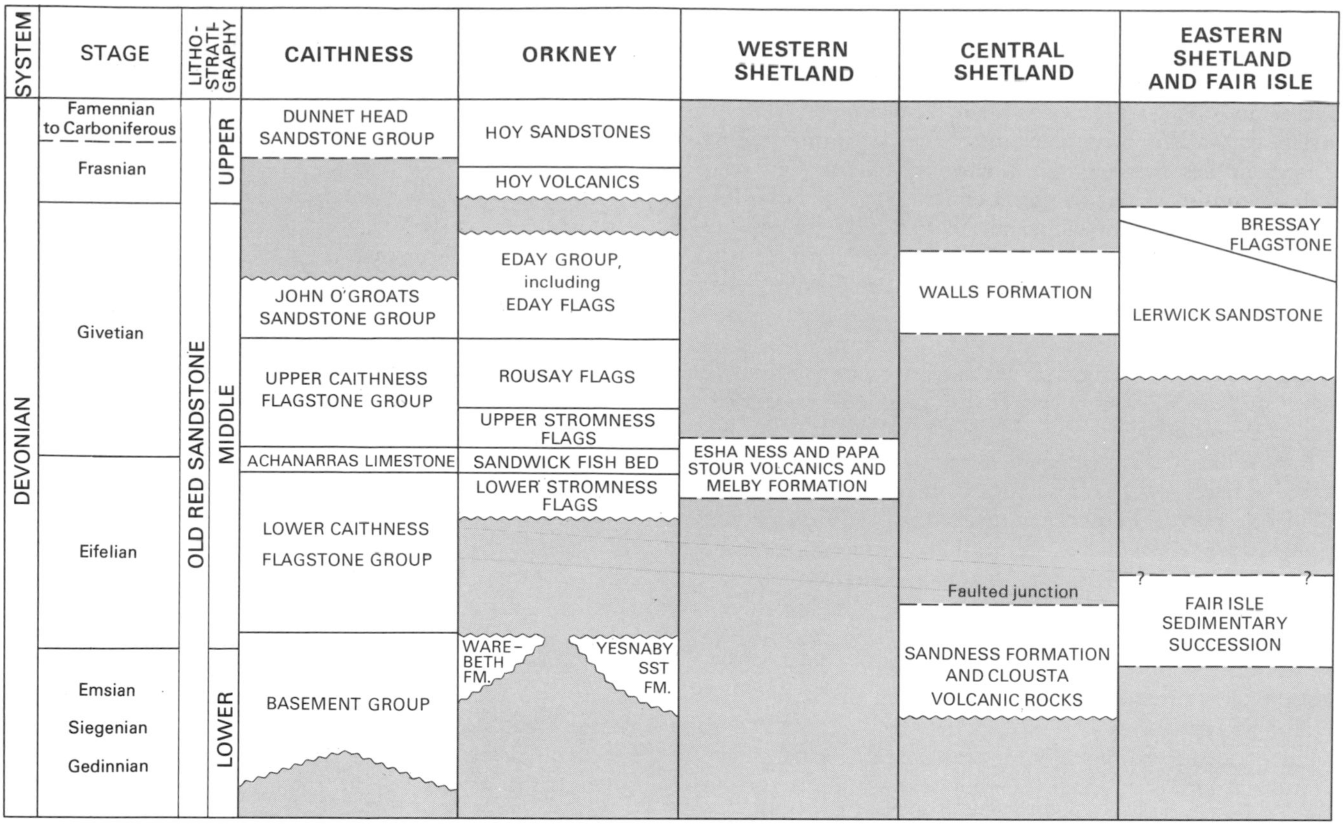

SYSTEM	STAGE	LITHO-STRATIGRAPHY	CAITHNESS	ORKNEY	WESTERN SHETLAND	CENTRAL SHETLAND	EASTERN SHETLAND AND FAIR ISLE
DEVONIAN	Famennian to Carboniferous	OLD RED SANDSTONE — UPPER	DUNNET HEAD SANDSTONE GROUP	HOY SANDSTONES			
	Frasnian			HOY VOLCANICS			BRESSAY FLAGSTONE
	Givetian	OLD RED SANDSTONE — MIDDLE	JOHN O'GROATS SANDSTONE GROUP	EDAY GROUP, including EDAY FLAGS		WALLS FORMATION	LERWICK SANDSTONE
			UPPER CAITHNESS FLAGSTONE GROUP	ROUSAY FLAGS			
				UPPER STROMNESS FLAGS			
			ACHANARRAS LIMESTONE	SANDWICK FISH BED	ESHA NESS AND PAPA STOUR VOLCANICS AND MELBY FORMATION		
	Eifelian		LOWER CAITHNESS FLAGSTONE GROUP	LOWER STROMNESS FLAGS		Faulted junction	FAIR ISLE SEDIMENTARY SUCCESSION
	Emsian	OLD RED SANDSTONE — LOWER	BASEMENT GROUP	WAREBETH FM. / YESNABY SST FM.		SANDNESS FORMATION AND CLOUSTA VOLCANIC ROCKS	
	Siegenian						
	Gedinnian						

Figure 22 Simplified stratigraphy of the Old Red Sandstone in Caithness, Orkney and Shetland. After Mykura (1983).

well data suggest that this basin may be flanked by a small granite pluton (Holloway et al., 1991). According to Gatliff et al. (1994), similar Devonian basins on the Mid North Sea High of the central North Sea may have formed between crustal blocks buoyed by Caledonian granites.

Lithostratigraphical divisions (Figure 22) of Lower, Middle and Upper Old Red Sandstone have commonly been taken as broadly corresponding to Lower, Middle and Upper Devonian rocks (Mykura, 1983). Most offshore ORS successions have not yielded fossils, and are therefore undifferentiated, as on the western part of the East Shetland Platform where reddish purple and greenish grey sandstones and mudstones have been recovered from gravity cores (BGS Shetland Solid Geology sheet). However, a complete suite of ORS sediments has been indicated on oil-company logs from a few wells in the northern North Sea and Moray Firth (Andrews et al., 1990).

Lower Old Red Sandstone

These largely Lower Devonian rocks have a limited distribution around the margins of the Orcadian Basin, but crop out around the coast of the Moray Firth, on Shetland, and on Orkney (Figure 22). The deposits are up to about 3000 m thick, and are generally made up of associations of interdigitating conglomerates, sandstones and mudstones (Mykura, 1983). They may have accumulated in areally restricted, intermontane, lacustrine basins, the margins of which may have been controlled, at least in part, by active faults (Mykura, 1983).

In the Moray Firth Basin, a few wells have drilled up to about 1000 m of possible Lower ORS comprising grey to reddish brown, micaceous mudstones with minor sandstones (Andrews et al., 1990). Supposed Lower ORS has also been reported just to the north of the Beryl Embayment, where

well 9/12-3 penetrated about 60 m of very fine- to very coarse-grained sandstone (Figure 20). Possible Lower to Middle Devonian rocks have been drilled in wells 9/7-1 and 3/29-2; these are considered together with the Middle ORS rocks.

Middle Old Red Sandstone

Middle Devonian rocks form most of the Orcadian Basin successions, and crop out mainly in Orkney and Caithness (Figure 22), but also intermittently to the south-west around the Moray Firth coast. They also occur on Shetland. There is a marked change in facies from, in the south, mainly sandstones and thick conglomerates with sedimentary structures indicating a fluvial origin, to mudstones and sandstones of lacustrine origin in the north. An angular unconformity commonly separates the Lower and Middle ORS, with the strongly diachronous base of the Middle ORS overstepping on to Caledonian basement. The lacustrine Middle Devonian succession reaches a thickness of about 4000 m in Caithness, and 2000 m in Orkney; it consists of well-defined rhythmic units, or 'cycles', of laminated, carbonate-rich siltstones and shales with subordinate, thinly bedded sandstones and fish beds (Mykura, 1983; Johnstone and Mykura, 1989). There are upward-coarsening and rarer upward-fining cycles, generally 5 to 10 m thick, but some are as much as 60 m in thickness (Mykura, 1983). Every rhythm represents a sequence of events caused by repeated fluctuations in lake level (Donovan, 1980; Rogers and Astin, 1991). Most upward-coarsening rhythms record gradual fluviatile incursions during phases of low lake level (Parnell, 1988).

Extensive outcrops of Middle ORS on Shetland comprise three separate groups differing in age, facies, and extent of deformation. They may have been juxtaposed by later dextral movements (Mykura, 1975; 1983) along the Melby and Walls Boundary faults (Figure 20). However, D A Rogers et al. (1989) proposed post-Devonian reverse movement with only minor strike-slip along the Melby Fault.

The thermally metamorphosed and deformed Walls Formation lies between the Melby and Walls Boundary faults; it consists of up to 9000 m of dark grey, fine- to medium-grained sandstones with thin rhythmic alternations of mudstones, and rare calcilutites. The sandstones have a high proportion of clastic matrix, and Mykura (1983) interpreted them as lacustrine mass-flow deposits. In contrast, Melvin (1985) divided the Walls Formation into three distinct lithofacies associations, and interpreted the succession as the product of meandering-stream, sheltered-floodplain, and braided-stream environments.

Miospore evidence indicates that the little-altered, mainly volcanic succession on Papa Stour to the west of the Melby Fault (Figures 20 and 22), is older than the Walls Formation (Marshall, 1988). Fish beds in the Melby Formation to the west of the Melby Fault are of late Eifelian age (Mykura, 1983). The Melby Formation comprises 600 m of cross-bedded, fluviatile sandstone with intercalated lacustrine mudstones, overlain by a volcanic suite of rhyolite, basalt and andesite (Mykura, 1983).

The Middle Devonian sequence of Shetland east of the Walls Boundary Fault consists of conglomerates and pebbly sandstones with thinly bedded, flaggy sandstones, calcareous siltstones, and laminated mudstones with fish beds. These are thought to have accumulated in fluvial floodplain and lake environments (Allen and Marshall, 1981). On Fair Isle (Figures 20 and 22), conglomerates, pebbly sandstones and mudstones over 1700 m thick are also largely of Mid-Devonian age (D A Rogers et al., 1989).

Mykura (1983) has reconstructed the Mid-Devonian palaeogeography of the region around north-east Scotland, Orkney and Shetland (Figure 23), taking into account postulated subsequent movements along the major transcurrent faults that traverse the area. The reconstruction suggests that alluvial plains extended over the southern Moray Firth area, and some sedimentary detritus may have been derived from the nearby South Halibut Granite (Andrews et al., 1990). The shallow Orcadian Lake extended from southern Caithness northwards beyond Orkney, and was flanked to the west by metamorphic highlands. To the north, highlands supplied clastic detritus to an alluvial plain on which the Melby Formation was deposited; this plain was bounded in the north-east by volcanic uplands. In the present Walls area of Shetland, a rapidly subsiding alluvial basin developed (Melvin, 1985). The eastern Shetland sediments were deposited in alluvial fans and on plains bounded in the southeast by a shallow lake (Allen and Marshall, 1981; Mykura, 1983). In the southern and central North Sea, Middle Devonian marine limestones with corals were deposited (Gatliff et al., 1994). According to Mykura (1983), a possible river connecting the Orcadian Lake with a tongue of the sea in the Central Graben may account for the lack of evaporites in the Orcadian Basin.

Seven wells in the northern North Sea have penetrated rocks presumed to be of Mid-Devonian age. Supposed Lower to Middle Devonian rocks were drilled at the bottom of well 9/7-1 (Figure 24), immediately to the west of the Beryl Embayment. These strata comprise about 260 m of grey, green and reddish brown, calcareous mudstone and fine-grained sandstone with a few beds of argillaceous limestone. In the middle to upper part of the succession, the gamma-ray log response suggests upward-fining cycles about 10 to 15 m thick, and possibly some thinner upward-coarsening units.

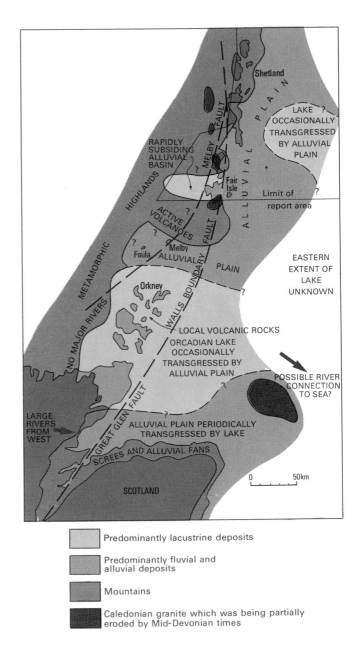

Figure 23 Mid-Devonian palaeogeographic reconstruction of north-east Scotland and the northern Isles. After Mykura (1983) with modifications after Andrews et al. (1990) and Melvin (1985). Displacements of 30 km, 80 km, and 80 km respectively have been made along the Great Glen, Walls Boundary and Melby faults to restore the present coastline to its inferred position during Mid-Devonian times.

In the Central Viking Graben, well 3/29-2 (Figure 20) penetrated about 230 m of pink, buff, greenish grey, and pale to dark grey sandstone and calcareous mudstone of Early to Mid-Devonian age, which overlie crystalline basement. A Lower to Middle Devonian sequence has also been penetrated at the bottom of wells 9/12-4, 9/12-6 (Figure 24), and well 9/12-7 (Figure 20). These wells drilled about 80 m, 150 m, and 80 m respectively of black, grey and reddish brown, calcareous, micromicaceous mudstones with interbedded grey and reddish brown, fine-grained sandstones. In wells 9/12-4 and 9/12-6, the strata contain rich assemblages of carbonised spores, including *Rhabdosporites langii* (Eisenack) Richardson, *Ancyrospora* and *Hystrichosporites;* these suggest an Eifelian to Givetian age. Some of the black mudstones are very radioactive, perhaps reflecting their high organic content.

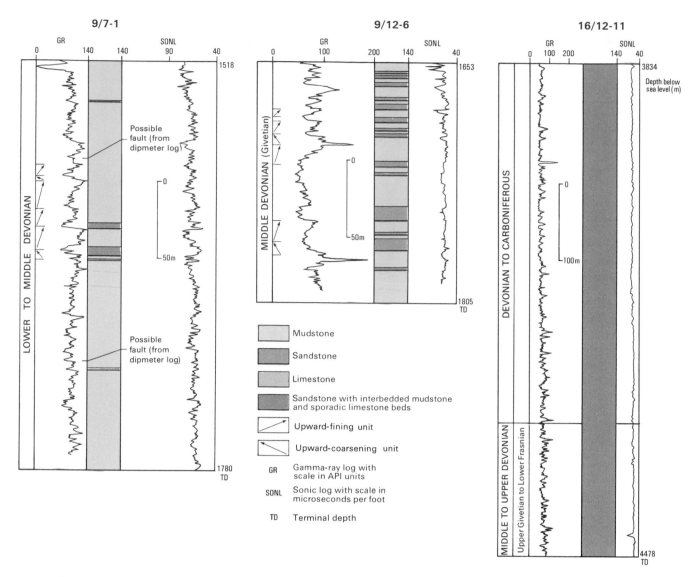

Figure 24 Devonian sections from selected wells in the northern North Sea. For locations see Figure 20.

Possible Middle to Upper Devonian rocks comprising interbedded, fine-grained sandstone and mudstone are reported at the bottom of well 9/11-2, west of the Beryl Embayment (Figure 20). In the South Viking Graben, well 16/12-11 (Figure 24) penetrated a thick succession of very fine- to medium-grained sandstone with interbedded mudstone, the lower 180 m of which have been assigned a Mid- to Late Devonian age (late Givetian to early Frasnian) on the oil-company log.

Upper Old Red Sandstone

Upper ORS rocks crop out in Caithness, Orkney, sporadically along the coast of the Moray Firth, and possibly in southeast Shetland (Mykura, 1983). Perhaps as a result of Mid-Devonian earth movements, the Upper Devonian sequences in many places lie unconformably upon Middle Devonian rocks. Onshore, the Upper ORS of the Orcadian Basin consists mainly of red, yellow or buff, cross-bedded sandstones with local lenses of conglomerate. The sandstones contain fewer lithic clasts, and a higher proportion of quartz grains, than those in the older Devonian sequences. These strata are generally considered to have accumulated in fluvial and aeolian environments. In the upper part of the succession there are many horizons of cornstone; these indicate phases of re-duced sedimentation during which caliche soils and sabkha conditions were able to develop (Mykura, 1983). Volcanic rocks are absent in the Upper ORS of the Scottish mainland, but occur on Orkney (Figure 22).

Very few wells in the northern North Sea region have proved Upper ORS. Recrystallised, quartz-rich sandstone overlying weathered Middle Devonian granite in well 3/11-6 on the Transitional Shelf and Terrace are reported to be of Late Devonian age. A thick succession of interbedded sandstones and mudstones in well 16/12-11, on the western flank of the South Viking Graben, may also be of Late Devonian age according to the oil-company log (Figure 24).

CARBONIFEROUS

Well 9/13-22 in the Beryl Embayment (Figure 25) is the only location in the northern North Sea where Carboniferous rocks have been penetrated. Ziegler (1982; 1990) suggested that nondeposition and erosion were prevalent in this region during the Carboniferous. However, in the Outer Moray Firth and Forth Approaches basins to the south, Old Red Sandstone facies sediments are overlain by a Carboniferous coal-bearing succession which is more than 1500 m thick in the Outer

Moray Firth Basin (Andrews et al., 1990). Miospore evidence shows this coal-bearing unit to be of Viséan to Namurian age (Andrews et al., 1990; Gatliff et al., 1994). Volcanic rocks of Viséan age are interbedded with the coal-bearing succession in the Outer Moray Firth Basin (Andrews et al., 1990; Leeder et al., 1990). In the Dutch Bank Basin, well 8/27-1 (Figure 25) drilled about 100 m of redbeds beneath Zechstein strata; these are inferred to be of Late Carboniferous age.

Gatliff et al. (1994) postulate that Carboniferous deposits may extend north-eastwards from the Forth Approaches Basin to the Fisher Bank Basin and north of the Jaeren High (Figure 25). It is likely that Carboniferous strata were deposited over a wider area than that in which they are now preserved (Leeder et al., 1990), but it is uncertain whether uplift and erosion in the Outer Moray Firth Basin was initiated during the Namurian, or as in much of northern Britain, during late Westphalian/Stephanian times. Ziegler (1982) favoured the former alternative, whereas Leeder et al. (1990) preferred the latter.

Haszeldine and Russell (1987) recognised north-trending Carboniferous lineaments in Britain and Norway, and postulated that the dominant Carboniferous stress field was east–west extension. About 75 m of reddish brown to grey mudstones with interbeds of sandstone at the bottom of well 9/13-22 in the Beryl Embayment (Figure 25) have been interpreted on the oil-company log as nonmarine Carboniferous deposits, and Haszeldine and Russell (1987) have reported a 4 m-thick, black shale near their base. Spore evidence from this shale suggests that it is no older than Bolsovian (Westphalian C). These Westphalian strata are overlain by about 300 m of unfossiliferous, reddish brown, interbedded sandstones, mudstones and conglomerates, which are capped by about 65 m of varicoloured and interbedded dolomite, anhydrite, sandstone and mudstone, with abundant Late Permian palynofloras. Haszeldine and Russell (1987) suggested that the presence of Carboniferous strata in the Beryl Embayment supports their view that the north-north-easterly trending Viking Graben had a Carboniferous rift history.

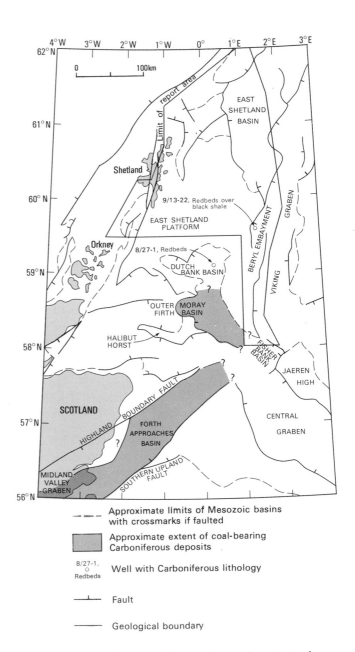

Figure 25 Distribution of Carboniferous deposits in the northern North Sea and adjacent areas.

4 Permian and Triassic

Permo-Triassic strata, mostly of redbed facies, occur in all basins across the northern North Sea (Figure 26). In the smaller basins where the strata commonly crop out at sea bed (Figure 2; BGS Solid Geology sheets), subdivision of the succession is not possible due to lack of biostratigraphical evidence. The trilete Unst Basin contains over 3600 m of Permo-Triassic redbeds. About 2700 m of undifferentiated Permo-Triassic sediments are preserved in the West Fair Isle Basin adjacent to the Walls Boundary Fault, and approximately 2000 m occur in the deepest parts of the East Fair Isle Basin.

In the graben areas, the Permian and Triassic can be differentiated locally; up to 300 m of Lower Permian (Rotliegend) and 464 m of Upper Permian (Zechstein) strata have been penetrated in the Beryl Embayment. About 450 to 500 m of Permian strata also occur in the Magnus Trough. It is, however, generally difficult to determine the maximum thickness of Permian strata elsewhere because the base of the Permian is not imaged on seismic sections. Over 1700 m of Triassic has been proved in the East Shetland Basin, where thickness is variable, and up to 4000 m may be preserved in the Viking Graben. It is likely that there are some 1500 m of Triassic sediments in the Magnus Trough, where no significant thickness variations are observed on seismic-reflection profiles.

PERMO-TRIASSIC BASIN DEVELOPMENT

According to Ziegler (1982), the overall size and shape of the depositional basin in the North Sea changed significantly during Permo-Triassic times. During the Early Permian, continental and lacustrine sediments were deposited in both the Southern and Northern Permian basins, separated by the Mid North Sea High. Ziegler (1982) suggested that the Northern Permian Basin extended northwards from the central North Sea into the Moray Firth and South Viking Graben. However, Lower Permian sediments have been encountered in wells in the Magnus Trough and Unst Basin, suggesting that the depositional area was more extensive.

The depositional area of the Northern Permian Basin is thought to have expanded during Late Permian times. Ziegler (1982) postulated that a succession of continental, coastal and evaporitic Zechstein sediments may have been deposited along the axial area of the developing Viking Graben, with the creation of a northwards link to the Boreal Ocean. However, Fisher and Mudge (1990) envisaged a wider depositional area across the Viking Graben during the Late Permian, and suggested that the basin may also have extended across the present-day East Shetland Basin, Unst Basin and East and West Fair Isle basins. Andrews et al. (1990) also suggested that Upper Permian clastic sediments are present in the southern part of the West Fair Isle Basin, where a BGS vibrocore sample (BGS Orkney Solid Geology sheet) recovered sediments with a diverse Later Permian miospore assemblage. Upper Permian strata have also been proved in the Unst Basin, where a rich and diverse palynoflora was recovered (Johns and Andrews, 1985).

The depositional area in the northern North Sea expanded farther during the Early Triassic (Ziegler, 1982), with continental sediments laid down throughout the Viking Graben, East Shetland Basin, Magnus Basin, Unst Basin, and East and West Fair Isle basins. Ziegler (1982) envisaged that much of the East Shetland Platform remained an area of nondeposition throughout Triassic times, and Deegan and Scull (1977) suggested a possible sediment source area in this region.

The major tectonic controls on Permo-Triassic basin development and sedimentation in the graben areas have been a matter of debate since Ziegler (1975; 1978) suggested that the Viking Graben began to form during the Permian by fault-controlled extension, and that movement continued on the western bounding fault throughout Triassic times. More recently it has been suggested that the first of two rifting phases in the northern North Sea probably started in Late Permian times, and continued through the Early Triassic, to be followed by a phase of thermally controlled subsidence that lasted into the later part of the Mid-Jurassic (Badley et al., 1988; Thorne and Watts, 1989). Steel and Ryseth (1990) concurred, but cited thickness variations in the Triassic succession of the East Shetland Basin as evidence that faults were active there during Triassic times.

Fisher and Mudge (1990) considered that the lithological sequence in the Beryl Embayment, where Triassic conglomerates overlie Permian carbonates, implies a significant degree of fault control on Triassic sedimentation at the basin margin that was not necessarily active during the Permian. The presence of Upper Permian sediments of similar thickness on both sides of the graben-bounding fault suggested to Frostick et al. (1992) that there was no Permian faulting. Ormaasen et al. (1980) implied that neither Permian nor Triassic sedimentation was fault controlled in the Beryl Embayment.

Permian halite and attendant halokinesis had a less significant effect on Triassic sedimentation and thickness distribution in the Viking Graben than in other parts of the North Sea. Indeed, halite has been recorded in only two wells in the Viking Graben. However, salt movement has affected Triassic thickness variations to some degree in the South Viking Graben. A seismic line through well 9/27-1 (Figure 27) demonstrates the presence of a pod of Triassic sediment whose distribution is almost certainly controlled by the effects of salt withdrawal.

Johns and Andrews (1985) suggested that the Unst Basin was initiated in Early Permian times, and that there was syndepositional movement on the basin-bounding faults throughout the Permo-Triassic. Indeed, considerable southward thickening of the Permo-Triassic succession can be demonstrated on seismic-reflection profiles in the Block 1/4 Graben (Figure 26), where the succession thickens from some 500 m in the north-east, to about 3000 m adjacent to the southern bounding fault. Johns and Andrews (1985) demonstrated a similar thickening of the Permo-Triassic succession south-eastwards within the north-east arm of the Unst Basin, where a wedge of sediment thickens from zero to about 2000 m adjacent to the Pobie Fault (Figure 16). However, the Permo-Triassic succession appears to be of uniform thickness within the north-west arm, suggesting that this part of the basin may not have been subjected to extension during the Permian and Triassic.

In the Magnus Trough, Permo-Triassic strata were encountered in well 210/4-1, near the northern margin (Figure 26), and can be imaged on seismic sections southwards across the trough to the bounding fault against the Magnus Ridge.

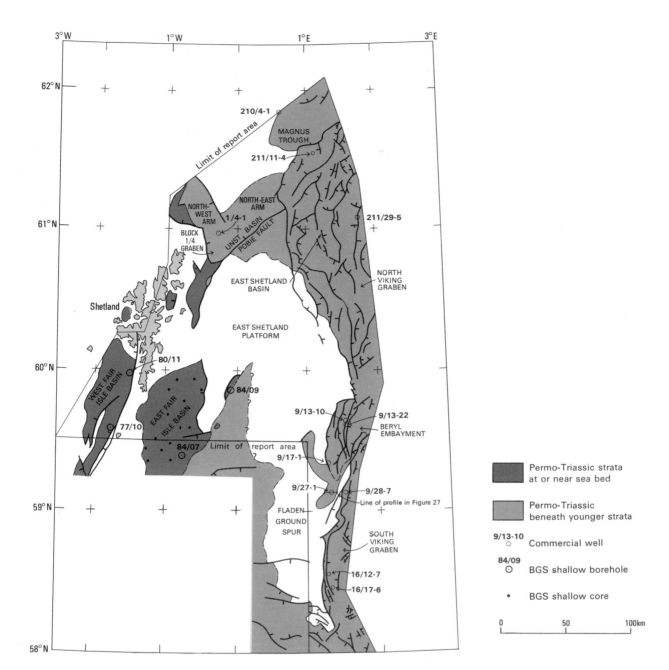

Figure 26   Distribution of Permo-Triassic strata in the northern North Sea.

There is no evidence for wedging of reflectors within the Permo-Triassic succession, suggesting that the sequence was not deposited during syndepositional extension of the basin.

Permo-Triassic strata crop out at sea bed in both the East and West Fair Isle basins (Figure 26). Seismic-reflection profiles across the West Fair Isle Basin show that the succession here comprises parallel, evenly spaced reflectors, with no evidence of stratigraphical thickening or wedging towards the bounding faults of the half-graben (Figure 18). It is likely that this Permo-Triassic succession was deposited in a much larger basin that originally extended over parts of the East Shetland Platform, the Orkney–Shetland Platform, and the Moray Firth, and have been preserved as separate, downfaulted wedges following later Mesozoic subsidence and Tertiary inversion.

PERMIAN

Lower Permian, Rotliegend, sediments have been recognised in only 13 wells in the report area, and the Upper Permian in 15. The wells provide insufficient information to allow depositional trends and facies belts to be delineated.

Lower Permian (Rotliegend)

Although the distribution of Rotliegend strata is incompletely known in the northern North Sea, Glennie (1990b) envisaged that deposition was probably largely continental and dominated by aeolian, fluvial and sabkha environments. Depositional patterns in the Northern Permian Basin were probably similar to those in the more fully documented Southern Permian Basin, although Glennie (1990b) has suggested that there were significantly different wind systems controlling aeolian sedimentation in the two basins. Aeolian sediments of the Southern Permian Basin were deposited by winds that blew towards the west and south-west, whereas the main wind direction in the Northern Permian Basin appears to have been towards the east or south-east.

There is no formal lithostratigraphical subdivision of Lower Permian sediments in the northern North Sea. In the

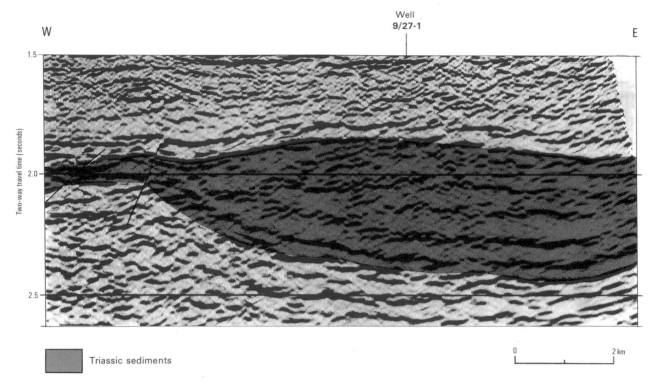

W   Well 9/27-1   E

Two-way travel time (seconds)

1.5

2.0

2.5

Triassic sediments

0   2 km

Figure 27   Seismic section through well 9/27-1 in the southern part of the Beryl Embayment, illustrating a pod of Triassic sediment formed as a result of local salt withdrawal. For location see Figure 26.

central North Sea, Deegan and Scull (1977) defined the sand-dominated, aeolian, Auk Formation sediments and the shale-dominated, sabkha-deposited Fraserburgh Formation. They described the northern North Sea succession as local occurrences of dune sands.

Some dominantly sandy Lower Permian successions in the Viking Graben have been informally assigned to the Auk Formation on oil-company logs. Many successions comprise varicoloured, partly conglomeratic sandstones that are similar to those of the Auk Formation, interbedded with shales similar to the Fraserburgh Formation, as in well 9/13-22 (Figure 28). A 26 m-thick conglomerate, with clasts of shattered metamorphic rock fragments, at the base of the Rotliegend succession in well 9/13-22 in the Beryl Embayment, is similar to basal conglomerates with quartz and schist clasts that are typically found at the base of the Auk Formation in the central North Sea.

A dominantly argillaceous Lower Permian succession has been recorded in well 16/17-6 (Figure 28), in the South Viking Graben. This 83 m-thick succession, dominated by reddish brown claystone with some evaporites and silty laminae, is similar to, but substantially less radioactive than, the Fraserburgh Formation as defined in the type well some 120 km to the south-west. The Fraserburgh Formation also occurs in the outer Moray Firth (Andrews et al., 1990) in a relatively low-radioactive mudstone facies similar to that in well 16/17-6.

Deegan and Scull (1977) noted that the Auk and Fraserburgh formations pass laterally into each other in the central North Sea, where the dominantly aeolian deposits of the Auk Formation are bordered by the dominantly sabkha environments of the Fraserburgh Formation. The interbedded sediments recorded in the northern North Sea, such as those in well 9/17-1 (Figure 28), may represent similar interdigitation of aeolian/fluvial and sabkha environments, but on a smaller-scale and representing repeated vertical alternations of environment.

Volcanic rocks of probable Early Permian age have been encountered in two wells in and around the Magnus Trough (Figure 26). In well 210/4-1 there is an approximately 6 m-thick unit of porphyritic extrusive igneous rocks with feldspar and green phenocrysts, interbedded with reddish brown siltstones. In the other well, 211/11-4 on the southern margin of the trough, the 77 m-thick Lower Permian succession comprises reddish brown, hard, splintery tuff and altered tuff with shards and phenocrysts of ferromagnesian minerals. Several extrusive porphyry beds up to about 5 m thick are interbedded with the tuffs. Earliest Permian volcanic rocks are common in Germany, Poland, the Oslo Graben and the Horn Graben, but there is insufficient age evidence from the Magnus Trough volcanics to enable correlation with these occurrences.

Upper Permian (Zechstein)

Redbed deposition under essentially desert conditions ceased at the start of Late Permian times due to flooding of the basin by the expansion of the Boreal Ocean (Ziegler, 1982). This transgression southwards into the North Sea probably resulted from a combination of North Sea rifting and sea-level rise (Taylor, 1990). Ziegler (1982) envisaged that the marine environments created by the transgression were restricted in the northern North Sea to the axial portions of the Viking Graben, although Andrews et al. (1990) and Fisher and Mudge (1990) postulated more widespread Zechstein deposition. Although most of the 15 records of Upper Permian deposits in northern North Sea wells are from the southern and central part of the Viking Graben, the succession has also been recorded in the Unst Basin and Magnus Trough.

Taylor (1990) suggested that the deposition of Zechstein halite, which is typical of the Upper Permian in other North Sea basins, may have extended no farther north than the Beryl Embayment. Indeed, no halites have yet been proved north of wells 9/17-1 and 9/27-1 in the southern part of the

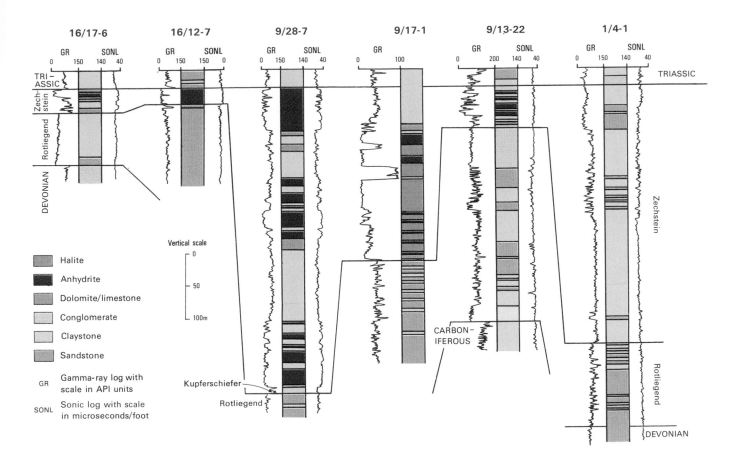

Figure 28 Permian successions in selected wells from the northern North Sea. For locations see Figure 26.

embayment (Figure 26). Up to 70 per cent of the 274 m-thick Zechstein sequence in well 9/17-1 is composed of halite (Figure 28), which Taylor (1990) suggested probably represents the Zechstein Z2 cycle that is developed over much of the central and northern North Sea.

A basal shale, possibly equivalent to the Kupferschiefer Formation, has been recorded in five wells in the central and southern Viking Graben, including well 9/28-7 (Figure 28). This formation is up to 9 m thick, and comprises highly radioactive anhydritic shales and silts.

Above the Kupferschiefer Formation, the Zechstein in most wells comprises interbeds of anhydrite, shales that are commonly anhydritic, dolomite, and siltstones/sandstones, as in well 9/28-7 (Figure 28). Up to 90 per cent of the succession is anhydritic in wells such as 16/12-7, although the dominant component can be mudstone (well 1/4-1) or dolomite.

There is no formal lithostratigraphical subdivision of Zechstein sediments in the northern North Sea. The mixed lithology of most sequences precludes their assignment to either the dominantly dolomitic Halibut Bank Formation, or the dominantly anhydritic Turbot Bank Formation recognised in the central North Sea by Deegan and Scull (1977), and in the outer Moray Firth by Andrews et al. (1990). However, Andrews et al. (1990) suggested that the anhydritic Turbot Bank Formation originally covered the Fladen Ground Spur, and it is therefore possible that anhydrite-dominated successions, such as that in well 16/12-7 (Figure 28), may represent local development of the Turbot Bank Formation.

TRIASSIC

The base of the Triassic has been reached in only 36 of the 300 penetrations of Triassic rocks in the report area, and in many of these the sequence may be incomplete due to erosion. The succession dominantly comprises red sandstones and claystones deposited in a range of fluvial, alluvial and lacustrine environments. Redbeds span the Triassic–Jurassic boundary in the northern North Sea, where the Rhaetian to Sinemurian Statfjord Formation (Figure 29) is developed in fluvial and coastal-fan/shallow-marine facies (see Chapter 5).

Only one lithostratigraphical unit, the Cormorant Formation (Figure 29), was erected by Deegan and Scull (1977) for the Triassic sediments of the area; they described the formation as an alternating sequence of fine-grained, argillaceous, white to reddish brown sandstones and siltstones, with some sandy claystones. Deegan and Scull (1977) also noted that the sequence comprises a greater proportion of conglomerates and coarser-grained sandstones to the west of the type well in the Cormorant Oilfield. They suggested that the formation was deposited in a continental setting, and that the apparent increase in sand content towards the west (Figure 30) suggests that a major source of sediment lay in that direction.

Deegan and Scull (1977) recognised the Skagerrak and Smith Bank formations in the Central Graben, but did not extend them northwards into the southern and central parts of the Viking Graben. However, these terms have since been used informally and erroneously; in the type area in the central North Sea, the Skagerrak Formation overlies the Smith Bank Formation, but in the Viking Graben, the Smith Bank Formation is placed stratigraphically above the Skagerrak Formation. Other informal terms have also been used locally in the Viking Graben, contributing to a confused nomenclature.

In another early review of the Triassic, Clemmensen et al. (1980) suggested that the bulk of the succession is alluvial, with fanglomerates adjacent to fault-bounded margins, and lacustrine or sabkha deposits commonly developed elsewhere in the basin. Ormaasen et al. (1980) similarly recognised the presence of alluvial fanglomerates at fault-bounded margins, with finer-grained sediments towards the middle of the basin.

In an attempt to unify UK and Norwegian Triassic and Jurassic lithostratigraphical nomenclature, Vollset and Doré (1984) introduced the term Hegre Group for the Triassic sediments of much of the northern North Sea region (Figure 29), but indicated that this new group and its constituent formations could not be recognised over parts of the East Shetland Basin, where the Triassic sequence is largely attenuated over structural highs. They therefore retained usage of the Cormorant Formation for such successions, and furthermore did not extend the Hegre Group south of 60°N. The three subdivisions of the Hegre Group recognised by Vollset and Doré (1984) are the Teist, Lomvi, and Lunde formations (Figure 29), all of which have type wells in the Norwegian sector.

Vollset and Doré (1984) postulated that the Teist Formation at the base of the Triassic succession normally exceeds 500 m in thickness and consists of interbedded, fine- to coarse-grained, reddish brown, fluvial sandstones, with green to dark grey claystones and red marls of lacustrine origin. These sediments form a gradually upward-coarsening sequence in the type well. Although originally recognised by Vollset and Doré (1984) between the Brent Oilfield and the southern edge of the Møre Basin, the formation can be identified over more western parts of the East Shetland Basin and in the Central Viking Graben.

Several wells in the East Shetland Basin, including well 211/29-5 (Figure 31), may provide suitable reference sequences for the overlying Lomvi Formation. The formation consists of fine- to coarse-grained kaolinitic sandstones with subordinate red marls and claystones, all deposited in a fluvial setting. In the UK sector, the formation usually comprises about 85 to 100 per cent sand, although in well 211/11-4 (Figure 26) only about 70 per cent of the formation is sandstone. The formation is identified over the same area as the underlying Teist Formation.

The Lunde Formation at the top of the Triassic succession has its UK reference section in well 211/29-5 (Figure 31). According to Vollset and Doré (1984), the formation comprises interbedded, white, pink or grey, fine- to coarse-grained fluvial sandstones, and reddish brown lacustrine/floodbasin claystones, siltstones and shales, some with thin limestones representing possible caliche deposits. Tuff horizons are present in the lower part of the formation around the Statfjord Oilfield. The lowermost part of the formation in well 211/29-5 comprises a brick-red, claystone-dominated unit which can be up to about 270 m thick. The formation was originally present throughout the northern North Sea Basin, but major parts of it may now be missing due to erosion over structural highs.

Lervik et al. (1989) suggested amendments to the Vollset and Doré (1984) lithostratigraphical scheme for the northern North Sea, and elevated the thick, basal claystone of the Lunde Formation to formation status, although all subdivisions of the succession were assigned to informal units (Figure 29).

A major problem with existing lithostratigraphical schemes is that they are based almost entirely on lithological criteria. Attempts to place the lithostratigraphical subdivisions into some form of biostratigraphical framework have been largely unsuccessful. Because of the paucity of palynomorphs within the sequence, Vollset and Doré (1984) were unable to provide precise ages for the lithostratigraphical subdivisions they identified within the Hegre Group (Figure 29). Nevertheless, they suggested that the Teist Formation probably ranges in age from Early Triassic to possibly Late Triassic; the age of

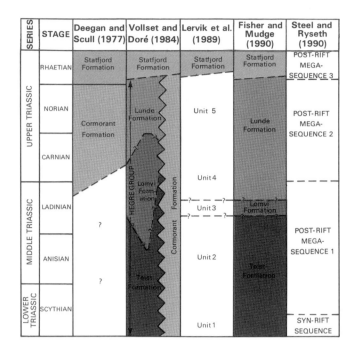

Figure 29 Stratigraphical schemes in use for the Triassic succession of the northern North Sea.

the Lomvi Formation is indeterminate, and the Lunde Formation was judged to be possibly of Carnian/Norian to Rhaetian age. Fisher and Mudge (1990) suggested a similar range of ages, but postulated that the Lomvi Formation may be Ladinian (Figure 29). The Cormorant Formation, used in the Vollset and Doré (1984) scheme to refer to attenuated sequences confined to structural highs, is also considered by them to be of indeterminate age.

Lervik et al. (1989) showed that palynomorphs from the Teist, Lomvi and lower Lunde formations suggest Scythian to Ladinian ages, with the greater part of the Lunde Formation yielding palynomorphs of Late Triassic age. In the Central Viking Graben and Beryl Embayment, Lervik et al. (1989) recorded Norian to Rhaetian ages for the upper part of the succession, their unit 5 (Figure 29).

In an attempt to overcome the problems associated with using a strictly lithostratigraphical framework for subdividing the Triassic, Steel and Ryseth (1990) proposed a megasequence stratigraphy related to tectonic control rather than to lithological/lithostratigraphical boundaries. These authors concentrated on the relationship between sand-rich and shale-rich intervals, and their significance in terms of a varying rate of base-level change during the Triassic evolution of the basin. Working mainly on the area north of the Beryl Embayment, they recognised four main units within the Triassic to Lower Jurassic interval. The lowest of their units is the syn-rift sequence, which was deposited during an Early Triassic episode of tectonic activity (e.g. Badley et al., 1988) when the sediments infilled topographic lows created by syn-depositional tilting of fault blocks. The three younger, post-rift megasequences span the remainder of the Triassic to earliest Jurassic succession. The bases of megasequence units are defined as the stratigraphical level where a main mudstone–siltstone interval overlies the level of maximum progradation represented by thick alluvial sandstones at the top of the underlying megasequence. The megasequences are up to 1000 m thick, and show a trend that is either upward fining overlain by upward coarsening, or crudely upward coarsening. Smaller-scale, upward-fining and upward-coarsening sequences are observed within the megasequences.

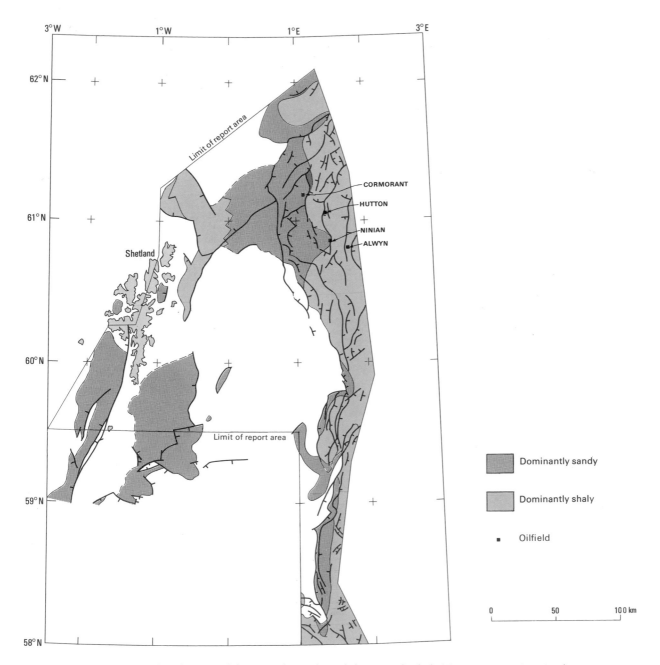

Figure 30 Generalised distribution of dominantly sandy and dominantly shaly Triassic successions in the northern North Sea.

According to Steel and Ryseth (1990), the thick, fine-grained intervals at the bases of megasequences in basinal areas represent dominantly overbank, floodbasin or lacustrine deposits that indicate retreat of the underlying, sand-dominated fluvial systems, and 'drowning' by floodbasin conditions. The finer-grained deposits contain marine indicators in places, confirming a transgressive interpretation. The thick sandstone-dominated intervals at the tops of the megasequences represent a return to fluvial deposition after progradation into the floodbasin area.

Post-rift megasequence 1 (PR1) of Steel and Ryseth (1990) is probably of late Scythian to Ladinian age, and comprises the Teist and Lomvi formations in a generally upward-coarsening cycle (Figures 29 and 31). This megasequence is up to about 900 m thick on and around the Tampen Spur, but may be absent from much of the East Shetland Basin according to Steel and Ryseth (1990). They suggested that the Teist Formation part of the megasequence represents sandy sheetflood and streamflood deposits generated from alluvial

fans along the basin margin while terminal floodbasins and lakes were developing in the basin centres, and that the Lomvi Formation part of the megasequence was deposited under waning-floodwater conditions in a fluvial system.

Post-rift megasequence 2 (PR2) is of Carnian to Rhaetian age (Figure 29), and comprises most of the Lunde Formation below its topmost shale (Steel and Ryseth, 1990). Unlike the earlier megasequence, PR2 is, in the view of Steel and Ryseth (1990), found over the East Shetland Basin. They interpreted the lower part of the megasequence as a retrogradational deposit, and the upper part as ephemeral, fluvial sandstones and interbedded lacustrine/lagoonal shales.

Post-rift megasequence 3 (PR3) is of Rhaetian to Sinemurian age (Figure 29), and equates largely with the alluvial parts of the Statfjord Formation (see Chapter 5).

A refinement of Steel and Ryseth's (1990) megasequence stratigraphy can be applied to the East Shetland Basin and Beryl Embayment, where four major upward-coarsening cycles can be recognised in many wells (Figure 31). The lower-

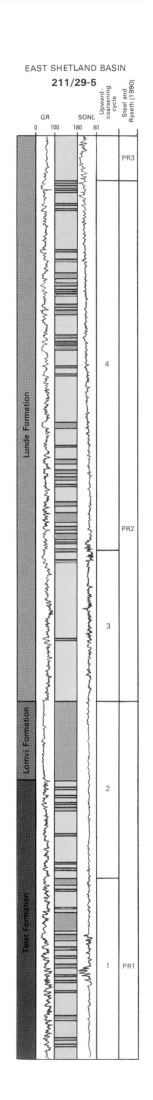

EAST SHETLAND BASIN
211/29-5

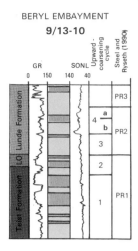

BERYL EMBAYMENT
9/13-10

Vertical scale

⌐ 0

⊢ 50

⌐ 100m

Claystone

Sandstone

GR Gamma-ray log with scale in API units

SONL Sonic log with scale in microseconds/foot

LO Lomvi Formation

Figure 31 Sequence-stratigraphical subdivisions of the Triassic in wells from the Beryl Embayment and East Shetland Basin. For locations see Figure 26.

most cycle occurs above Steel and Ryseth's (1990) syn-rift sequence, and encompasses the lower to middle parts of the Teist Formation. The sequence overlying this cycle comprises the upper part of the Teist Formation as well as the Lomvi Formation. Together, these two upward-coarsening cycles equate with megasequence PR1.

The two overlying upward-coarsening units recognised in the East Shetland Basin and Beryl Embayment correspond to the lower and middle/upper Lunde Formation respectively (Figure 31). Combined, these cycles equate with the PR2 megasequence. The uppermost cycle proposed here can itself be subdivided into two upward-coarsening units in places, particularly in the Beryl Embayment, although no equivalent subdivision of the upper part of the PR2 megasequence was recognised by Steel and Ryseth (1990).

The four upward-coarsening cycles can be identified only to the east of the Alwyn–Ninian–Hutton fault trend (Figure 30). However, although Steel and Ryseth (1990) noted that only megasequence PR2 (post-Lomvi Formation) deposits are generally recorded in the East Shetland Basin, it can be demonstrated that the Lomvi Formation, and therefore part of megasequence PR1, is recognisable over much of the basin.

Like the megasequences identified by Steel and Ryseth (1990), the four upward-coarsening cycles described here appear to represent more-or-less basinwide sequence stratigraphical units. Each cycle begins with a succession of dominantly floodbasin silts and shales with only minor channels, and passes upwards to sand-dominated successions composed of stacked channel deposits. The upward trend to channel domination within each cycle may reflect an upward decrease in subsidence rate and increase in progradation rate (Steel and Ryseth, 1990). It may also represent a progressive increase in basinwide tectonic rejuvenation of the source areas that provided sandy detritus. Tectonically controlled shedding of sediment and the concentration of channel sands in the basinal areas at the end of each cycle may have given way to floodplain development as the sediment source retreated due to erosion. Under such tectonic/sedimentary control, the encroaching floodbasins need not be viewed as transgressive deposits representing an increase in the relative rate of base-level rise or increasing subsidence, as proposed by Steel and Ryseth (1990), but can be interpreted as the result of a slow-down in marginal uplift.

Whatever the controls on the sand-to-shale transitions, it is clear that they operated basinwide. Furthermore, the cycle–megasequence boundaries in part correspond to defined lithostratigraphical subdivisions, suggesting that the existing lithostratigraphical scheme of Vollset and Doré (1984) may be sufficiently durable to adequately subdivide the Triassic over much of the northern North Sea.

5 Jurassic

The Jurassic is economically the most important succession in the northern North Sea, and consequently has been extensively studied. Most of the UK's oil reserves have been found in Middle Jurassic sandstones in the tilted fault blocks of the East Shetland Basin, and significant reserves are also located in Upper Jurassic fan-type sands in the South Viking Graben. Additionally, relatively small amounts of oil are found in Lower Jurassic sands in the Viking Graben. As well as providing an array of reservoirs, the Jurassic includes the main source rock, the largely argillaceous Upper Jurassic Kimmeridge Clay Formation.

Jurassic strata comprise a maximum composite thickness of 4000 m in the northern North Sea, and are confined largely to the downwarped areas defined by the Viking Graben, the Beryl Embayment and the East Shetland Basin. A 640 m-thick succession is also preserved in the Unst Basin, but Jurassic strata appear to be absent over most of the East Shetland Platform. Only in the north-west arm of the Unst Basin (Figure 2) do Jurassic rocks crop out at or near the sea bed (BGS Miller Solid Geology sheet). The Jurassic succession is generally draped over tilted fault blocks which rotated intermittently, possibly from Late Permian to Early Cretaceous times. Variations in the rates of block tilting and/or basin extension have resulted in complex differences in both the thickness and geometry of the Jurassic depositional packages across the basins. Generally, the Lower and Middle Jurassic successions form a 'postrift' unit deposited during a thermal-sag phase following Late Permian to Early Triassic rifting. The Upper Jurassic represents a second synrift sequence in the evolution of the northern North Sea (Badley et al., 1988).

The Lower to Middle Jurassic strata commonly thicken markedly towards the axis of the Viking Graben, but the Upper Jurassic thickens towards the margins of the basin, where faulting was active during sedimentation. Complex thickness variations of Jurassic successions occur across the mostly northerly and north-north-easterly trending faults that traverse the area, as well as across north-easterly trending, reactivated, Caledonian structures in the East Shetland Basin.

Another significant aspect of tectonic control on the evolution of the Jurassic sequence concerns the presence, extent, and degree of influence on sedimentation, of a thermally domed area to the south of the Viking Graben. This domed area, centred mostly on the central North Sea, supplied volcanic detritus to the South Viking Graben and outer Moray Firth areas during the Mid-Jurassic. Estimates of the size of the domed area vary up to 270 000 km^2 in areal extent, with relief ranging from 3000 m (Ziegler, 1982) to as little as 60 m (Leeder, 1983). It was suggested that its growth started in the Mid-Jurassic, cutting off a link between the Boreal and Tethyan oceans; the resulting erosion of Lower Jurassic strata provided a source for the Middle Jurassic sediments which now form the main oil reservoirs in the Viking Graben and East Shetland Basin (Budding and Inglin, 1981; Ziegler, 1982; Johnson and Stewart, 1985). More recent reconstructions of depositional environments and basin evolution suggest that the domed area may have existed earlier in the Jurassic, when it prevented widespread connection between the Boreal and Tethyan oceans, and may have contributed far less sediment to the Viking Graben during the Mid-Jurassic

than was previously thought (Richards et al., 1988; Richards, 1990b).

The lithostratigraphical terminology used here (Figure 32) is largely that of Deegan and Scull (1977), with additions, where appropriate, from studies by Vollset and Doré (1984) and Richards (1989). Boreal chronostratigraphical terms are used for the Upper Jurassic and lowermost Cretaceous.

TRIASSIC TO LOWER JURASSIC TRANSITIONAL BEDS

The Triassic to Lower Jurassic transitional beds of the North Viking Graben and East Shetland Basin are referred to the Statfjord Formation (Figure 32), which ranges in age from Rhaetian to Sinemurian. The base of the formation is defined by an upward change from the predominantly red, shaly, Cormorant Formation, to a more arenaceous, varicoloured sequence. In the central and southern parts of the Viking Graben, redbeds of Triassic affinity may also extend into the Hettangian, but have not been assigned to the Cormorant Formation.

Where most fully developed in the East Shetland Basin, the Statfjord Formation consists of three members. The Raude Member and the overlying Eiriksson Member are restricted to the east of the major north-north-easterly trending fault that defines the Dunlin and Hutton oilfields (Figure 33), but the superjacent Nansen Member extends across the East Shetland Basin. The Raude Member is of Rhaetian age, deposition of the Eiriksson Member spanned the Rhaetian–Hettangian boundary, and the Nansen Member is probably Hettangian to Sinemurian in age (Deegan and Scull, 1977).

The Raude Member is up to 160 m thick in the East Shetland Basin. It has been differently interpreted as a braided-stream deposit (Deegan and Scull 1977), a floodplain-dominated succession with meander channels (Kirk, 1980; Chauvin and Valachi, 1980), and as a complex system of distal fans and coastal floodbasins (Røe and Steel, 1985). The member has a generally low sand:shale ratio, but with sands forming up to 75 per cent of the succession locally. The sandstones occur in beds averaging 2.5 m in thickness, and are fine to very coarse grained, varicoloured, micaceous and kaolinitic. Interbedded siltstones are varicoloured, up to 4 m thick, and locally carbonaceous.

The overlying Eiriksson Member is also up to about 160 m thick in the East Shetland Basin. In the north of the basin it has a generally higher sand:shale ratio than the Raude Member, with sandstones up to 5 m thick interbedded with hard, grey shales. These white to pale grey, medium- to very coarse-grained, cross-bedded sandstone beds are generally laterally correlatable. Coals occur locally, and Deegan and Scull (1977) reported marine fossils near the top of the member. The environment of deposition of the Eiriksson Member in this northern part of the East Shetland Basin has been variously interpreted as coastal barrier, mouth bar and swamp (Deegan and Scull, 1977), sinuous stream, braided stream and coastal plain (Kirk, 1980; Chauvin and Valachi, 1980), or coastal alluvial-fan, coastal floodbasin and lagoonal bay (Røe and Steel, 1985).

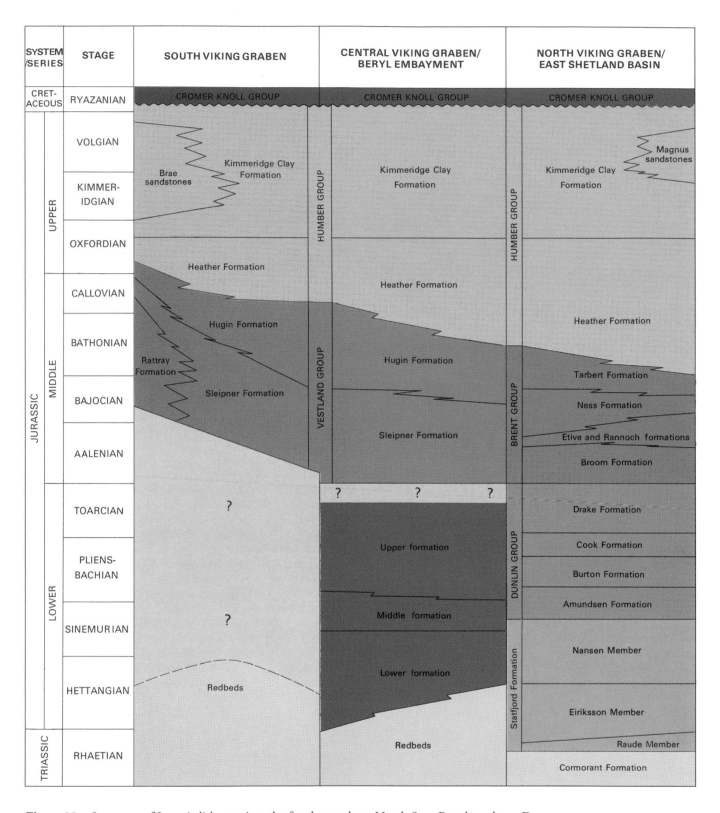

Figure 32 Summary of Jurassic lithostratigraphy for the northern North Sea. Based partly on Deegan and Scull (1977), Vollset and Doré (1984) and Richards (1989).

In the southern part of the East Shetland Basin, the Eiriksson Member is composed predominantly of sharp-based, fine- to very coarse-grained sandstones. These are usually 0.5 to 1 m thick, but range up to 4 m, and are stacked in upward-fining units up to 23 m thick. Matrix-supported quartz clasts occur throughout, but are commonly concentrated near the bases of beds. These sandstones are interpreted as the deposits of braided streams which were carrying bed loads of sand and gravel. The sandy units are separated by siltstones up to 7 m thick, in which rootlets are developed in

places. Unlike the Eiriksson Member farther north, there is no evidence of marine influence.

The Nansen Member approaches 50 m in thickness in the East Shetland Basin, and oversteps the older members of the Statfjord Formation towards the west (Figure 33). It is composed mostly of medium- to coarse-grained sandstones with some pebble lags, and has calcareous cement over much of the East Shetland Basin. Where calcite cemented (Figure 33), it is termed the Nansen Calcareous Sandstone Bed (Deegan and Scull, 1977). Thin shale beds with marine fossils are in-

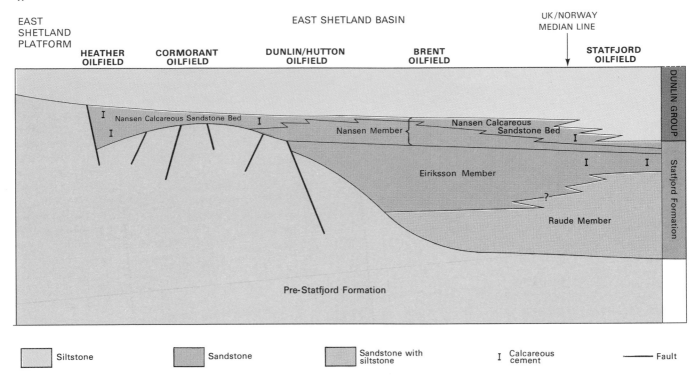

W   E

Figure 33 Schematic cross-section through the East Shetland Basin, illustrating the distribution of subdivisions of the Statfjord Formation.

terbedded with the sandstones in the northern part of the East Shetland Basin, where the member has been interpreted as a marine-reworked unit above the coastal alluvial-fan deposits of the Eiriksson Member (Røe and Steel, 1985), or as a transgressive shallow-marine sand (Johnson and Stewart, 1985). In the southern part of the East Shetland Basin, the Nansen Member appears to be lithologically similar to the underlying, fluvially dominated Eiriksson Member, and no evidence of marine conditions have been recorded. However, the uppermost 5 m or so of the member here have not been cored, and it is possible that marine sands occur at this level.

The upward increase in marine influence observed within the Statfjord Formation in the northern part of the East Shetland Basin has been interpreted as the result of eustatic sea-level rise, which Røe and Steel (1985) have compared to similar transgressions elsewhere in the North Sea, East Greenland and western Scotland. This sea-level rise resulted in flooding of the Statfjord Formation, the creation of a marine environment across the basin, and the deposition of the overlying Lower Jurassic sediments.

LOWER JURASSIC

Lower Jurassic sediments above the Statfjord Formation in the northern North Sea are referred to the Dunlin Group, which is divided into the Amundsen, Burton, Cook and Drake formations (Deegan and Scull, 1977). Over much of the area, the group is dominated by siltstones or shales, but sandstone-dominated successions that have not been formally assigned to existing formations are recorded in both the Central Viking Graben and the Unst Basin. Lower Jurassic strata appear to be largely absent from the South Viking Graben, although wells with unconfirmed Lower Jurassic successions, such as well 16/28-3 (see Figure 35), have been reported (Richards, 1990b).

Two contrasting models have been published to explain both the distribution of Lower Jurassic strata and the evolution of the Viking Graben region during the Early Jurassic. The first suggests that Lower Jurassic strata were deposited throughout the North Sea graben system, but were subsequently eroded from the South Viking Graben region due to uplift of a thermally domed area to the south (Ziegler, 1982; 1988a). The other model, implied first by Skarpnes et al. (1980) and developed by Richards (1990b), suggests that there was no extensive marine connection between the Boreal and Tethyan oceans throughout most of the Early Jurassic, and that the general absence of marine Lower Jurassic sediments from the South Viking Graben is the result of nondeposition.

The Early Jurassic was a time of relative tectonic quiescence in the northern North Sea; Badley et al. (1988) suggested this was a phase of thermal subsidence in the evolution of the basin, following Permian to Early Triassic rifting. Although local thinning on, and erosion over, tilted-block crests is observed in the East Shetland Basin, this is probably a result of localised footwall uplift rather than tilting during rifting (Badley et al., 1988). Syndepositional faulting, and possibly localised extension, may have been more important in the Central Viking Graben, where depositional patterns and thickness trends were to some extent controlled by movements on major normal faults (Richards, 1991a).

East Shetland Basin

The four predominantly argillaceous formations of the Dunlin Group are recognised in almost all released wells in this basin, but are absent from the crests of some tilted fault blocks (Figure 34). All four formations thicken towards the Viking Graben; they attain a thickness in excess of 250 m within the East Shetland Basin, and thin to zero near its

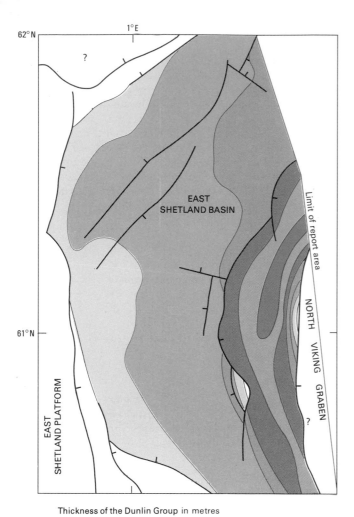

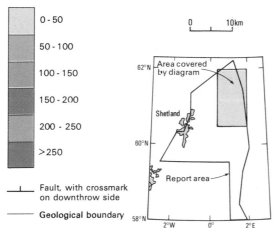

Thickness of the Dunlin Group in metres

	0 - 50
	50 - 100
	100 - 150
	150 - 200
	200 - 250
	>250

⊥— Fault, with crossmark on downthrow side

—— Geological boundary

Figure 34 Isopach map of the Lower Jurassic Dunlin Group in the East Shetland Basin.

faulted western margin (Figure 34). No shoreline deposits are found at this western margin, which is considered to be an erosional limit of strata once developed over part of the East Shetland Platform (Richards, 1990b).

The Amundsen Formation at the base of the group is probably of Sinemurian to Pliensbachian age (Deegan and Scull, 1977), and is up to 109 m thick in the East Shetland Basin. Although composed predominantly of grey siltstones with some burrows, there are thin, sharp-based, silty to coarse-grained sandstones. The formation was probably deposited under marine conditions resulting from continued inundation of the Statfjord Formation coastal alluvial-fan as sea level rose during the Early Jurassic. The sandstones are thick-

est in a broad zone trending subparallel to the basin margin, and may have been deposited from some form of offshore-directed flow originating near the palaeocoastline.

The overlying Burton Formation is of Pliensbachian age, and is over 65 m thick in the East Shetland Basin. Lithologically similar to the underlying formation, but with fewer sandstones, it is also probably of marine origin.

The succeeding Cook Formation is of Pliensbachian to Toarcian age (Richards, 1990b) and up to 70 m thick. Like the other formations, it thickens eastwards towards the axis of the Viking Graben, with marked thickness increases across some of the major north-north-easterly trending faults that transect the basin. Like the underlying formations, it is composed mostly of siltstones, but up to 20 per cent of the succession in the eastern part of the basin comprises fine- to coarse-grained sandstones. These sandstones form a reservoir in the Statfjord Oilfield (Buza and Unneberg, 1987) as well as in the Gullfaks and Oseberg oilfields in Norwegian waters (Figure 10). In the UK sector, the sandstones tend to occur in the upper part of the formation, whereas in Norwegian waters the sandstones are more persistent throughout. The Cook Formation was probably deposited in an offshore setting. The sandstones found in the UK sector have been interpreted as turbidites derived from the east, and coeval sands in Norwegian waters as shallow-marine, shoal, prograding-shelf and coastal deposits (Hazeu, 1981; Vollset and Doré, 1984; Buza and Unneberg, 1987).

The Toarcian Drake Formation at the top of the Dunlin Group is up to 60 m thick, and has a similar distribution to underlying formations, thickening towards the Viking Graben but thinning over intrabasinal highs. This formation is finer grained than the underlying units, and was termed the 'Shale Member' by Bowen (1975); it comprises carbonaceous, very fine-grained siltstones and shales. Unlike the other Dunlin Group formations in the East Shetland Basin, there are no sandstones in this formation, and it is easily recognisable on gamma-ray log profiles because of its higher radioactive response, reflecting relatively high levels of carbonaceous matter. A number of sideritic and/or chamositic oolite beds are found, particularly near the top of the formation, and belemnites have been recovered.

Beryl Embayment and Central Viking Graben

The Lower Jurassic succession here is significantly different to that in the East Shetland Basin, and three distinct, but as yet formally unnamed formations have been identified (Figure 32). The Lower and Middle formations are predominantly sandy, coastal deposits (Richards, 1989; 1991b). The siltstone-dominated Upper formation is probably an offshore deposit, overlain, possibly with local unconformity, by Middle Jurassic sediments.

The Lower formation is of Hettangian to Sinemurian age, and is composed of interbedded sandstones, siltstones and minor coals. It attains a maximum thickness of about 80 m in the Beryl Embayment. Sandstones comprise about 55 per cent of the formation in sharp-based, upward-fining beds; these were probably deposited in fluvial channels (Richards, 1989; 1991a). The interbedded siltstones, mudstones and coals are of coastal-marsh and lacustrine origin (Richards, 1989; 1991a).

The Sinemurian to Pliensbachian Middle formation is up to about 70 m thick in the Beryl Embayment, and is dominated by fine- to coarse-grained, sporadically upward-fining sandstones with rare planar laminae in 0.5 m-thick sets. The sandstones are interbedded with pebbly siltstones at a number of levels, particularly near the base of the formation. The

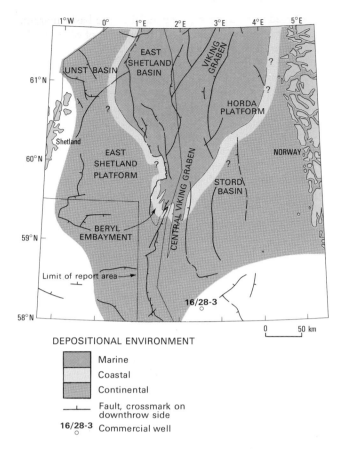

Figure 35 Hettangian to Pliensbachian palaeogeographic reconstruction of the northern North Sea. After Richards (1990b).

Unst Basin

Jurassic strata are absent over most of the East Shetland Platform, but are preserved within the downfaulted Unst Basin. Here, the 81 m-thick succession of grey-green sandstones and subordinate siltstones below Middle Jurassic sediments were attributed to the Dunlin Group by Johns and Andrews (1985). They suggested that these sand-dominated deposits are nonmarine clastic equivalents to the marine sediments of the adjacent East Shetland Basin. These continental sediments were probably deposited to the west of a coastal fringe of clastic sediments developed near the eastern margin of the East Shetland Platform (Figures 35 and 36).

MIDDLE JURASSIC

The term 'Middle Jurassic sediments' is often used informally in the northern North Sea to describe the predominantly sandy Brent Group and equivalent successions (Figure 32). The precise age of the Brent Group in the north of the report area is disputed, with suggestions of its age ranging from late Toarcian to early Bathonian (Ryseth, 1989), or entirely post-Aalenian (Helland-Hansen et al., 1989). Richards et al. (1990b) have suggested that the bulk of the group is probably of Aalenian to earliest Bajocian age, although deposition of the upper part may have extended into the Bathonian. Lithologically similar sediments in the central and southern portions of the Viking Graben may range in age from Aalenian to Callovian or Oxfordian (Figure 32). Deegan and Scull (1977) subdivided the Brent Group into five formations:

commonly coarse grain size of the sandstones, their upward-fining profiles, and the presence of cross-bedding, suggests they were deposited from waning traction flows, possibly within channels in a coastal-fan/fan-delta setting (Richards, 1989; 1991a). Associated pebbly siltstones display characteristic features of alluvial debris-flow deposits.

Coastal-fan or fan-delta sedimentation probably began during the Sinemurian as a result of faulting and the generation of source material in uplifted footwall areas both within the Beryl Embayment and possibly also near its western margin. The fans probably built out into the embayment from the west or south-west (Richards, 1989).

The Upper formation is of Pliensbachian to Toarcian age (Richards, 1990b), and is composed predominantly of grey, bioturbated siltstones in which dinoflagellate cysts indicate marine deposition. Although possibly deposited at the same time as the Drake, Cook and Burton formations farther north, it is lithologically more similar to the Amundsen Formation at the base of the Dunlin Group, for both formations represent the first marine deposit developed above coastal-fan systems.

The three formations recognised in the Beryl Embayment probably extend across the Central Viking Graben, suggesting that a shoreline was developed across the graben from Hettangian to Pliensbachian times (Figure 35). The presence of a shoreline sequence in this region at that time led Richards (1990b) to postulate that there may already have been thermally domed high ground to the south, earlier than envisaged by Ziegler (1982). This coastal system was probably drowned during Pliensbachian to Toarcian times, when eustatic sea level rose and the Upper formation was deposited in the Central Viking Graben (Figure 36).

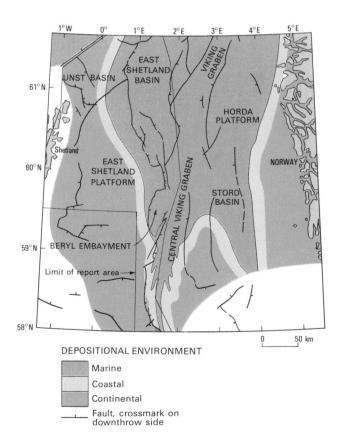

Figure 36 Pliensbachian to Toarcian palaeogeographic reconstruction of the northern North Sea. A more widespread marine link may have been established between the Boreal and Tethyan oceans at this time via the Viking Graben. After Richards (1990b).

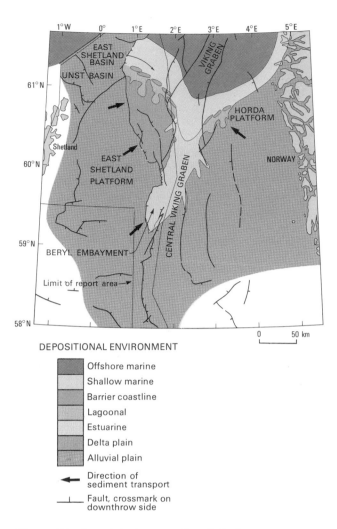

Figure 37 Late Aalenian to earliest Bajocian palaeogeographic reconstruction of the northern North Sea. The map depicts progradation of deltaic sediments into the basin before the phase of maximum progradation and silting-up of the basin. After Richards et al. (1988).

Broom, Rannoch, Etive, Ness and Tarbert (BRENT). Lithologically similar strata in the central and southern parts of the Viking Graben were termed the Sleipner and Hugin formations by Vollset and Doré (1984).

The Brent Group probably lies conformably upon the underlying Dunlin Group in the East Shetland Basin, although Hallett (1981) noted the presence of local unconformities. Farther south in the Central Viking Graben, well logs commonly show an unconformity between the Lower and Middle Jurassic successions. In the South Viking Graben, the Middle Jurassic strata rest unconformably on Triassic rocks (Larsen and Jaarvik, 1981; Graué et al., 1987).

The Brent Group has been described as a deltaic, regressive–transgressive wedge (Brown et al., 1987; Graué et al., 1987). The regressive part of the succession is usually considered to be the Broom, Rannoch, Etive and lowermost Ness formations, with the succeeding upper Ness and Tarbert formations deposited during retreat of the delta system as relative sea levels rose. While this general hypothesis is largely accepted, there is debate regarding both the regional controls on sedimentation and the palaeogeographic configuration of the basin.

The older, more-conventional model to explain build-up of regressive sedimentation (Budding and Inglin, 1981; Eynon, 1981; Johnson and Stewart, 1985; Graué et al., 1987) suggests that, following the latest Early Jurassic or ear-

liest Mid-Jurassic growth of a thermally domed area to the south, erosional products were shed off the dome and prograded northwards along the Viking Graben. This resulted in the deposition of the regressive sequence in a system of facies belts arranged concentrically across the graben.

A number of authors (Morton and Humphreys, 1983; Leeder, 1983; Morton, 1985; Hamilton et al., 1987) have disputed a southerly origin for the bulk of the regressive sediments on the basis of their mineralogy, preferring a source on the adjacent platforms. An alternative model has been postulated by Richards et al. (1988) and Richards (1990b) to account for this apparent derivation of material from adjacent platforms. This model envisages rapid sea-level fall and/or basin-margin uplift in latest Toarcian or earliest Aalenian times, resulting in rapid clastic supply transversely into the graben. At the same time, a marine connection is envisaged to have been maintained into the Central Viking Graben, where estuarine sediments were deposited. The resultant late Aalenian to earliest Bajocian palaeogeography, recording a phase during the early progradation of the delta, but before the time of complete silting up of the basin, is shown in Figure 37.

There has also been debate regarding the timing of basin extension/rifting during the Jurassic. Badley et al. (1988) suggested that the second phase of Viking Graben rifting did not start until the Bathonian, after deposition of the Brent Group. Evidence cited in favour of a model of thermal subsidence rather than rifting during Mid-Jurassic sedimentation includes the geometry of the succession, which generally thins towards the basin margin and thickens towards the axis of the graben. However, Hallett (1981) and Livera (1989) have demonstrated that syndepositional faulting partially controlled Brent Group deposition, and Richards (1990b) and Ziegler and Van Hoorn (1989) have cited evidence of intrabasinal thickness variations which may suggest limited amounts of rifting/extension during this time. Yielding et al. (1992) have since calculated this extension to be about 1 per cent.

East Shetland Basin

Brent Group sediments are recorded virtually throughout this basin, where they are up to about 300 m thick, but are absent over some fault-block crests and over the Magnus Ridge to the north. They are also absent over the Transitional Shelf and Terrace in the north-west of the basin, although possibly partly coeval sediments (the Emerald Formation) have been recorded there by Wheatley et al. (1987). Although the succession is virtually complete across much of the basin, the Tarbert Formation is locally thin or missing over tilted fault-block crests. This thinning can hinder differentiation of the Tarbert Formation from the underlying Ness Formation, as the two formations locally comprise similar facies.

BROOM FORMATION

The Broom Formation at the base of the group ranges in thickness from about 50 m along the western margin of the basin to zero towards the east and north-east (Figure 38). Considerable thickness variations occur across intrabasinal faults, and although a lack of core prevents detailed identification of possible facies variations across these faults, large-scale variations are recorded across the basin.

At the Heather Oilfield (Figure 38), the Broom Formation is composed dominantly of medium- to coarse-grained, poorly sorted, commonly carbonate-cemented sandstones, with bifurcated, subparallel to wavy, carbonaceous streaks. Mudstones with floating, coarse, sand grains are also common. Burrows are abundant at some horizons, and include shallow-water forms such as the bivalve *Arenicola*. Slightly

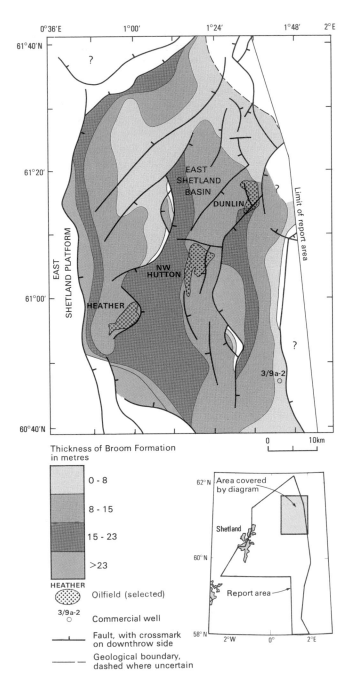

Thickness of Broom Formation in metres

	0 - 8
	8 - 15
	15 - 23
	>23

HEATHER 〔oilfield symbol〕 Oilfield (selected)

3/9a-2 ○ Commercial well

⊥ Fault, with crossmark on downthrow side

— Geological boundary, dashed where uncertain

0   10km

Area covered by diagram

Shetland

Report area

Figure 38 Isopach map of the Broom Formation in the East Shetland Basin. After Brown et al. (1987). Thickness values are converted from feet.

farther east in the NW Hutton Oilfield, the formation predominantly comprises moderately well-sorted, medium- to coarse-grained sandstones with metre-scale planar cross-bedding and shallow-marine burrows. Farther east again, in well 3/9a-2, the formation ranges in coarseness up to pebbly sandstone or conglomerate, interbedded with hummocky cross-stratified, shoreface sands of the Rannoch Formation. In contrast, the Broom Formation around the Dunlin Oilfield in the north-east of the basin is represented by relatively thin, coarse-grained, oolitic sandstones. The formation here marks the transition from offshore, silty shales of the Dunlin Group to the fissile, highly micaceous, prodeltaic siltstones of the lower part of the Rannoch Formation.

The Broom Formation sediments were probably derived by erosion of the East Shetland Platform area (Morton, 1985; Richards, 1990b), and have been variously interpreted as transgressive tidal-flat sands (Hay, 1978), offshore sheet-sands (Budding and Inglin, 1981), and cliff-base beach deposits (Eynon, 1981). However, the eastward thinning of the succession, coupled with the eastward change from shallow- to deeper-water deposits, may suggest that the Broom Formation was deposited as a fan-delta system, like the coeval, but geographically separate Oseberg Formation on the eastern side of the Viking Graben (Graué et al., 1987).

RANNOCH AND ETIVE FORMATIONS

The Rannoch and Etive formations overlie, and partly interdigitate with, the Broom Formation. They form a generally upward-coarsening succession, and can be considered together as a single genetic package representing the main, marine to coastal, progradational phase of the Brent delta. The two formations attain a combined maximum thickness of about 150 m, and are thickest in a north-west to south-east-trending zone in the north-eastern part of the basin (Figure 39).

Over much of the East Shetland Basin, the Rannoch Formation has a micaceous, siltstone-dominated unit with thin, sharp-based sands at its base, and generally coarsens upwards to very fine-grained sandstones. These sandstones are micaceous, with the micas and carbonaceous detritus concentrated preferentially into low-angle laminae. The laminae are mostly planar, with some low-angle truncations defining hummocky cross-stratification (Richards and Brown, 1986). In some beds, hummocky cross-stratification passes upwards to undulose lamination or symmetrical wave ripples. Individual beds generally range in thickness from 0.2 to 1.5 m, and tops of beds are commonly bioturbated. The most common burrow types are *Rosselia* and *Planolites*, with other forms such as *Schaubycylindrichus* recorded in places. These sands were probably deposited under storm-wave influence in a shoreface setting (Richards and Brown, 1986; Brown et al., 1987; Graué et al., 1987).

In the south-western part of the East Shetland Basin, the Rannoch Formation is sometimes coarser grained than elsewhere, with the dominant grain size in the fine, rather than the very fine, range. These deposits are also probably of shoreface origin; their coarser grain size may reflect a south-west to north-east proximal to distal progradational trend within the formation (Richards et al., 1988). In places, for example parts of the Lyell Oilfield (Figure 39), the lower part of the formation is coarser grained than the upper portion.

The Etive Formation overlies the Rannoch Formation, usually either as part of an upward-coarsening sequence, or as a distinct upward-fining unit (or complex of units) above a sharp base. The Etive Formation is missing locally where sediments more typical of the overlying Ness Formation rest directly on the Rannoch Formation (Brown et al., 1987; Brown and Richards, 1989).

Where the Etive Formation occurs as part of an upward-coarsening sequence above the Rannoch Formation, it is usually composed dominantly of fine-grained, moderately well-sorted, structureless sandstones, commonly with sharp bases. In such sequences, the Etive Formation usually has a blocky, low, and upward-decreasing gamma-ray response (Figure 40); a prominent mid-formation gamma-ray peak is commonly recorded in this type of Etive sequence. Units like this are usually overlain by lagoonal siltstones or coals of the Ness Formation, and are generally interpreted as barrier-bar/beach deposits formed by progradation of the coastline over the Rannoch Formation shoreface deposits (Johnson and Stewart, 1985; Brown et al., 1987; Graué et al., 1987).

The sharp-based, upward-fining variation of the Etive Formation changes from medium- or coarse- to fine- or very fine-grained sandstone, and two or more such beds may be stacked vertically. These sandstones are generally parallel lami-

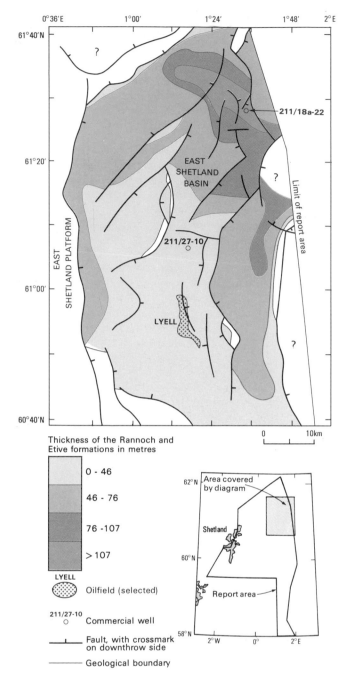

Figure 39 Isopach map of the Rannoch and Etive formations in the East Shetland Basin. After Brown et al. (1987). Thickness values are converted from feet.

units can be identified in the formation to the north of 61°N: a Lower Ness unit, a Middle Ness unit recognised as a more-or-less correlatable siltstone layer; and an Upper Ness unit.

The Lower Ness unit is up to about 60 m thick and consists dominantly of lagoonal siltstones with wavy bedding and a brackish to marine microflora. There are also lagoonal, beach and washover sands with wave ripples, parallel lamination and flaser bedding, as well as mouth-bar deposits forming minor, upward-coarsening cycles, minor fluvial channel sands displaying upward-fining profiles, and thin (less than

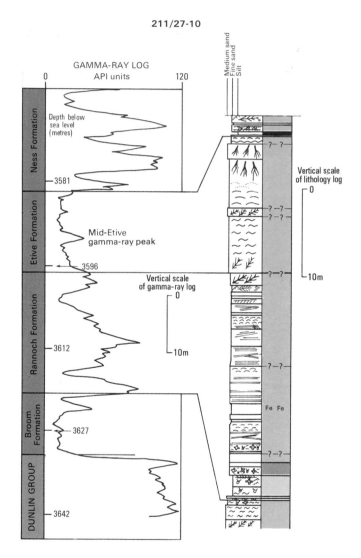

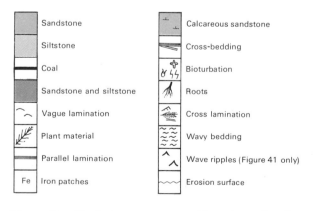

Figure 40 Typical gamma-ray profile and core log through upward-coarsening Rannoch and Etive formation sediments in the NW Hutton Oilfield. For location see Figure 39.

nated or planar cross-bedded, and gamma-ray profiles tend to show an upward increase in radioactivity, reflecting the upward fining. However some are of erratic ('ratty') appearance (Figure 41) because of greater concentrations of finer-grained, channel-abandonment facies. Such 'ratty' Etive Formation sequences tend to be most common in the north-east of the East Shetland Basin, where barrier-bar Etive Formation successions are largely absent in favour of distributary-channel deposits (Brown and Richards, 1989). Similar sediments are found in the overlying Ness Formation, to which they may be genetically related.

NESS FORMATION

The Ness Formation is lithologically the most variable unit of the Brent Group, and is up to about 180 m thick. The thickest succession is found in the structurally low area in the east, and the formation thins westwards (Figure 42). Three informal

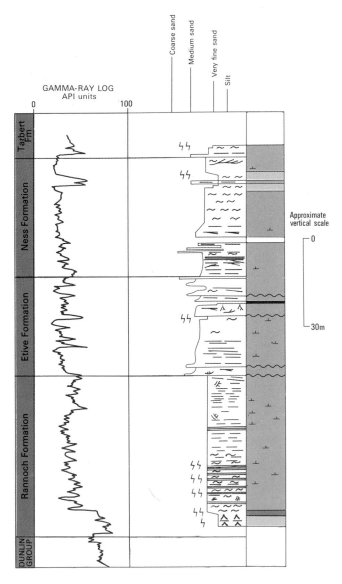

211/18a-22

Figure 41 Typical erratic gamma-ray profile and core log through an Etive Formation interval in which the units tend to consist of upward-fining channel sands. For location see Figure 39, for key see Figure 40. After Brown and Richards (1989).

The Mid Ness Shale may have been deposited isochronously across much of the basin, and its base therefore possibly provides one of the few recognisable time markers within the Brent Group. Palynomorph assemblages in this unit contain marine and brackish-water species, which like those from the other Ness units, are dominated by long-ranging miospores. However, samples from near the northern limit of the Ness Formation in the East Shetland Basin contain the dinoflagellate cyst *Nannoceratopsis triceras* Drugg (J B Riding, written communication, 1987); the range of this species is Toarcian to lowermost Bajocian (Woollam and Riding, 1983). This suggests that the Mid Ness Shale and all Brent Group strata below it may be of earliest Bajocian age or older (Richards et al., 1990). However, Cannon et al. (1992) have suggested that the Mid Ness Shale is not isochronous, but youngs towards the north.

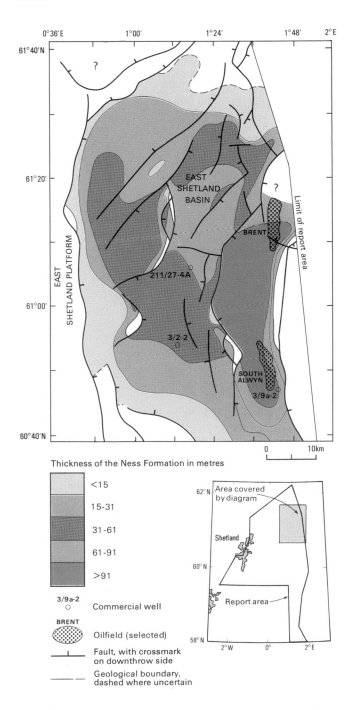

Figure 42 Isopach map of the Ness Formation in the East Shetland Basin. After Brown et al. (1987). Thickness values are converted from feet.

1 m) coal seams, some with roots below. The infaunal deposit-feeding trace fossil *Planolites montanus* is common, accompanied by *Diplocraterion* and *Arenicolites* structures. This lower unit was interpreted as a lagoonal or lower delta-plain sequence by Budding and Inglin (1981), although Livera (1989) noted upper delta-plain environments at some levels.

The Middle Ness unit, often termed the Mid Ness Shale, reaches a maximum thickness of 18 m to the north of the Dunlin Oilfield. It more usually has a thickness range of 4.5 to 8 m, and is found over an area of some 2100 km² (Brown et al., 1987). The unit is predominantly composed of medium to dark grey, lenticular- to wavy-bedded siltstones with some sharp-based, possibly wave-ripple, cross-laminated sandstones. Budding and Inglin (1981) have shown that in the Cormorant Oilfield area the unit consists of a succession of facies similar to those seen in the underlying Lower Ness unit, and formed in a large, high-energy lagoon which developed when subsidence temporarily exceeded sediment supply.

The Upper Ness unit usually varies in thickness from 10 to 15 m, but a thickness of up to 41 m has been recorded in the NW Hutton Oilfield area. However, the top of the unit is commonly eroded, which may mask original thickness trends. For the most part, the Upper Ness unit has a higher sand:shale ratio than the Lower Ness unit, and has been interpreted as a dominantly upper delta-plain deposit (Livera, 1989). The more sandy parts of the unit predominantly comprise sharp-based, medium- to very fine-grained, upward-fining, fluvial sands in beds 0.6 m to about 5 m thick. There are some flood-plain mudstones, and lagoonal mudstones occur between the channel sands, as do laterally persistent coals. The topmost part of the Upper Ness Unit has a much lower sand:shale ratio and is dominated by lenticular-bedded siltstones with thin sandstones and some coals. These siltstones tend to be highly bioturbated, and contain a marine microflora; in the Statfjord Oilfield area they include chamositic ooids (Parry et al. 1981). This siltstone-dominated succession at the top of the Upper Ness unit possibly results from a fall in the supply of coarser-grained sediment due to a rise in base levels. It may represent a brackish transgression that developed before deposition of the overlying, largely shallow-marine, Tarbert Formation, as the area was transgressed from the north.

Where the Etive Formation is totally or largely missing, the Ness Formation displays local facies variations. For example, in well 211/27-4A (Figure 42) in the NW Hutton Oilfield, a few tens of centimetres of Etive Formation sandstone is overlain by a lithologically complex and variable Ness succession of interbedded siltstones and sandstones. The Ness Formation sandstones display steeply inclined, muddy laminae, and scattered mud clasts; the siltstones contain burrows and a marine microflora. Such successions can be interpreted as tidal-channel deposits with overlying tidal flat/lagoonal sediments (Brown et al., 1987). The muddy laminae possibly represent mud-draped tidal foresets or side-of-channel slump blocks. Although such facies are relatively rare, sufficient examples can be observed within some oilfield areas to allow the delineation of tidal-inlet trends; these tend to be orientated in a north-west to south-east direction.

TARBERT FORMATION

The Tarbert Formation is a distinct stratigraphical sequence deposited during the retreat of the Brent delta, although it contains elements of progradational as well as transgressive sediments. The formation base is commonly defined by a sharp-based, coarse- to very coarse-grained sandstone interpreted as a transgressive lag deposit developed above a ravinement surface (Brown et al., 1987). Sandstones overlying the lag are fine grained and highly bioturbated, with rare, planar, dipping laminae in places. Further ravinement surfaces and associated transgressive lags can be developed at a number of horizons (Figure 43). Some of the fine-grained units are highly bioturbated, and Livera (1989) suggested they are similar to Upper Jurassic shelf sandstones found in the central North Sea, and probably represent shelf-ridge deposits. The finer-grained, laminated sands locally pass up to micaceous, parallel-laminated to hummocky cross-stratified, shoreface sandstones identical to those in the Rannoch Formation (Brown et al., 1987).

Where distinct regressive sedimentation can be observed between transgressive pulses, such as in the South Alwyn Oilfield (Figure 42), the Tarbert Formation again consists dominantly of marine sediments, although barrier-washover, lagoon and coal-swamp deposits of nonmarine affinity are found at many levels (Rønning and Steel, 1987). Although the top, and locally all, of the Tarbert Formation is eroded over the crests of some tilted fault-blocks, a conformable tran-

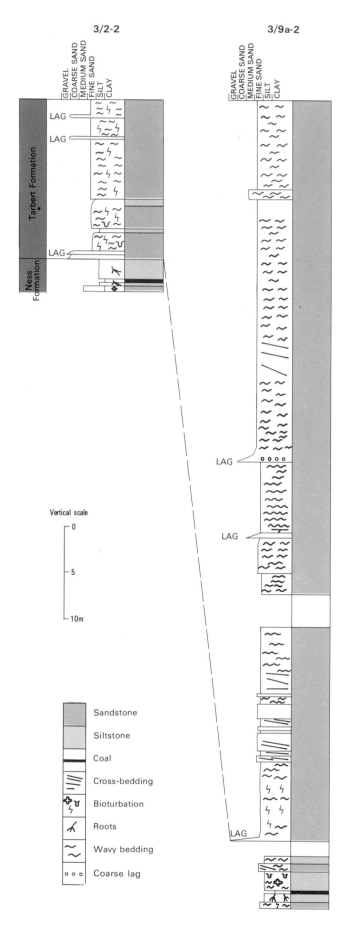

Figure 43 Examples of core logs through the Tarbert Formation, showing multiple ravinement surfaces. Modified from Brown et al. (1987). For locations see Figure 42.

46

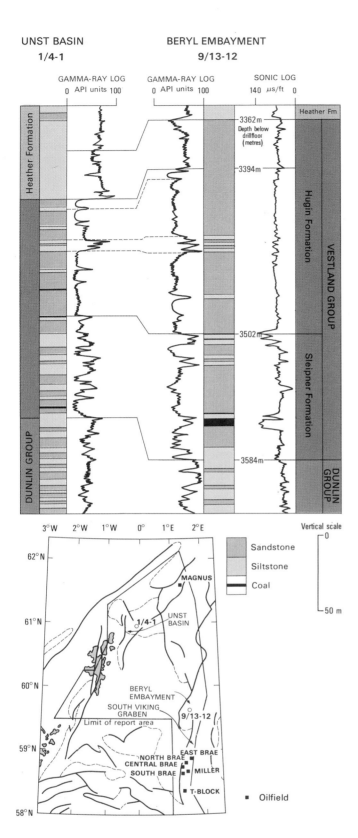

Figure 44 Correlation between Lower and Middle Jurassic strata of the Beryl Embayment and those of the Unst Basin. After Richards (1990b). For key to lithology see Figure 43.

sition up to Heather Formation mudstones is seen in the Brent Oilfield (Livera, 1989).

Unst Basin

Although Middle Jurassic strata are absent over most of the East Shetland Platform, a 144 m-thick succession of Brent Group strata has been penetrated in the Unst Basin (Johns and Andrews, 1985). This consists of friable, pale grey and brown, fine- to coarse-grained sandstones interbedded with carbonaceous shales and lignites. The only fossils reported from these sediments are microflora which are not age-specific. The gross lithology of the succession led Johns and Andrews (1985) to suggest that it is similar to the Ness and Tarbert formations in the adjacent East Shetland Basin, but a greater similarity to the Middle Jurassic of the Beryl Embayment (Figure 44) has been proposed by Richards (1990b).

Beryl Embayment and the Central Viking Graben

The sand-dominated Middle Jurassic sediments of this region are lithologically similar in many respects to the Brent Group, and range in age from Aalenian to Callovian (Figure 32). No Broom, Rannoch or Etive formation-type sediments are recorded, but coal-bearing sediments similar to the Ness Formation, and marine sediments comparable to those in the Tarbert Formation, have been identified. Vollset and Doré (1984) assigned the sequence in the central and southern parts of the Viking Graben to the Vestland Group, subdividing it into the coal-bearing Sleipner, and shallow-marine Hugin formations.

SLEIPNER FORMATION

The Sleipner Formation here ranges in age from Aalenian to possibly earliest late Bajocian (Richards, 1990b), and possibly rests unconformably on Lower Jurassic siltstones. Within the Beryl Embayment, the formation ranges up to about 130 m in thickness, and is thickest on the downthrown sides of major normal faults. Thicknesses of up to 485 m are recorded in the Central Viking Graben to the east of the Beryl Embayment.

Three informal subdivisions of the Sleipner Formation can be recognised in the region. An Interbedded unit is overlain by a Lower Coal marker, which is capped by the bulk of the formation, termed the 'Estuarine Succession' by Richards (1991b). The Interbedded unit ranges from 1 to 21 m thick in the Beryl Embayment, where it comprises interbedded sandstones and siltstones. It represents a transitional environment between the Lower Jurassic marine shales and the subaerial Lower Coal marker. The latter is widespread across the Beryl Embayment, and probably represents the acme of a regressive phase in earliest Aalenian times.

The 'Estuarine Succession' is up to 120 m thick in the Beryl Embayment, and is characterised by an upward-fining sequence of variable lithology. In the northern part of the embayment the unit is dominated by sharp-based, upward-fining sandstones interpreted by Richards (1991b) as estuary-mouth, tidal-channel deposits. Farther south in the Beryl Oilfield area, the succession tends to be more variable, with upward-fining, tidal-channel sands passing up to an interbedded sand/silt sequence with coals at the top. The siltstones are dominantly of the lenticular-bedded, tidal-flat type; the sands are parallel-laminated to herringbone cross-laminated, and are probably of sandy tidal-flat origin. At the top of the succession, the siltstones are less sandy and have a blocky fracture and abundant rootlets; these probable marshy-soil deposits are interbedded with coals and minor creek sands, and are interpreted by Richards (1991b) as estuarine saltmarsh deposits. The lithologically more variable succession around the Beryl Oilfield may represent the middle and upper reaches of the estuary, compared with the estuary-mouth environment envisaged for the northern part of the embayment. The marine connection to the estuary probably lay (Figure 37) along the structurally lowest, axial part of the Viking Graben (Richards et al., 1988; Richards, 1990b).

HUGIN FORMATION

The Hugin Formation in the Beryl Embayment region ranges in age from earliest late Bajocian to probably Callovian (Figure 32), and is possibly conformable on the Sleipner Formation. The Hugin Formation is up to 290 m thick in the embayment, and 310 m thick in the graben to the east. The formation is partly equivalent to the transgressive Tarbert Formation farther north, and in the Central Viking Graben represents the drowning phase above the Sleipner Formation estuarine deposits. The lower part of the formation comprises very fine-grained, laminated and rippled sands deposited under shoreface conditions; these pass up to a shallower-water, channellised, barrier deposit composed largely of very fine- to coarse-grained, upward-fining, cross-bedded sandstones (Richards, 1989). These barrier deposits were drowned during a renewed phase of marine transgression partway through deposition of the Hugin Formation, possibly resulting from renewed tectonic subsidence. This second phase of drowning was followed by deposition of a succession of very fine-grained, shoreface sandstones and highly bioturbated, lower shoreface to offshore siltstones with thin, storm-sand beds (Richards, 1989). These sediments were deposited under progressively deeper-water conditions, and pass transitionally to the offshore siltstones of the overlying Heather Formation.

South Viking Graben

The 'Middle Jurassic' succession in this region is similar to that in the Central Viking Graben, but ranges up into the upper Callovian or Oxfordian (Figure 32). It also comprises units that contain volcanic rocks, that were termed the Pentland and Rattray formations by Deegan and Scull (1977); these were not included in the Sleipner Formation by Vollset and Doré (1984), but are broadly coeval with it. The Rattray Formation is dominated by volcanic material, and is considered here as a separate unit, but the sediment-dominated Pentland Formation is regarded in this review as an integral part of the Sleipner Formation.

The Rattray Formation extends as far north as about 59° 20'N in the Viking Graben, and consists of basic lavas and tuffs with interbedded siltstones; it attains a drilled thickness of over 873 m. The proportion of volcanic material in the formation tends to decrease upwards, and both lateral and vertical contacts with the Sleipner/Pentland Formation are commonly gradational. A Triassic to Bathonian age has been proposed for these volcanic rocks by Howitt et al. (1975), although Ritchie et al. (1988) suggested a Callovian or early Oxfordian age for at least some of the volcanic material in the Fisher Bank Basin.

The Sleipner Formation partly overlies, and is partly laterally equivalent to, the Rattray Formation (Figure 32). Composed dominantly of interbedded siltstones, shales, sandstones and coals, it has been variously detailed in this region as a fluviodeltaic deposit (Vollset and Doré, 1984), a delta-top/coastal-plain deposit (Ranaweera, 1987), and as deltaic sands (Faerseth and Pederstad, 1988). Palynomorph assemblages are dominated by terrestrial forms, but prominent marine shales with Bathonian dinoflagellate cysts have been recorded.

The overlying Hugin Formation ranges in age up to Oxfordian; it has been interpreted largely as a progradational deposit laid down between pulsed transgressive phases (Harris and Fowler, 1987). The sediments are dominated by large-scale (c. 20 m) upward-fining or upward-coarsening cycles of sandstones that are separated by siltstones, coals, and thin, marine sands. The formation varies across the area, and sedimentary environments recognised include coastal plain (Ostvedt, 1987), prodelta to lower delta-plain (Christiansen and Strand, 1987), or barrier, tidal-delta, estuary and lagoon (Faerseth and Pederstad, 1988). Four major regressive episodes separated by trangressive events have been detailed by Harris and Fowler (1987), who described the bulk of the formation in this region as a series of barrier-shoreline sand bodies of lenticular geometry occurring in distinct facies belts parallel to the contemporary coast.

UPPER JURASSIC

There is much greater lateral continuity of facies in the Upper Jurassic compared with the Middle Jurassic, so that the interval can be considered over the entire report area. Although dominantly of Late Jurassic age, the 'Upper Jurassic' sediments of the northern North Sea, which are referred to the Humber Group, range in age from Bathonian to Ryazanian (Early Cretaceous). The succession is over 3000 m thick locally (Figure 13), and is variably made up of siltstones and shales of the Heather and Kimmeridge Clay formations, together with distinctive sandstones informally referred to the Brae and Magnus sandstones (Figure 32). The Upper Jurassic is generally deeply buried, but occurs at or near sea bed in the north-west arm of the Unst Basin (Figure 2), where hard, black clay of late Kimmeridgian to early Volgian age has been sampled in BGS borehole 84/08 (Figure 1; BGS Miller Solid Geology sheet).

Heather Formation

At the base of the Upper Jurassic succession, the Heather Formation rests with local unconformity on the underlying Brent and Vestland groups, and consists dominantly of grey silty claystones, with some limestones. It ranges in age from probably Bathonian to late Oxfordian. A marine molluscan fauna was identified by Callomon (1975), and Deegan and Scull (1977) interpreted the formation as a continuation of the transgressive sedimentation which was initiated during the late Bajocian with the deposition of the shallow-marine Tarbert Formation.

Continuation of the transgression that deposited the Tarbert and Heather formations may have been partly caused by eustatic sea-level rise, and may have been maintained by increased subsidence related to the second major phase of Viking Graben rifting. According to Badley et al. (1988), this rifting phase had two stages: an early stage characterised by deposition of the Heather Formation, and a later stage during deposition of the Kimmeridge Clay Formation. Both formations thicken markedly towards the basin margin faults, and display internal wedging of seismic reflectors; they therefore conform to the features Badley et al. (1988) considered to be diagnostic of synrift sediments.

Kimmeridge Clay Formation

Deposition of the Kimmeridge Clay Formation corresponded with the later rifting stage from the late-Oxfordian to the Ryazanian. This was characterised in part by uplift of the surrounding platform areas and the local influx of coarse-grained, clastic sediment (Badley et al., 1988). However, the bulk of the Kimmeridge Clay Formation, which was renamed the Draupné Formation by Vollset and Doré (1984), is composed of dark grey to black, noncalcareous, carbonaceous siltstones, with a high gamma-ray response reflecting the high

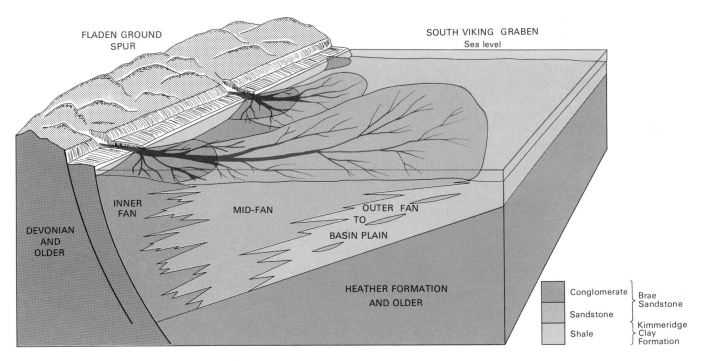

Figure 45 Three-dimensional, schematic block-diagram of the depositional setting of Upper Jurassic sediments in the Brae Oilfield area (Figure 44). After Stoker and Brown (1986).

organic content. Three main sedimentary facies have been recorded in the formation by Stow and Atkin (1987): silt-laminated mudrocks deposited as turbidites; fissile-laminated mudrocks of hemipelagic/turbiditic origin; and silty, bioturbated mudrocks deposited in shallow seas adjacent to the main graben areas.

Measurements of total organic carbon content of the Kimmeridge Clay Formation range up to 15 per cent (Stow and Atkin, 1987), although average values are more usually about 5 per cent (Cornford, 1990). These relatively high carbon values, together with a favourable burial history, make the Kimmeridge Clay Formation the principal hydrocarbon source rock of the central and northern North Sea.

The main criteria governing the deposition of such organic-rich rocks are high nutrient concentration, high sedimentation rate, and low concentration of dissolved oxygen (Demaison and Moore, 1980). Despite this apparent simplicity, two contrasting models have been proposed to explain the high organic content of the Kimmeridge Clay Formation. The first envisages that the seasonal formation of phytoplankton blooms resulted in temporary de-oxygenation of the water mass, and therefore the creation of anaerobic bottom conditions suitable for the preservation of algal and other organic matter (Gallois, 1976). The second model, postulated by Tyson et al. (1979), suggests that the algal blooms are the result, rather than the cause, of anoxic conditions. They envisaged a stratified water body with anoxia at depth, which overturned periodically, freeing nutrients and thereby producing algal blooms at the surface. Water depths may not have been great, but Cornford (1990) has estimated a depth of possibly 200 m.

Magnus and Brae sandstones

Coarse-grained, clastic sediments, generated as a result of uplift of surrounding platform areas during and after the Oxfordian, form discrete reservoirs at a number of localities in the Viking Graben. These occur at a variety of stratigraphical levels within the Kimmeridge Clay Formation. Sandstones and conglomerates are found in the Magnus

Oilfield (De'Ath and Schuyleman, 1981), and at several fields in the South Viking Graben, including the Brae oilfields.

Magnus (see front cover) is the most northerly oilfield in the Viking Graben (Figure 44), and gives its name to the Magnus sandstones. These sediments range up to 202 m in thickness, and occur near the top of the Kimmeridge Clay Formation. They are dominantly fine- to medium-grained subarkoses or arkoses with granitic and gneissic fragments (De'Ath and Schuyleman, 1981). Four major advances of a sand-rich submarine fan have been recognised, each of which produced a broadly lobate sand body (Barraclough, 1987).

Upper Jurassic reservoirs in the oilfields in the South Viking Graben (Harms and McMichael, 1983; Kessler and Moorhouse, 1984; Stoker and Brown, 1986; Turner et al., 1987) consist of sandstone and conglomerate sequences that range in age from Oxfordian to late Volgian (Riley et al., 1989). Different parts of the Brae sandstones fan complex are recognised as discrete oilfields, and developed at different times during this interval.

During the Oxfordian and Kimmeridgian, submarine-fan sedimentation may have been confined to a narrow belt close to the graben-margin fault zone, with thick sands possibly developed only in the region of the Tiffany Oilfield (see Figure 86). Deposition on several other small fans probably ceased at various times during the early Volgian, while the fans responsible for deposition of sand in the South Brae and Miller oilfields (Figure 44) were probably expanding into the graben. Although the mid-Volgian was a time of widespread mud deposition, fan sediments continued to accumulate in parts of the T-Block area and in the East Brae region (Figure 44). Fan sedimentation had ceased virtually everywhere in the South Viking Graben by the end of the mid-Volgian, with the exception of the North Brae area where sand deposition may have continued into the middle of the late Volgian. Late Volgian to Ryazanian mudstones of the Kimmeridge Clay Formation form a veneer above the fan sandstones and conglomerates.

The Brae-type fan deposits are lithologically variable, and four facies have been documented by Stoker and Brown

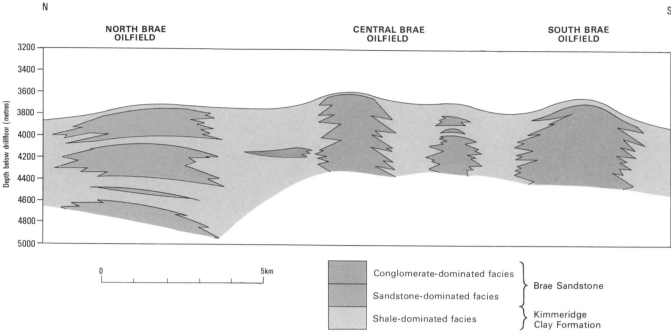

N   S

Figure 46   Longitudinal section along the western margin of the South Viking Graben (Figure 44). The Central and South Brae oilfields are about 1 km from the graben-margin fault, whereas the North Brae Oilfield is some 3.5 km away. After Stoker and Brown (1986).

(1986): 1. massive, disorganised conglomerates and pebbly sandstones of debris-flow origin; 2. graded and massive sandstones of sandy debris-flow or high-density, turbidity-flow origin; 3. thin-bedded sandstones and shales of low-density turbidite origin; and 4. mixed sand-and-mud-matrix conglomerates of cohesive debris-flow or slump origin. The debris-flow and high-density turbidite deposits are found closest to the graben margin, with sandy and muddy turbidites farther out into the graben (Figure 45). The fans do not overlap everywhere along the graben margin, but are separated by zones where deposition of Kimmeridge Clay Formation mudstones continued throughout Late Jurassic and earliest Cretaceous times (Figures 45 and 46).

Early models to explain the origin of the Brae-type successions in the South Viking Graben suggested that deposition occurred in fan-delta complexes (Harms et al., 1981; Harms and McMichael, 1983; Kessler and Moorhouse, 1984). This fan-delta hypothesis owed much to the interpretation of the coarser-grained sediment as subaerial topset deposits on the fan surface. However, interpretations of the entire system in terms of a submarine-fan model (Stow, 1984a, 1984b; Stoker and Brown, 1986) have become accepted (Figure 45). The recognition of marine fossils in the conglomerate matrix of the topset deposits enabled Turner et al. (1987) to confirm the submarine origin.

THE JURASSIC–CRETACEOUS BOUNDARY

The change from deposition of dark grey to black mudstones of the Kimmeridge Clay Formation to the less organic-rich

mudstones of the Lower Cretaceous Cromer Knoll Group occurred within the Ryazanian (Figure 32), rather than at the Jurassic–Cretaceous boundary (Lott et al., 1989). This lithological change produces a distinct seismic reflector that is easily mappable throughout most of the Viking Graben. This reflector has commonly been interpreted as an unconformity (Johnson, 1975; Fyfe et al., 1981) and has been termed the 'late-Cimmerian' unconformity by Ziegler (1982). Badley et al. (1988) have challenged the use of this term, arguing that it implies an inappropriate scale for its use. They argued that the unconformity is related to local tectonic conditions, specifically the cessation of extensional block-tilting in the graben, and the change to a phase of thermal subsidence.

Detailed palynological analyses of sediments near the Kimmeridge Clay Formation–Cromer Knoll Group boundary led Rawson and Riley (1982) to suggest that there is no major unconformity at this level, but that over much of the North Sea the base of the Cromer Knoll Group is isochronous. The boundary possibly represents a facies change marking a late Ryazanian transgression, which caused flushing and overturning of the anaerobic basins in which the Kimmeridge Clay Formation was deposited. Rawson and Riley (1982) did, however, recognise hiatuses between the Kimmeridge Clay Formation and the Cromer Knoll Group over tilted fault-block crests, but suggested that these may pass into several breaks down-dip, with condensed sequences contributing to the local complexity of the boundary.

6   Cretaceous

LOWER CRETACEOUS

Lower Cretaceous strata occur over much of the northern North Sea (Figure 47), and although the succession is dominated by argillaceous lithologies, sandstones form hydrocarbon reservoirs in the southern part of the Viking Graben, as well as in the Agat Oilfield in Norwegian waters. The thickest successions are recorded in the deepest, axial areas of the Viking Graben in Norwegian waters; over most of the UK sector the thickness is highly variable, ranging from about 3 m over parts of the East Shetland Basin to over 600 m in the graben. A thin Lower Cretaceous sequence of some 10 m thickness may occur over parts of the East Shetland Platform, with possibly a thicker succession cropping out in a small basin east of south Shetland (Figure 2). Lower Cretaceous strata, including a minor sandstone component, are also found in the Magnus Trough, and in the Unst Basin where Valanginian sandstone has been drilled at BGS borehole 84/05 (Figure 47; BGS Miller Solid Geology sheet).

The base of the Cretaceous in the northern North Sea occurs within the Kimmeridge Clay Formation, and the overlying upper Ryazanian to upper Albian strata are referred to the Cromer Knoll Group (Deegan and Scull, 1977). Cromer Knoll Group sediments drilled in the northern North Sea are dominantly marls, claystones and siltstones, although some limestones and a few sandstones are also found. Throughout Early Cretaceous times, deposition probably occurred in relatively deep-water, marine environments (Ziegler, 1982; Hancock, 1986). Badley et al. (1988) have noted the presence of canyon and fan-like features near the eastern margin of the basin in the Norwegian sector. Eustatic sea level may have been rising through the Early Cretaceous (Hancock, 1986), although Haq et al. (1987) have constructed a variable coastal onlap curve for this time. In the Haq et al. (1987) curve, a marked lowering of the long-term eustatic level is recorded in the latest Ryazanian. This contrasts with the transgression which Rawson and Riley (1982) proposed; they envisaged a basin-flushing event responsible for overturning the anoxic water body in which the Kimmeridge Clay Formation was deposited.

Although the boundary between the Kimmeridge Clay Formation and the Cromer Knoll Group may be conformable over parts of the area (see previous chapter), the junction is commonly interpreted as an unconformity in wells sited over structural highs. Badley et al. (1988) have suggested that such regional unconformities tend to form as a result of primary tectonic effects. They envisaged the causal mechanism to be the cessation of the extensional block tilting which characterised the early Bathonian to early Ryazanian rifting episode, and the subsequent change to a phase of thermal subsidence in the late Ryazanian.

Badley et al. (1988) subdivided the Cretaceous to Tertiary thermal subsidence phase into four stages, the earliest of which corresponds to the late Ryazanian to Albian interval. At that time, the most rapid subsidence occurred in the centre of the basin, and was achieved by movement on planar, normal faults. The sequence deposited during this interval onlapped and overlapped older strata both to the east and west of the basin axis, thickening as it infilled the remnant tilt-block topography. Thermal subsidence became more regionally extensive during Cenomanian to Turonian times.

Lithostratigraphical subdivision of the Cromer Knoll Group is complicated by the many different stratigraphical schemes in current use. Deegan and Scull (1977) did not subdivide the Cromer Knoll Group in the northern North Sea, although they recognised subdivisions elsewhere. Isaksen and Tonstad (1989) erected five units within the group in the Norwegian sector, and a modified version of their terminology is used here for the UK sector of the northern North Sea (Figure 48). The Cromer Knoll Group of the various basins can be considered together, except for the Magnus Trough.

Cromer Knoll Group in the East Shetland Basin, Unst Basin and Viking Graben

Although the Cromer Knoll Group is of late Ryazanian to Albian age, Hancock (1986) has suggested that pre-Barremian strata are not preserved over large parts of the report area. However, pre-Barremian strata have been recorded in a relatively small number of wells in parts of the East Shetland Basin, South Viking Graben and Unst Basin. Over the rest of the area, Lower Cretaceous strata do appear to be Barremian or younger in age, with an unconformity, postulated from geophysical-log interpretations, separating the Cromer Knoll Group from the underlying Kimmeridge Clay Formation. The upper boundary of the Lower Cretaceous sequence is also commonly interpreted as an unconformity, with Cenomanian and locally younger strata missing.

In the Isaksen and Tonstad (1989) lithostratigraphical scheme, the oldest subdivision of the Cromer Knoll Group in the deepest parts of the northern North Sea is the argillaceous Åsgard Formation, although the coeval Mime Formation limestone is recognised at the margins of the northern North Sea Basin (Figure 48). These two basal formations are overlain in turn by the largely argillaceous Sola and Rødby formations, with the Ran/Bosun sands developed locally.

MIME AND ÅSGARD FORMATIONS

The Mime Formation is identified on many composite logs of wells in the UK sector of the northern North Sea as 'The Basal Limestone'. These basal limestones are locally interbedded with marls or claystones, and Isaksen and Tonstad (1989) reported the presence of oolites in some wells in the East Shetland Basin. The formation is probably of Barremian age over much of the East Shetland Basin, but is diachronous, and may range from Ryazanian to Barremian in age (Isaksen and Tonstad, 1989). Nevertheless, the Mime Formation forms the basal unit of the Lower Cretaceous wherever it has been drilled. It is probably absent from the structurally deeper, axial parts of the Viking Graben.

The Åsgard Formation forms the bulk of the pre-Aptian succession in the northern North Sea; its age ranges from late Ryazanian to early Aptian, and it is broadly coeval (Figure 48) with the Valhall Formation of the outer Moray Firth (Andrews et al., 1990). The Åsgard Formation is typically developed in well 211/27-10 at the NW Hutton Oilfield (Figure 49), where it is 223 m thick above the Mime Formation. It comprises reddish brown to grey, partly silty marls with reddish brown to grey, blocky to subfissile, locally calcareous claystones, as well as bands of whitish, blocky limestones that are in part argillaceous. Isaksen and Tonstad

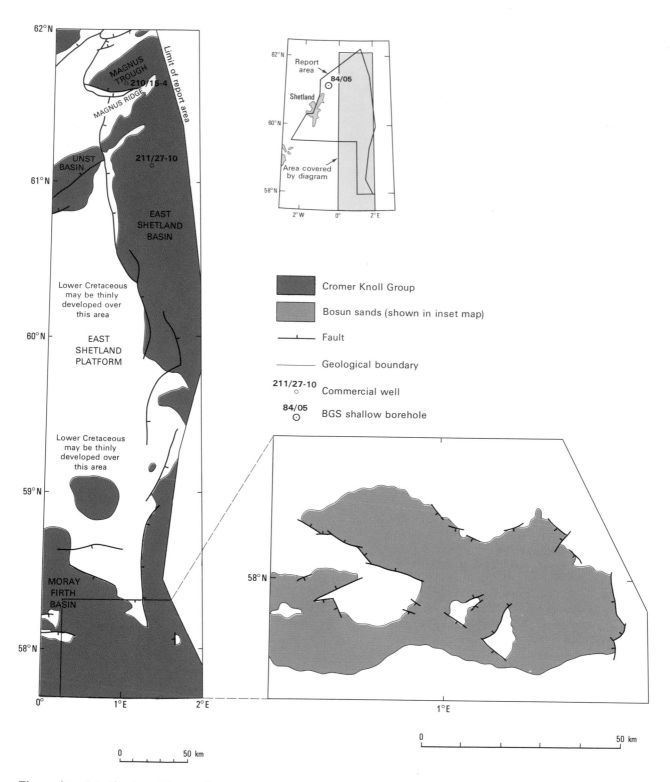

Figure 47 Distribution of Lower Cretaceous strata in the eastern part of the northern North Sea.

(1989) reported that mica, pyrite and glauconite are commonly found in the formation; sandstones are rare, and usually less than a few metres thick. The Valhall Formation in the outer Moray Firth comprises similar lithologies to the Åsgard Formation, but contains the important fan-sandstone and conglomerate reservoirs of the Scapa sands, that are derived from horsts in the region of the Claymore Oilfield (Andrews et al., 1990).

SOLA AND EQUIVALENT FORMATIONS

The base of the Sola Formation (Isaksen and Tonstad, 1989) is marked by a slight increase in gamma-ray log response and

an associated decrease in interval velocity. This formation ranges in age from early Aptian to early Albian. In well 211/27-10 (Figure 49) it comprises 70 m of claystones with thin limestones. Although the succession is lithologically similar to the underlying Åsgard Formation, the carbonate content of the Sola Formation is significantly lower.

In the South Viking Graben, Sola Formation claystones locally pass laterally into sandstones. These sandy deposits are termed the Bosun sands in the outer Moray Firth and South Viking Graben (Andrews et al., 1990), although they have also been called the Kopervik or Åsgard formations. The Bosun sands typically consist of interbedded sandstones and

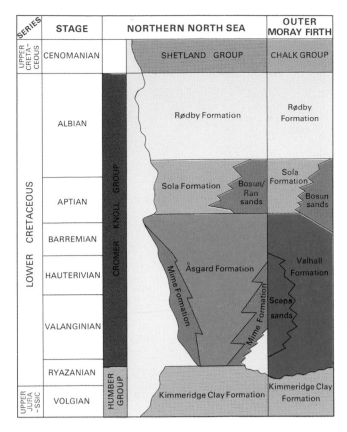

SERIES	STAGE	NORTHERN NORTH SEA	OUTER MORAY FIRTH
UPPER CRETACEOUS	CENOMANIAN	SHETLAND GROUP	CHALK GROUP
LOWER CRETACEOUS	ALBIAN	Rødby Formation	Rødby Formation
	APTIAN	Sola Formation / Bosun/Ran sands	Sola Formation / Bosun sands
	BARREMIAN	Åsgard Formation	Valhall Formation
	HAUTERIVIAN	Mime Formation	Scapa sands
	VALANGINIAN		
	RYAZANIAN	Kimmeridge Clay Formation	Kimmeridge Clay Formation
UPPER JURASSIC	VOLGIAN		

(CROMER KNOLL GROUP / HUMBER GROUP shown vertically)

Figure 48 Lower Cretaceous lithostratigraphy in the northern North Sea and outer Moray Firth; the former modified from Isaksen and Tonstad (1989), the latter from Andrews et al. (1990).

mudstones arranged in upward-fining cycles which become thin towards the top of the succession. The sandstones are fine to coarse grained, poorly sorted, massive to poorly laminated, and contain minor rip-up clasts and coal fragments. Dish and pillar structures are common, and the sandstones are interpreted as the deposits of turbidity currents and debris flows in submarine fans (Andrews et al., 1990).

The Bosun sands are probably restricted to the South Viking Graben and the adjacent Moray Firth area (Figure 47), although Isaksen and Tonstad (1989) also reported the presence of similar sandstones, which they referred to the Ran Formation, in a small area of the East Shetland Basin around the Magnus Oilfield. This separate development, commonly termed the Ran sands, is found in only three wells, and has a maximum thickness of about 3 m; its age range is Barremian to Albian, slightly longer than that of equivalent sands elsewhere in the UK sector.

Isaksen and Tonstad (1989) noted that the Agat Formation also forms a sandstone-dominated succession that is partly coeval with the Ran/Bosun sands. The Agat Formation is, however, encountered only in a small area of the Norwegian North Sea around 62°N, where it is laterally equivalent to both the Sola and Rødby formations. The Agat Formation sandstones are up to 401 m thick in the Agat Oilfield, where they form the main reservoir interval.

Figure 49 The Lower Cretaceous succession in well 211/27-10 in the East Shetland Basin. For location see Figure 47.

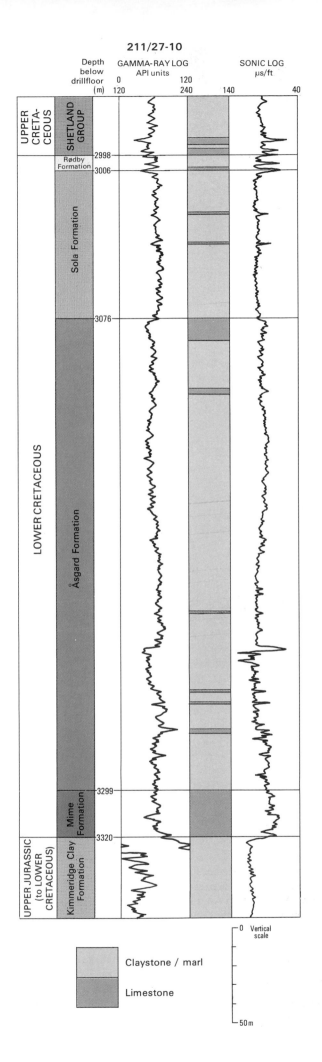

211/27-10

Depth below drillfloor (m)

GAMMA-RAY LOG
API units

SONIC LOG
µs/ft

Claystone / marl

Limestone

Vertical scale

The Rødby Formation at the top of the Cromer Knoll Group is of Albian age, and forms a widespread unit generally only a few metres thick. In well 211/27-10 (Figure 49), it comprises 8 m of reddish brown to pale green or grey claystone, calcareous claystone and limestone. Isaksen and Tonstad (1989) have noted that siltstones may also occur, and that the rocks are glauconitic and pyritic in places.

Cromer Knoll Group in the Magnus Trough

The north-easterly plunging Magnus Trough forms a discrete basin separated from the East Shetland Basin by the Magnus Ridge. The southern bounding fault of the Magnus Trough has a displacement of up to 3050 m, and the Permian to Cretaceous succession within the basin thickens markedly towards this fault. Lower Cretaceous strata are thin or absent in many wells around the margins of the basin, but in well 210/15-4, drilled some 4 km north of the southern bounding fault, the Lower Cretaceous sequence is over 1590 m thick (Figure 47). The Åsgard and Sola formations, and a particularly thick Rødby Formation (731 m), can all be recognised in the uppermost 970 m of the succession in well 210/15-4; they form a sequence of reddish brown to grey mudstone with thin, whitish limestone and some sandy stringers.

A 620 m-thick unit, referred to on the oil-company log as 'Devil's Hole Formation Equivalent' is penetrated in the lower part of the well 210/15-4 sequence, below the Åsgard Formation. This sequence comprises interbedded, reddish brown siltstone and fine- to coarse-grained, poorly to moderately well-sorted, varicoloured, quartz- or calcite-cemented sandstone. The Devil's Hole Formation was defined by Deegan and Scull (1977) as having a limited distribution in the UK sector of the central North Sea, so usage of the term in the Magnus Trough is inappropriate. However, the Devil's Hole Formation does have the same age range (Ryazanian/Valanginian to early Hauterivian) as the sand-dominated basal succession in well 210/15-4.

Well 210/15-4 terminated within Lower Cretaceous rocks, so that the full age range of the succession in the Magnus Trough has not yet been proved. Late Valanginian to early Hauterivian ages have been assigned to the lower part of the succession, and an Albian age to the upper part. If the age of the sequence is sufficiently constrained, then strata of late Hauterivian, Barremian and Aptian age are missing between the Åsgard and Sola formations. An unconformity can be seen at this level on some seismic sections, particularly near the margins of the basin. Structurally deeper areas in the middle of the basin may contain a more complete Cromer Knoll Group sequence.

UPPER CRETACEOUS AND LOWER DANIAN

During Late Cretaceous and very earliest Palaeogene times, eustatic sea level was exceptionally high (Hancock and Kauffman, 1979), and the Boreal Ocean extended southwards across much of western Europe to form a large, epicontinental sea (Ziegler, 1982). This particularly extensive Late Cretaceous sea effectively reduced the size of potential source areas for terrigenous clastic sediment, providing conditions suitable for the widespread deposition of thick chalk.

North Sea chalk is composed mainly of the debris of minute planktonic algae and calcareous nannofossils which formed the diet for copepod crustaceans. The sediment probably accumulated largely in the form of crustacean faecal pellets, in 100 to 600 m of water, although the water depth may have reached up

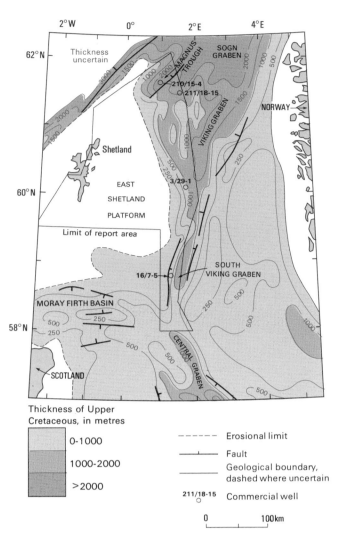

Figure 50 Upper Cretaceous isopach map. Modified after Ziegler (1982).

to 1000 m over the graben system (Hancock, 1990). A nonseasonal, arid climate may have been an additional factor in inhibiting clastic input to the transgressive Chalk Sea, the surface temperature of which may have been about 25°C (Black, 1980). Most North Sea chalk outside the graben system accumulated by settlement from suspension, and commonly shows a rhythmic alternation of paler, and darker, more clay-rich units known as 'periodites'. The cycles are thought to reflect climatic fluctuations which may have been controlled by perturbations of the Earth's orbit (Kennedy, 1987). However, in the Central Graben, some thick chalk sequences have been interpreted to be resedimented, mass-flow deposits (Perch-Nielsen et al., 1979; Kennedy, 1980; 1987).

In contrast to the chalk succession of the central and southern North Sea, the laterally equivalent Upper Cretaceous of the northern North Sea north of about 59°N contains a thick sequence of terrigenous mudstones. These argillaceous deposits display an increase in silt-grade material northwards; this has been interpreted to indicate a northern provenance for the mudstones, possibly from Greenland (Hancock and Scholle, 1975; Hancock, 1990). The mudstone succession may have been deposited in around 120 to 200 m of water (Hancock, 1990).

The northward change from chalk- to mudstone-dominated lithologies in the Central Viking Graben is gradational, both laterally and vertically. Even at the northern limits of the Viking Graben, there are a few metres of Maastrichtian

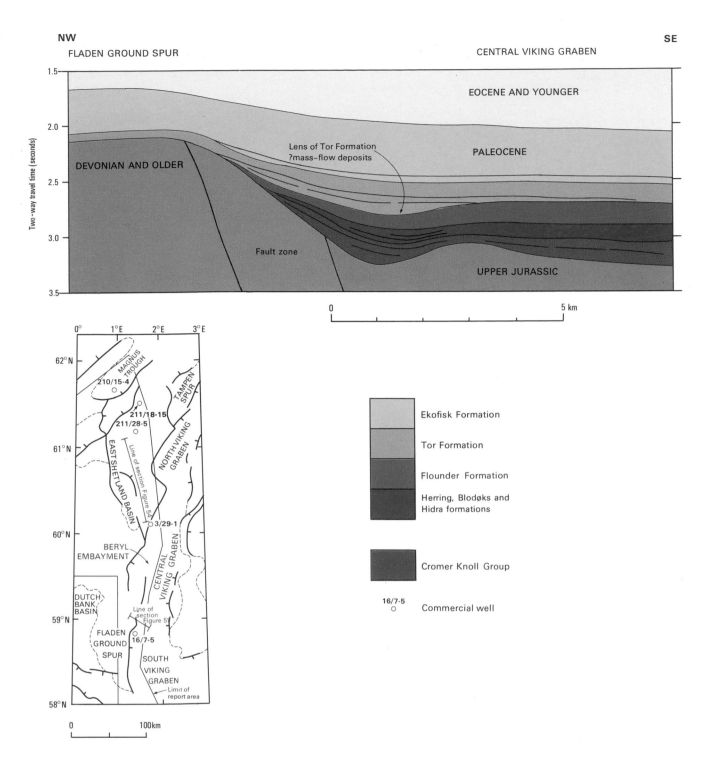

Figure 51 Line drawing of an interpreted seismic profile across the western margin of the Central Viking Graben.

chalk (Hancock, 1990). The thick Coniacian to Campanian succession in the northern and central North Sea Basin is generally more mud-rich than both the underlying and overlying Upper Cretaceous deposits, although thin muds were widely deposited during the Turonian.

The main Late Cretaceous depocentres are located in the Viking Graben, East Shetland Basin and Magnus Trough; thicknesses commonly exceed 1000 m, with over 2000 m in the Magnus Trough (Figure 50). According to Ziegler (1982), Upper Cretaceous strata largely infill the Early Cretaceous rift topography, and relatively thin Upper Cretaceous sediments are present over the eastern part of the East Shetland Platform. However, the western limits of origi-

nal Late Cretaceous to early Danian sedimentation remain unclear because of erosion associated with extensive uplift of the Orkney–Shetland Platform during the early Tertiary, which resulted from the onset of sea-floor spreading between the Rockall Plateau and Greenland.

The general pattern of Late Cretaceous subsidence in the North Sea (see Chapter 2) is largely consistent with a phase of tectonically quiet, thermal sag following Late Jurassic to earliest Cretaceous crustal extension (Thorne and Watts, 1989). Nevertheless, variable sediment thickness on the western margins of the Viking Graben and East Shetland Basin shows that the Late Cretaceous subsidence pattern was complex. Many faults in the Viking Graben and East Shetland Basin

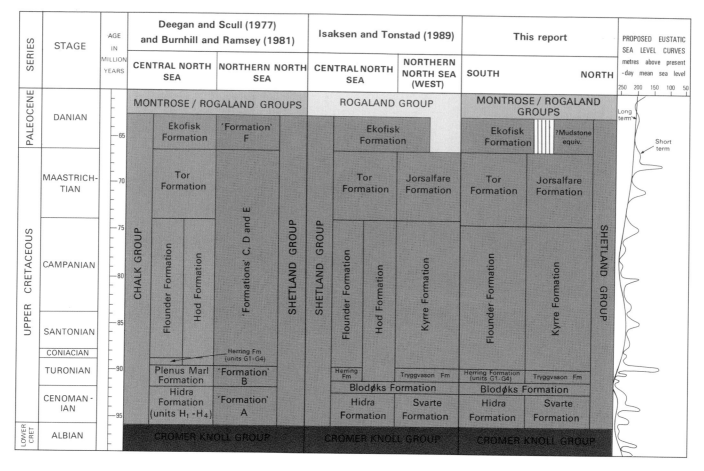

Figure 52 Stratigraphical chart of the Upper Cretaceous and Danian, showing the relationship between current lithostratigraphical schemes. The Isaksen and Tonstad (1989) scheme is slightly modified for this report. Sea-level curves after Haq et al. (1987).

became inactive prior to the Late Cretaceous, and seismic evidence commonly suggests that the Upper Cretaceous succession thins due to onlap on to basin-marginal and intrabasinal highs (Figure 51; BGS Solid Geology sheets). However, some faults truncate the succession, for example the fault defining the western margin of the East Shetland Basin in the vicinity of the Heather Oilfield (Figure 15; BGS Cormorant and Halibut Bank Solid Geology sheets). Marginal faulting may not have significantly modified the lateral distribution of lower units, as only the uppermost Upper Cretaceous strata (Campanian to Danian) encroached significantly on to the East Shetland Platform and Fladen Ground Spur (Figure 51). In a study of the North Viking Graben, Badley et al. (1988) postulated that thermal subsidence during the Cenomanian to Turonian was accompanied by movement on planar faults separating the Tampen Spur from the North Viking Graben. Subsequently, during Santonian times, the locus of faulting shifted westwards to the East Shetland Basin (Badley et al., 1988).

Thick mass-flow successions have been interpreted in the Upper Cretaceous chalk of the Central Graben (Kennedy, 1987). Because these deposits are closely associated with graben margin fault zones, Hatton (1986) suggested that earthquake activity was the triggering mechanism for the mass flows. The Upper Cretaceous of the northern North Sea has been less intensively studied than the Central Graben chalk reservoirs, and the amount of resedimentation that may have accompanied syndepositional faulting is largely unknown. However, mass-transport deposits have been postulated in the lowermost Upper Cretaceous of the North

Viking Graben in the Norwegian sector (Alhilali and Damuth, 1987).

Few cored sections have been drilled in the Upper Cretaceous of the northern North Sea, and stratigraphical divisions (Figure 52) are based on wireline-log response and micropalaeontological dating. Deegan and Scull (1977) proposed a lithostratigraphical scheme which separates the Upper Cretaceous of the North Sea Basin into the chalk-dominated Chalk Group and the mudstone-dominated Shetland Group; both are of Cenomanian to Danian age. They divided the Chalk Group into the Hidra, Plenus Marl, Herring, Flounder, Hod, Tor and Ekofisk formations; the Herring and Flounder formations together being laterally equivalent to the Hod Formation. On the basis of log responses, Burnhill and Ramsay (1981) subdivided the Hidra and Herring formations into informal units. Deegan and Scull (1977) divided the Shetland Group into six units which were informally designated formations A to F, and it was noted that some of these units equate with formations in the Chalk Group.

Isaksen and Tonstad (1989) revised the lithostratigraphy (Figure 52). Because of difficulties associated with the transition from chalk-dominated to mudstone-dominated facies, and the conventions of lithostratigraphical nomenclature, they abandoned the terms Chalk Group and Plenus Marl Formation. The two main facies of the Upper Cretaceous were separated at formation level, and the Plenus Marl Formation was renamed the Blodøks Formation, but all formations of the former Chalk Group were included in the Shetland Group. Formations A to E were given new names and defined as the Svarte, Blodøks, Tryggvason, Kyrre and

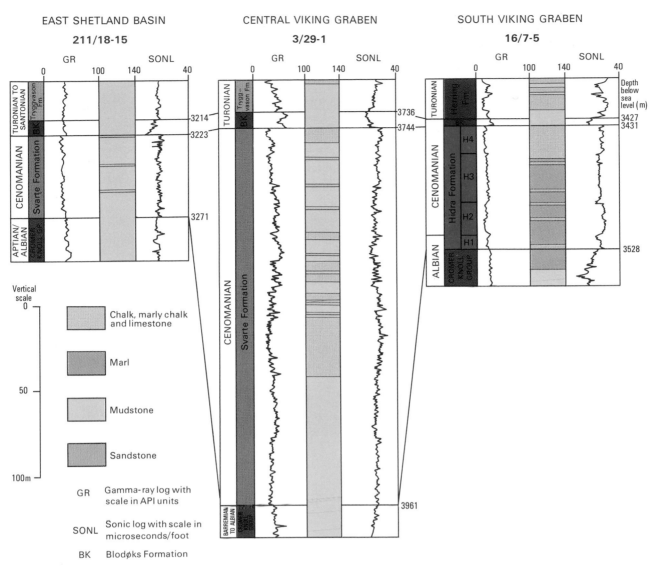

EAST SHETLAND BASIN
211/18-15

CENTRAL VIKING GRABEN
3/29-1

SOUTH VIKING GRABEN
16/7-5

Chalk, marly chalk and limestone

Marl

Mudstone

Sandstone

GR   Gamma-ray log with scale in API units

SONL   Sonic log with scale in microseconds/foot

BK   Blodøks Formation

Note: Facies changes may be gradational or interbedded on a fine scale

Figure 53   Correlation of the Hidra, Svarte and Blodøks formations in wells from the northern North Sea. For locations see Figure 50.

Jorsalfare formations; formation F was renamed the Ekofisk Formation (Isaksen and Tonstad, 1989).

This report follows the stratigraphical scheme of Isaksen and Tonstad (1989), with only minor modification, and incorporates the log units of Burnhill and Ramsay (1981). Most of the major stratigraphical breaks are thought to have occurred synchronously across the basin, which is consistent with the widely held view that eustatic sea-level changes were a major control on the Upper Cretaceous succession (Haq et al., 1987; Nybakken and Bäckstrøm, 1989).

Shetland Group in the Viking Graben and East Shetland Basin

HIDRA AND SVARTE FORMATIONS

The northward transition from the dominantly calcareous Hidra Formation to the dominantly mudstone Svarte Formation can be traced in the Central Viking Graben between about 59°N and 59°30'N. These coeval formations are mainly Cenomanian in age, but in basinal areas where sedimentation was continuous from the Rødby Formation of the Cromer Knoll Group, the basal part of the Shetland Group

may be of latest Albian age (Deegan and Scull, 1977; Burnhill and Ramsay, 1981).

The Hidra Formation is composed of argillaceous chalky limestones and calcareous mudstones. The lower boundary of the formation with the Cromer Knoll Group is marked by the upward passage into lower gamma-ray and higher sonic-velocity log values, reflecting an upward increase in calcareous lithologies (Figure 53). The Hidra Formation is mainly confined to basinal depocentres of the South Viking Graben, where it reaches over 85 m in thickness. Condensed sequences occur over some intrabasinal highs, and the formation pinches out at basin margins and on major intrabasinal structural highs (Figure 51). Burnhill and Ramsay (1981) recognised four units in the Hidra Formation that can be widely correlated, which suggests that the strata may have accumulated in a dominantly pelagic environment; units H1 and H3 are more marly than units H2 and H4 (Figure 53).

The Svarte Formation generally consists of mudstones interbedded with limestones (Figure 53), and the ratio of limestone to mudstone decreases northwards (Isaksen and Tonstad, 1989). The formation is mainly confined to basinal depocentres of the Viking Graben, where it reaches over

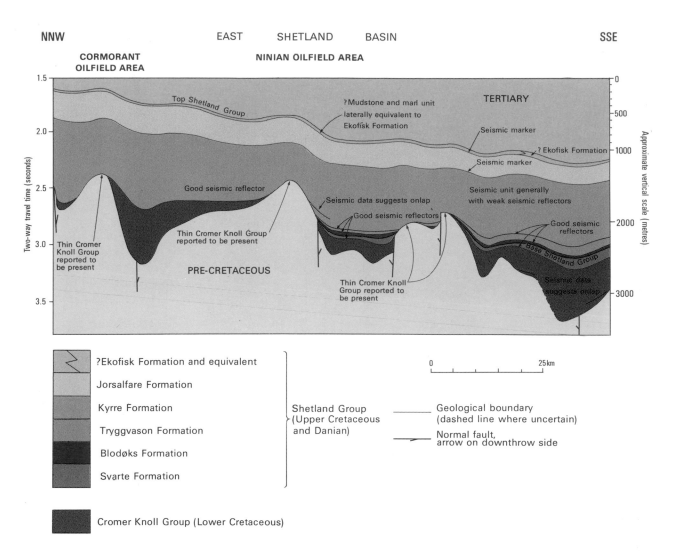

Figure 54   Line drawing of an interpreted seismic section illustrating the Shetland Group in the East Shetland Basin. For location see Figure 51.

200 m in thickness. In the Norwegian Sogn Graben (Figure 50) it is up to 350 m thick (Nybakken and Bäckstrøm, 1989). As with the Hidra Formation, the Svarte Formation pinches out against intrabasinal and basin-marginal highs, and the formation is thin or absent in all but the most basinal parts of the East Shetland Basin (Figure 54). Log responses in the Svarte Formation display a broad similarity with those of the Hidra Formation, albeit with higher overall gamma-ray values and lower sonic velocities (Figure 53). On seismic profiles, the Svarte Formation commonly displays relatively high-amplitude, continuous, subparallel reflections, rather similar to the underlying Rødby Formation.

BLODØKS FORMATION

The Blodøks Formation is generally composed of black, grey, red and green pyritic shales and mudstones of latest Cenomanian to early Turonian age (Figure 52). The formation has a sharp base, which is marked by a high gamma-ray peak and reduced sonic velocity (Figure 53). In the Viking Graben, the formation reaches over 25 m in thickness; like the Svarte Formation it is thin or absent across all but the basinal parts of the East Shetland Basin (Figure 54). It remains unclear whether a mid-Cretaceous unconformity, similar to that in the Outer Moray Firth Basin (Burnhill and Ramsay, 1981; Andrews et al., 1990), affected the northern North Sea, and whether significant erosion of the Blodøks Formation occurred over structural highs during a mid-Turonian regression.

The Blodøks Formation correlates with black shales of Cenomanian/Turonian age that are widespread in Europe, and represents a phase when oceanic bottom waters were 'anoxic' (Hart and Leary, 1989). These black shales are generally considered to be isochronous, and the environmental conditions which favoured their accumulation may have been related to a particularly high sea level (Figure 52, Hancock and Kauffman, 1979; Farrimond et al., 1990).

HERRING AND TRYGGVASON FORMATIONS

Limestones, marls and calcareous mudstones of the Herring Formation in the South Viking Graben region are gradually replaced northwards by mudstones with interbedded limestones of the Tryggvason Formation in the central and northern parts of the Viking Graben (Figure 55). These laterally equivalent formations are generally considered to be of Turonian age, and Nybakken and Bäckstrøm (1989) postulated that their tops may correspond with a late Turonian sea-level lowstand (Figure 52).

The Herring Formation limestones are generally white to pale grey, hard and cryptocrystalline. The formation is thickest in basinal depocentres and reaches over 200 m in the Fisher Bank Basin just to the south of the report area (Figure 10). Like the Hidra and Blodøks formations, the Herring Formation pinches out against basin-marginal highs (Figures 51 and 54). Burnhill and Ramsay (1981) recognised four units in the Herring Formation (Figure 55), and indicated a

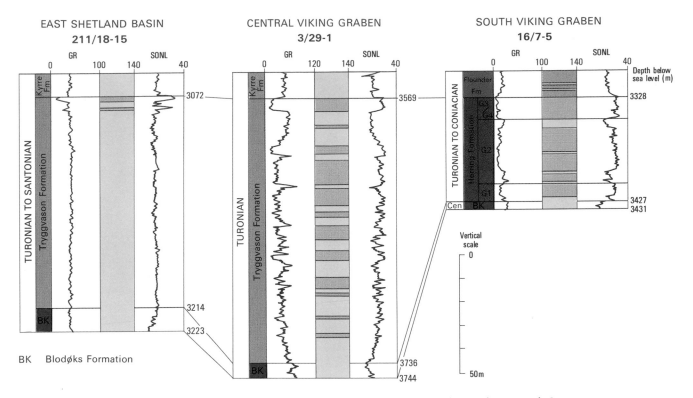

Figure 55 Correlation of the Herring and Tryggvason formations in wells from the northern North Sea. For key to lithology see Figure 53, for locations see Figure 50.

stratigraphical discontinuity over structural highs in the central North Sea, where Herring units onlap the Hidra Formation. The extent of this stratigraphical break in the northern North Sea is unknown.

The Tryggvason Formation mudstones are pale to dark grey, and commonly calcareous; the limestones are white to grey and argillaceous (Isaksen and Tonstad, 1989). The top of the Tryggvason Formation is characterised by an upward increase in gamma-ray values and a decrease in sonic velocity (Figure 55). In the Central Viking Graben, the formation shows log responses similar to those of the Herring Formation, but with higher gamma-ray values and lower sonic velocities (Figure 55). The Tryggvason Formation is widely distributed across basinal depocentres, and onlaps basin-margin highs; it is very thin or absent over many intrabasinal highs in the East Shetland Basin (Figure 54). There is a gradual northward increase in its thickness from about 150 m in the Central Viking Graben to about 350 m in the Sogn Graben (Nybakken and Bäckstrøm, 1989).

FLOUNDER AND KYRRE FORMATIONS

The laterally equivalent Flounder and Kyrre formations range in age from mid- or late Turonian to Campanian (Figure 52), and their tops may correspond to a lowstand in sea level close to the Campanian–Maastrichtian boundary (Nybakken and Bäckstrøm, 1989; Isaksen and Tonstad, 1989). The lack of significant variation in acoustic impedance within both the Flounder and Kyrre formations gives them seismic characters relatively free of reflections.

Although largely confined to the central North Sea, the Flounder Formation extends into the South Viking Graben where it generally consists of pale to dark grey, calcareous mudstones and shales grading upwards into pale to dark grey limestones; it is commonly capped by a red marl marker. The Flounder Formation is both underlain and overlain by formations containing a much higher proportion of harder limestone, and therefore it has a higher gamma-ray response and a

lower average sonic velocity (Figure 56) than these formations (Deegan and Scull, 1977).

The Flounder Formation was deposited over a much longer passage of time than any of the underlying formations of the Shetland Group (Figure 52), and is much thicker, reaching over 500 m in the Fisher Bank Basin immediately to the south of the report area (Figure 10). It is also more widely distributed than the older Shetland Group deposits, and onlaps or covers many intrabasinal highs (Figure 54).

The Kyrre Formation consists of grey mudstones with sporadic limestone beds (Isaksen and Tonstad, 1989); the mudstones are less calcareous and contain fewer limestones than those of the underlying Tryggvason Formation and the overlying Jorsalfare Formation, giving it a higher gamma-ray response and lower average velocity (Figure 56). The Kyrre Formation is widely distributed across the Viking Graben and East Shetland Basin; it onlaps and covers many intrabasinal highs (Figure 54), and increases in thickness northwards from about 500 m in the Central Viking Graben to 1300 m in the Sogn Graben (Nybakken and Bäckstrøm, 1989).

TOR AND JORSALFARE FORMATIONS

The laterally equivalent Tor Formation chalks and Jorsalfare Formation mudstones (Figure 52) range in age from late Campanian to Maastrichtian or possibly earliest Danian (Knox et al., 1981). The tops of the formations may correspond to a sea-level lowstand near the Cretaceous–Tertiary boundary (Nybakken and Bäckstrøm, 1989).

The Tor Formation, which consists of white to pale grey, hard limestones and chalks with minor mudstones, marls and shales, is widely distributed over the South Viking Graben. The Tor Formation generally has a lower gamma-ray response and higher sonic velocity than the surrounding formations, due to its higher carbonate content (Figure 57). The acoustic impedance contrast at its base gives rise to a prominent seismic reflector. The formation is a blanket deposit about 200 to 350 m thick over most of the South Viking

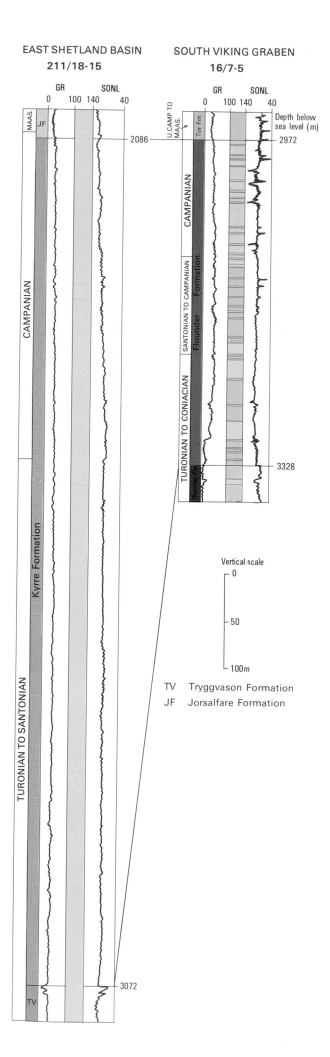

EAST SHETLAND BASIN
211/18-15

SOUTH VIKING GRABEN
16/7-5

TV   Tryggvason Formation
JF   Jorsalfare Formation

Graben, and may have been deposited over much of the North Sea (Ziegler, 1982), for its present western limit is erosional. The formation thickens to about 500 m over the faulted western margin of the Central Viking Graben, where seismic profiles (Figure 51) indicate a local angular discordance at its base, which is marked by the offlap and downlap of geographically restricted sedimentary units. Speculatively, and by analogy with the Central Graben (Kennedy, 1980; 1987), this lens of downlapping Tor Formation may represent massflow deposits, derived from the Fladen Ground Spur, that accumulated during syndepositional faulting and subsidence in the marginal zone of the graben.

The Jorsalfare Formation generally consists of grey, calcareous mudstones interbedded with thin, pale-coloured limestone beds which may be no thicker than 5 m and are commonly absent in the north (Figure 57; Isaksen and Tonstad, 1989). The lower boundary of the formation is marked by an increase in sonic velocity which gives rise to a seismic marker horizon at which there is, in general, no angular discordance. The formation is widely distributed over the Viking Graben and East Shetland Basin as a blanket about 300 to 350 m thick (Figure 54) that covers even major intrabasinal highs such as the Tampen Spur (Nybakken and Bäckstrøm, 1989). The western extent of the formation is limited by Tertiary faulting and erosion (BGS Solid Geology sheets). In the Norwegian part of the East Shetland Basin to the north-east, there is a decrease in thickness of the Jorsalfare Formation from about 400 m in the west to about 150 m in the east (Nybakken and Bäckstrøm, 1989).

EKOFISK FORMATION

The Ekofisk Formation is of Danian (early Palaeogene) age, and is the youngest formation of the Shetland Group (Figure 52). Regional studies indicate that its deposition was preceded, at least locally, by a break in sedimentation, and was followed by widespread uplift and erosion (Knox et al., 1981).

The full extent of the Ekofisk Formation in the northern North Sea is uncertain. In the southern and central parts of the Viking Graben, the Ekofisk Formation consists dominantly of argillaceous limestone and marl. The western limit of the Ekofisk Formation on the East Shetland Platform is erosional, and the formation may also be absent due to erosion over most of the North Viking Graben and East Shetland Basin. Locally developed Danian mudstones in the East Shetland Basin may either be lateral equivalents of the Ekofisk Formation or younger deposits overlying an unconformity. In the Norwegian sector, these strata have been included in the Rogaland Group (Isaksen and Tonstad, 1989).

In the South Viking Graben and Outer Moray Firth Basin, the lower boundary of the Ekofisk Formation is generally marked by an upward increase in gamma-ray response and a lower sonic velocity compared to the purer chalks of the Tor Formation (Figure 58). However, in the Central Viking Graben, the Ekofisk Formation is locally more calcareous than the underlying Maastrichtian strata, and its base is indicated by an upward decrease in radioactivity, and greater sonic velocity. The top of the Ekofisk Formation generally corresponds to a decrease in sonic velocity, and where the Ekofisk Formation is thick enough to be resolved on seismic records, both its top and bottom produce marker horizons (Figure 54). The Ekofisk Formation reaches over 75 m in thickness in the

Figure 56   Correlation of the Flounder and Kyrre formations in wells from the northern North Sea. For key to lithology see Figure 53, for locations see Figure 50.

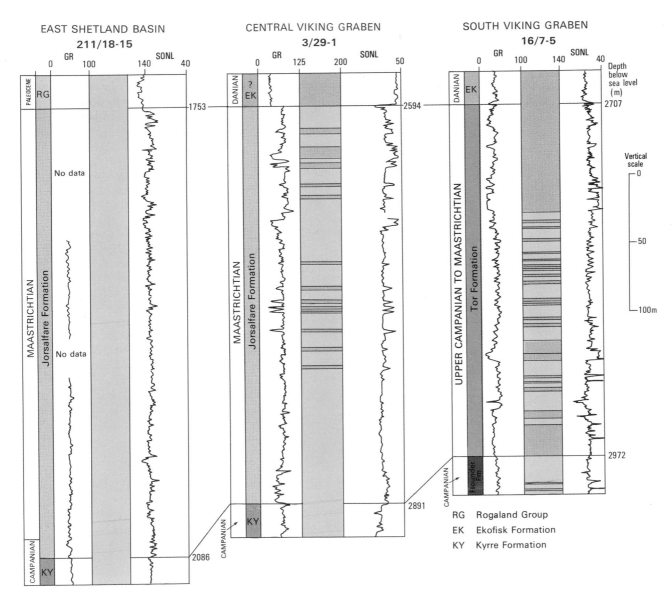

Figure 57 Correlation of the Tor and Jorsalfare formations in wells from the northern North Sea. For key to lithology see Figure 53, for locations see Figure 50.

South Viking Graben, but becomes thinner towards the north (Figure 58); over parts of the East Shetland Basin, the formation has been eroded following early Tertiary uplift.

Shetland Group in the Magnus Trough

Relatively few wells have been drilled in the Magnus Trough, where Upper Cretaceous mudstones are exceptionally thick at over 2000 m (Figure 50). The available data indicate that formations of the Shetland Group can be only tentatively recognised from wireline-log responses in the Magnus Trough.

Svarte Formation mudstones can be over 57 m thick, but pinch out against basin-marginal highs. The formation still shows broadly similar log responses to those recognised in the Viking Graben, but mudstones of the Blodøks Formation do not have a distinctive gamma-ray signature in the Magnus Trough because their level of radioactivity is not significantly higher than that of the overlying strata, although their base is clearly defined (Figure 59). The Blodøks Formation may be up to about 40 m thick, and the succeeding Tryggvason

Formation calcareous mudstones with thin interbedded limestones are up to about 475 m thick in basinal parts of the trough. The upper boundary of the latter formation corresponds to an increase in average gamma-ray response, and a decrease in sonic velocity.

The Kyrre Formation in the Magnus Trough consists of slightly calcareous mudstones with thin, interbedded limestones, and may locally be over 1200 m thick. The upper boundary is generally marked by a small upward increase in average sonic velocity. Maastrichtian mudstones with thin interbedded limestones of the Jorsalfare Formation reach over 580 m in thickness. Apart from a few peaks in the sonic log, and corresponding troughs in the gamma-ray log which correlate with thin limestone beds, the overall log responses of the Tryggvason, Kyrre and Jorsalfare formations are rather characterless. Thin mudstones, which are assigned to the Danian on oil-company logs, locally overlie the Jorsalfare Formation, and may either be lateral equivalents of the Ekofisk Formation or deposits of the Rogaland Group that unconformably overlie the Shetland Group.

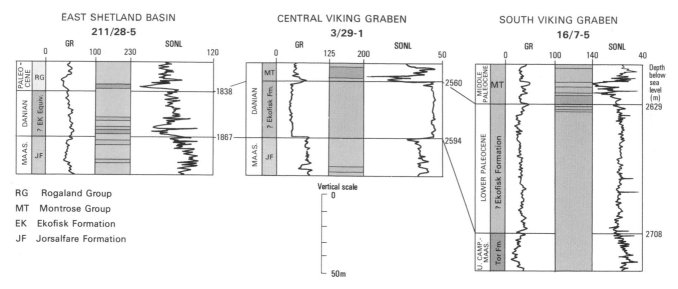

Figure 58 Correlation of the Ekofisk Formation and possibly equivalent mudstones in wells from the northern North Sea. For key to lithology see Figure 53, for locations see Figure 51.

RG Rogaland Group

MT Montrose Group

EK Ekofisk Formation

JF Jorsalfare Formation

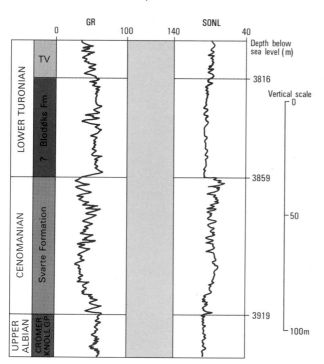

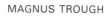

TV Tryggvason Formation

Figure 59 The lower part of the Shetland Group in the Magnus Trough. For key to lithology see Figure 53, for location see Figure 51.

7 Tertiary

The broad, symmetrical, Cenozoic (Tertiary and Quaternary) northern North Sea Basin (Figure 60) contains up to about 2500 m of sediment (Ziegler, 1982). The axis of the Tertiary basin coincides closely with the trace of the Mesozoic Viking Graben, and Tertiary subsidence can be largely explained by thermal cooling of the lithosphere following Mesozoic rifting (e.g. Thorne and Watts, 1989). From mid-Eocene times onwards, there was little fault control on sedimentation.

At the base of the succession, over 1000 m of coarse-grained Paleocene strata blanket the western Viking Graben and immediately adjacent areas (Figure 61), presenting a striking lithological contrast with the chalks, marls and mudstones of the underlying Upper Cretaceous and lowermost Tertiary (Danian) Shetland Group. The influx of coarse-grained sediment reflects a major phase of tectonic uplift of

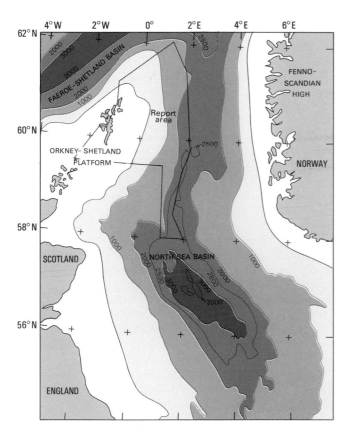

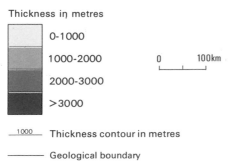

Figure 60 Generalised Cenozoic (Tertiary and Quaternary) sediment thickness in the North Sea. After Ziegler (1982).

both the Scottish mainland and the Orkney–Shetland Platform (Figure 60). This phase, and its associated volcanicity, resulted in tilting and eastward-directed drainage on the East Shetland Platform, and is widely considered to be related to early Tertiary opening of the North Atlantic (Bott, 1975; Hailwood et al., 1979).

Lower to middle Paleocene deposits are mainly confined to the Viking Graben, where subsidence was apparently controlled by reactivated Mesozoic graben faults, particularly along the western margin of the East Shetland Basin and Beryl Embayment (Rochow, 1981; Morton, 1982). However, the geometry of lower Paleocene depositional sequences in the Viking Graben suggests that syndepositional faulting was not related to a new phase of rifting, as proposed by Beach et al. (1987), but probably to thermal subsidence (Badley et al., 1988).

A major control on Tertiary sedimentation was fluctuation in relative or eustatic sea level (Stewart, 1987; Harding et al., 1990; Cloetingh et al., 1987). Kockel (1988) and Gramann and Kockel (1988) have recognised nine major transgressive/ regressive cycles in the North-West European Tertiary Basin.

Estimates of water depths in the North Sea Basin during Paleocene to early Eocene times are varied. On the basis of depositional models largely based on seismic reflection profiles and the fossil content of depositional sequences, Parker (1975) and Héritier et al. (1979) envisaged a deep-water basin with depths of about 1000 m. However, Berggren and Gradstein (1981) indicated that benthic foraminiferal assemblages in the lower Palaeogene of the central North Sea could have developed in water depths of as little as 200 m. Morton (1982) suggested that although sedimentological investigations indicate that much of the Paleocene sequence in the Viking Graben is of mass-flow origin, such a mode of deposition need not be confined to deep water.

In contrast to most studies, Mudge and Bliss (1983) disputed the gravity-flow origin for lower Paleocene sequences in the Viking Graben. They suggested that the microfloral assemblages (dominated by spores and pollen), the commonly well-sorted nature of massive sandstones, and the presence of lignites (which they interpreted as being in situ), indicate deposition in a shallow-water environment dominated by offshore bars.

In their lithostratigraphical scheme for the Tertiary of the northern North Sea (Figure 62), Deegan and Scull (1977) recognised a Paleocene, lower submarine-fan complex, called the Montrose Group; it is disconformably overlain by the basinward-prograded, shelf-deltaic deposits of the Moray Group. A relatively thin sequence of marine mudstones and tuffs, the Rogaland Group, was considered to be the distal equivalent of both the Montrose and Moray groups, and its age is now recognised to extend into the early Eocene.

An alternative stratigraphical scheme for the Paleocene of the central part of the North Sea was proposed by Knox et al. (1981) who, on the basis of sand mineralogy, shale lithology, tuff beds and fossil assemblages, erected ten post-Chalk Group stratigraphical units and subunits (Figure 62). These were related to the stratigraphical divisions of Deegan and Scull (1977), and to cycles of transgression, regression, uplift and subsidence. Morton (1982) used sand mineralogy to identify four phases of sand deposition in the northern North Sea.

On the basis of seismic and palaeontological data, Stewart (1987) divided post-Chalk Group lower Palaeogene strata in

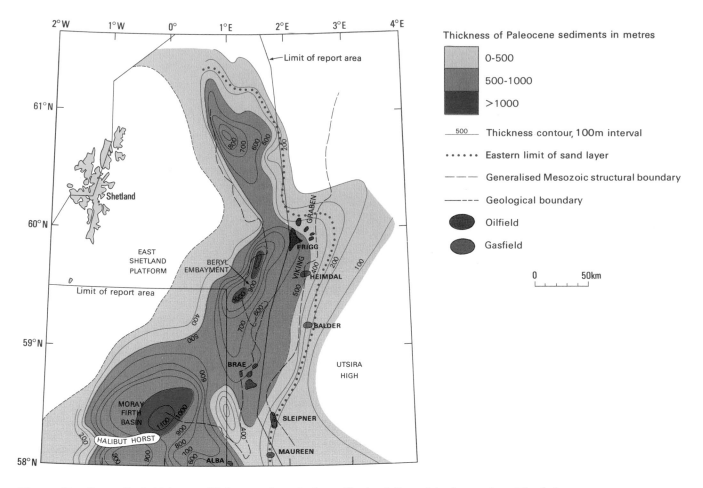

Figure 61 Generalised thickness of Paleocene deposits (post-Shetland Group) in the northern North Sea. After Kockel (1988).

the central part of the North Sea into nine genetically related sequences separated by transgressions and regressions. Stewart's (1987) sequences are closely related to the stratigraphical units identified by Knox et al. (1981). One of the advantages of this genetic, sequence-stratigraphy approach is that it provides a means of correlating contemporaneous sequences that show rapid lateral and vertical facies changes, and thus aids analysis of basin development.

In a revision of Tertiary lithostratigraphical nomenclature in the Norwegian North Sea, Isaksen and Tonstad (1989) abandoned the term Montrose Group and proposed that all its constituent formations be included in the Rogaland Group (Figure 62). However, Isaksen and Tonstad (1989) retained the Deegan and Scull (1977) formations, as well as defining new ones.

Mudge and Copestake (1992) revised Deegan and Scull's (1977) Danian to Ypresian lithostratigraphy for the central and northern North Sea within a framework of biostratigraphy and published a seismic sequence stratigraphy (Figure 62). They also modified the Norwegian sector nomenclature of Isaksen and Tonstad (1989). Mudge and Copestake (1992) allocated formation status to claystone units with basinwide distribution, and member status to more localised sandstone units that are enclosed within the claystones. They abandoned use of the Rogaland Group, and assigned its constituent formations to the laterally equivalent Montrose and Moray groups. The scheme of Mudge and Copestake (1992) has considerable merit, but as it awaits acceptance, this chapter is based around the framework of Deegan and Scull (1977).

Higher in the stratigraphical column, Deegan and Scull (1977) and Isaksen and Tonstad (1989) identified the domi-

nantly argillaceous Hordaland (Eocene to lower Miocene) and Nordland (middle Miocene to Recent) groups in the Norwegian sector of the northern North Sea Basin (Figure 62). These groups have not been formally subdivided in the UK sector. The lower Eocene Frigg Formation is the only unit Deegan and Scull (1977) defined within the Hordaland Group; it is generally considered to be a submarine-fan deposit (Héritier et al., 1979, 1981; Williams, 1983; Conort, 1986). Isaksen and Tonstad (1989) defined the sandy Grid and Skade formations in the Hordaland Group, and the Utsira Formation in the Nordland Group of the Norwegian Viking Graben.

The lower Palaeogene strata contain many commercially significant hydrocarbon accumulations (see Chapter 10), and consequently have been the subject of intensive study. Significant reserves of oil have also been discovered in middle Eocene sands in the southern part of the report area at the Alba Oilfield (Figure 61). No commercial hydrocarbon discoveries have so far been made in Neogene strata, which are relatively poorly documented.

MONTROSE GROUP

Across the Viking Graben, the Montrose Group is divided into the Maureen Formation and the overlying Heimdal Formation (Figure 62). The Maureen Formation consists of mixed lithologies; it is commonly conglomeratic, with clasts of reworked limestones and shales of Danian and Late Cretaceous age in a matrix of, and interbedded with, shales, siltstones and sandstones (Deegan and Scull, 1977). Stewart

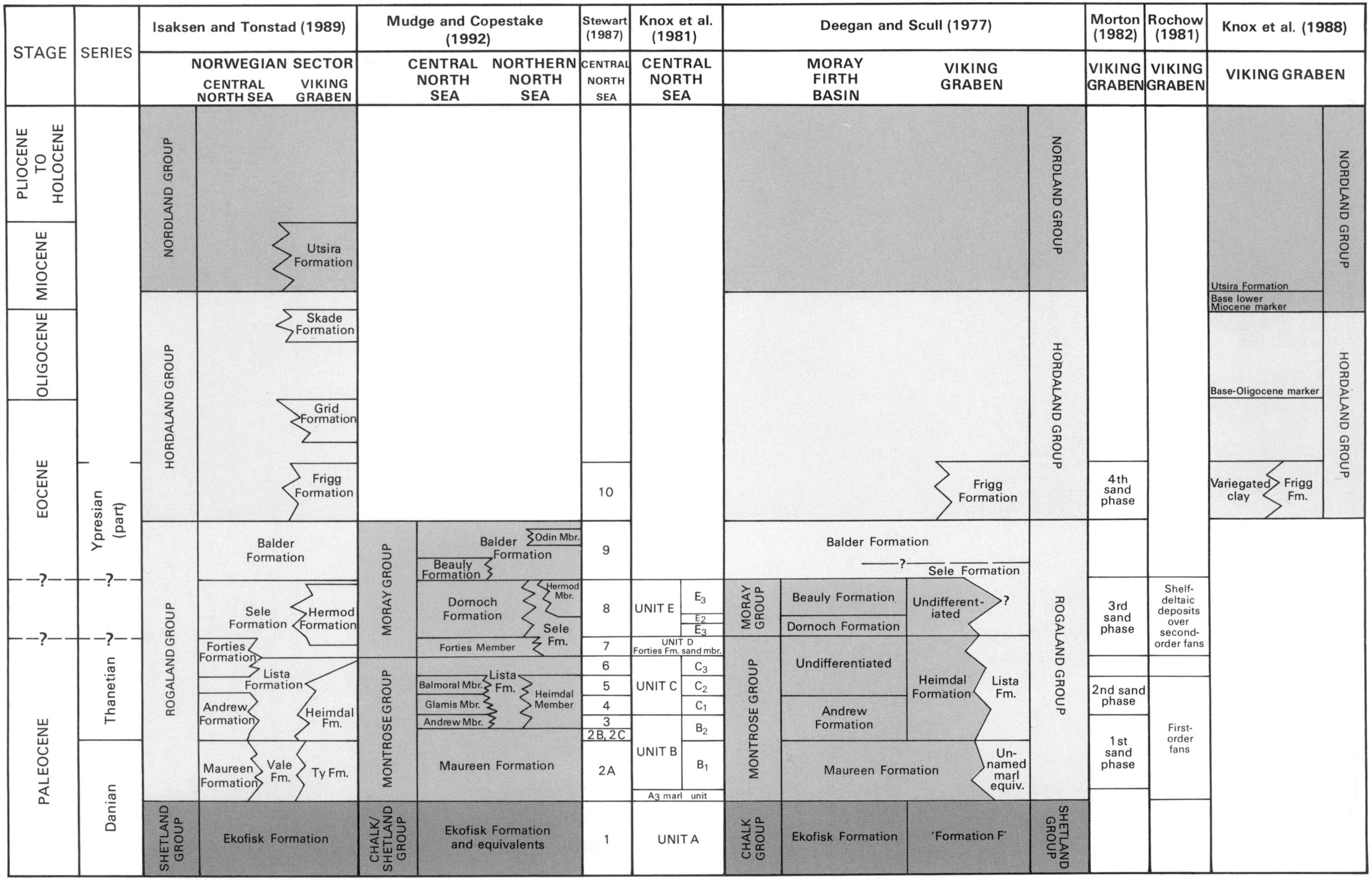

Figure 62 Stratigraphical chart of the Cenozoic showing the relationship between the lithostratigraphical schemes of Deegan and Scull (1977), Isaksen and Tonstad (1989), and Mudge and Copestake (1992). Also shown are the division of submarine-fan and shelf-deltaic deposits of Rochow (1981), the stratigraphical units of Knox et al. (1981) and Morton (1982), and the depositional sequences of Stewart (1987). Note that Stewart (1987) equated the base of sequence 7 with the base of the Moray Group.

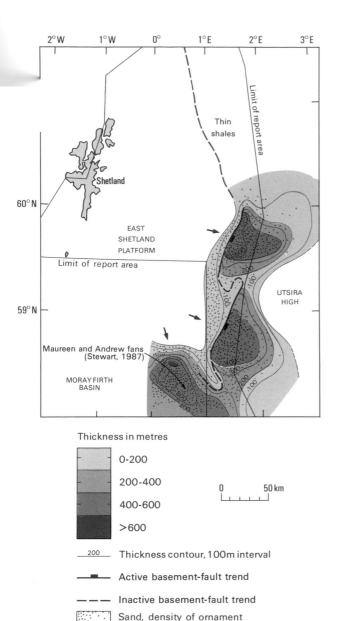

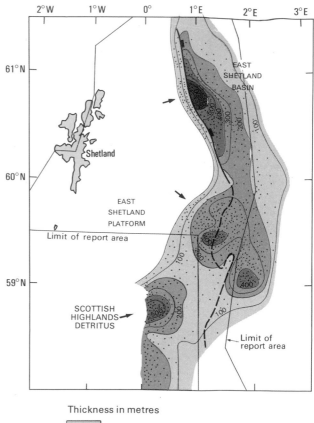

Thickness in metres

0-200

200-400

400-600

>600

0   50 km

———200——— Thickness contour, 100m interval

Active basement-fault trend

- - - - Inactive basement-fault trend

Sand, density of ornament indicates relative abundance

Direction of sediment influx

——— Geological boundary

Figure 63 Distribution and thickness of Maureen and lower Heimdal formation sediments (unit B of Knox et al., 1981) and coeval deposits. After Morton (1982).

(1987) considered these rocks to be debris-flow deposits of late Danian age (subsequence 2A, equivalent to sub-unit B_1 of Knox et al., 1981) which resulted from widespread erosion of the basin flank following regression.

The formation has an irregular distribution pattern, but is mainly confined to areas which overlie the Mesozoic grabens. It is best developed farther south in the central North Sea and Moray Firth, although Nielsen et al. (1986) indicated that the Maureen Formation reaches over 400 m in thickness in southern and central parts of the Viking Graben. Around the Maureen Oilfield, a marl equivalent of the Maureen Formation is overlain by submarine-fan deposits termed the Maureen Fan by Stewart (1987; his subsequence 2B); the distal, unnamed, marl facies equivalent to the Maureen Formation is part of the Rogaland Group (Figure 62). Mudge and Copestake (1992) consider the Maureen Formation to be of mid-Danian to earliest Thanetian age, and equate it to se-

quence 2 of Stewart (1987). Mudge and Copestake (1992) report two northern North Sea depocentres which contain thick Maureen Formation sandstones; one located in the Beryl Embayment, and the other in the southern part of the East Shetland Basin, although the latter (Figure 63) was not recognised by Morton (1982).

The Heimdal Formation is locally over 800 m thick and is distributed (Figures 63 and 64) across the southern and central parts of the Viking Graben, the southern East Shetland Basin, and over the western flanks of the grabens (Lilleng, 1980; Rochow, 1981; Morton, 1982; Mudge and Bliss, 1983). The formation is dominated by massive, fine- to coarse-grained, poorly cemented sandstone units up to about 30 m thick, but which are locally over 100 m thick due to amalgamation of beds. The sandstones are interbedded with grey and black shales, limestones and sandy limestones, and form an important hydrocarbon reservoir on the eastern flank

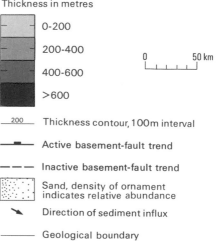

Thickness in metres

0-200

200-400

400-600

>600

0   50 km

———200——— Thickness contour, 100m interval

Active basement-fault trend

- - - - Inactive basement-fault trend

Sand, density of ornament indicates relative abundance

Direction of sediment influx

——— Geological boundary

Figure 64 Distribution and thickness of middle Heimdal Formation sediments (unit C of Knox et al., 1981) and coeval deposits. After Morton (1982).

of the Viking Graben (Mure, 1987a; Hanslien, 1987; Ostvedt, 1987). Bouma sequences have been described from the succession at the Heimdal Oilfield (Mure, 1987a), and Heimdal Formation sandstones are generally interpreted as submarine-fan deposits (Sarg and Skjold, 1981; Enjolras et al., 1986; Conort, 1986).

Rochow (1981) postulated two types of sand deposit in the Paleocene succession (Figure 62). Thick, areally restricted, first-order submarine fans that are laterally equivalent to the Maureen and Heimdal formations developed along the western margin of the Viking Graben. These are overlain by broader, more-extensive, second-order fans that include the upper Heimdal Formation and infill the depressions between the earlier fans. Rochow (1981) suggested that the first-order fans developed at the foot of a fault at the western margin of the Viking Graben, and that their cone-like shape indicates radial outflow of sediment from point sources, perhaps related to seismically defined channels at the base of the Paleocene on the western flank of the graben. In contrast, from a study of well logs, Enjolras et al. (1986) postulated that early Paleocene Heimdal Formation sandstones in the South Viking Graben accumulated from turbidity flows that travelled axially northward along the graben.

Although Rochow (1981) did not subdivide his first-order fan sequence, both Héritier et al. (1979) and Lilleng (1980) regarded the northern fan, in the East Shetland Basin area (Figure 64), as younger than those to the south. On the basis of sand mineralogy and correlation of geophysical-log responses of the sand bodies, Morton (1982) perceived two phases of sand deposition that equate with Rochow's (1981) first-order fans (Figures 62, 63 and 64).

During the first phase of sand deposition (Morton, 1982), rapid subsidence was concentrated in the southern and central parts of the Viking Graben, associated with movement on north-north-easterly trending basement faults (Figure 63). However, seismic evidence indicates only minor faulting of Paleocene strata in the South Viking Graben (BGS Fladen Solid Geology sheet), in contrast to the half-graben model proposed by Morton (1982). Sands up to about 600 m thick were deposited; these are epidote-free and mineralogically identical to the unit B sands in the central North Sea (Knox et al., 1981), being derived from the same source of Jurassic sandstones on the Orkney–Shetland Platform. This phase of sand deposition is therefore considered to be contemporaneous with deposition of unit B of Knox et al. (1981), and sequences 2 and 3 of Stewart (1987); it is of late Danian to early Thanetian age, and incorporates both the Maureen and Heimdal formations (Figure 62).

The second phase of sand deposition in the first-order fans (Morton, 1982) corresponds to rapid subsidence above a north-north-westerly trending basement fault in the southern part of the East Shetland Basin (Figure 64), leading to the accumulation of up to about 800 m of sandstones. To the southeast of Shetland, the unit is represented by up to 400 m of sandstones and claystones, commonly with abrupt variations in sand:shale ratios, although total thicknesses remain relatively uniform, even over the East Shetland Platform. The sands are epidote bearing, and were derived from metamorphic basement immediately to the west. This phase of sedimentation from early to mid-Thanetian times (Figure 62) was accompanied by deposition of volcanic ash (Jacqué and Thouvenin, 1975), and correlates with subunits C_1 and C_2 of Knox et al. (1981), and sequences 4 and 5 of Stewart (1987). There was accumulation of reworked sandy tuffs and tuffaceous sands, together with graded ash layers up to a few centimetres thick. The proposed age range for the ashes is about 58 to 57 Ma (Knox and Morton, 1983); their composition, and a well-defined contem-

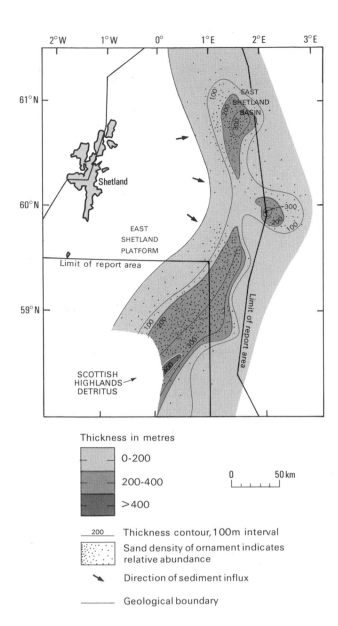

Figure 65 Distribution and thickness of units D and E, the second-order fans of the Montrose Group, the shelf-deltaic deposits of the Moray Group, and coeval deposits. After Morton (1982).

poraneous phase of uplift and erosion of central Scotland, suggest derivation from the Hebridean volcanic province (Knox and Morton, 1983; 1988).

Montrose Group submarine-fan deposits derived from the Moray Firth Basin extend south-eastwards into the southern part of the report area (Figures 61 and 63), where Stewart (1987) identified an easterly trending depositional lobe of a late Danian to earliest Thanetian submarine fan that he termed the Maureen Fan (subsequence 2B). Stewart (1987) loosely attributed the term mid-fan to this lobe, and described convex-up, broken reflectors that he interpreted as a channellised section. Laterally and downdip from the mid-fan area, the seismic character passes into a more layered reflection pattern that relates to a thinly bedded facies, with upward-fining cycles evident in well sections. Stewart (1987) also mapped a younger, south-easterly trending, channellised, submarine-fan lobe, termed the Andrew Fan (sequence 3); it is of early Thanetian age (Figures 62 and 63).

Overlying the first-order fan sands throughout the northern North Sea is a mid-Thanetian transgressive unit of green shale which equates with subunit C_3 of Knox et al. (1981)

and sequence 6 of Stewart (1987). Overlying this green shale unit (Figures 62 and 65) are the second-order fan deposits recognised by Rochow (1981), which show a more widespread distribution and more variable sand:shale ratios than the first-order fan deposits. Rochow (1981, p.262) indicated that they were fed by 'relatively dispersed transport processes', which carried sediment across the shelf to the graben edge, where suprafan channel systems and turbidity flows distributed them into the areas between the first-order fans. From seismic evidence, Rochow (1981) suggested that a southward axial palaeoslope existed in the central and southern parts of the Viking Graben during this accumulation.

MORAY GROUP

Rochow (1981) identified prograding and upward-coarsening shelf-deltaic deposits in the northern North Sea that largely equate (Figure 62) with the Moray Group in the Moray Firth Basin (Deegan and Scull, 1977). These possibly late Thanetian deposits, which are up to about 400 m thick (Figure 65), accumulated in a broadly north-trending belt that extends from the Moray Firth Basin, along the western margin of the Central Viking Graben, and across the southern portion of the East Shetland Basin (Rochow, 1981; Morton, 1982; Mudge and Bliss, 1983). The western limit of these strata is erosional (Mudge and Bliss, 1983), and in-situ lignitic deposits (Beauly Formation) that cap the Moray Group in the Moray Firth Basin wedge out north of about 59° 15'N to the west of the southern part of the report area (Rochow, 1981).

Rochow (1981) divided the shelf-deltaic deposits in the northern North Sea into an older, nonprograding, inner-shelf sequence composed of monotonous mudstones and younger, eastward-prograding, outer-shelf, upward-coarsening sands. He concluded that the Moray Group sands were transported across the inner shelf in channels, and that the arcuate or deltaic shape of the shelf front probably resulted from shelf-front currents and the pattern of distributary currents. According to Mudge and Bliss (1983), the Moray Group sands in the Viking Graben resulted from the outbuilding of a coastal-margin complex fed by longshore drift from the large delta system in the Moray Firth area. They interpreted sand units as northerly trending offshore-bar deposits with associated easterly trending tidal channels.

In contrast to Deegan and Scull (1977), Stewart (1987) suggested that the base of his sequence 7 (unit D or Forties Formation sand member of Knox et al., 1981) marks the base of the Moray Group (Figure 62). This interpretation is supported by Mudge and Copestake (1992). Morton (1982) showed that sands of the second-order fans (Montrose Group), and the shelf-deltaic deposits (Moray Group) described by Rochow (1981), are mineralogically identical. Morton (1982) regarded both deposits as belonging to one genetic unit; this is his third phase of sand deposition (Figures 62 and 65), that is equivalent to units D and E of Knox et al. (1981), and to sequences 7 and 8 of Stewart (1987). Morton (1982) suggested that a major regression at the end of unit C deposition had initially confined sedimentation to areas where water depths had been greatest in the preceding phases of sedimentation, such as in the vicinity of the Frigg Gasfield (Figure 61). Renewed clastic input at this time suggests contemporaneous uplift of the northern Orkney–Shetland Platform. The succeeding transgressive phase led to deposition of clays and nonprograded sands, the latter probably as offshore bars, but gradual shallowing led to increasing energy conditions and eastward progradation of sands.

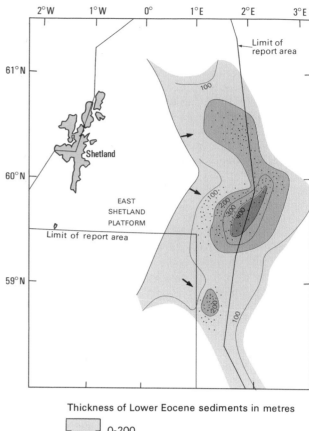

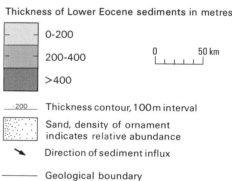

Thickness of Lower Eocene sediments in metres

- 0-200
- 200-400
- >400

0   50 km

-200- Thickness contour, 100 m interval

Sand, density of ornament indicates relative abundance

Direction of sediment influx

Geological boundary

Figure 66 Distribution and thickness of lower Eocene deposits, including the Balder and Frigg formations. After Morton (1982).

ROGALAND GROUP

The Rogaland Group consists predominantly of argillaceous marine deposits, and was initially considered to be the distal equivalent of the Paleocene Montrose and Moray groups (Deegan and Scull, 1977). However, the upper part is now known to be of early Eocene age, younger than the Moray Group (Figure 62). The Rogaland Group is up to about 200 m thick, and is typically developed in the eastern part of the northern North Sea, particularly in the Norwegian sector. Three divisions have been defined for the Rogaland Group in the northern North Sea: the Lista, Sele and Balder formations (Figure 62). A locally developed, unnamed, pale grey marl unit beneath the Lista Formation is equated with the Maureen Formation.

The Lista Formation is of Thanetian age, and consists predominantly of up to about 150 m of mudstones which are generally nontuffaceous and nonlaminated, and contain only minor sandy interbeds. In the central North Sea, Stewart (1987) and Knox et al. (1981) related the hemipelagic mudstones equivalent to the Lista Formation (Figure 62) to episodes of high sea level when coarse-grained sediments were trapped on the contemporaneous shelf areas.

The Sele Formation is composed of up to about 45 m of black or greenish grey, tuffaceous, laminated mudstones, siltstones and minor sandstones; these are at least partly equivalent to unit E of Knox et al. (1981). Both Mudge and Bliss (1983) and Knox et al. (1981) suggested that the presence of black, laminated shales, and the absence of foraminifera from the Sele Formation, indicate a phase of restricted marine circulation. The establishment of a continental basin to the south-west, and reduced marine connection to the north as a result of progradation of sediment wedges across the Viking Graben, may explain the stagnant bottom conditions during a phase of deposition which Knox et al. (1981) and Kockel (1988) regarded as transgressive. Stewart (1987), however, postulated a lowstand of sea level during deposition of the Sele Formation.

The lower Eocene Balder Formation is composed of up to about 75 m of laminated, varicoloured, fissile mudstones with significant beds of tuff and local sandstones. These are thought to have accumulated in a restricted marine environment (Knox et al., 1988). Pyroclastic sedimentation in the Sele and Balder formations is characterised by graded ash layers, generally up to a few centimetres thick, which range in composition mainly from basic to intermediate (Knox and Morton, 1983; 1988). The ash-rich Balder Formation is widely distributed across the North Sea Basin and west of Shetland, and forms a regional seismic marker because of the anomalously high sonic velocity of the ashes. The composition and overall distribution pattern of the Sele and Balder ashes suggests derivation from volcanic activity in the Rockall–Greenland rift, with a maximum phase of explosive eruptions taking place immediately before the onset of oceanic crust generation, at about 54 Ma (Knox and Morton, 1983; 1988).

In the southern and central Viking Graben, separate thick units of submarine-fan sandstone, which are marked by pronounced mounded features on seismic data, are present within the Sele and Balder formations. These are the Hermod and Odin members (Figure 62) of Mudge and Copestake (1992). The sands are fine to coarse grained, and fan progradation in the Sele Formation is indicated by cycles of upward bed-thickening in which the sands become cleaner upwards (Stewart, 1987). On the Norwegian flank of the Central Viking Graben (Figure 61), thin Balder Formation sandstones form a secondary reservoir in the Balder Oilfield (Hanslien, 1987), and lenticular sandstone bodies are also reported in the Balder and Sele formations around the Frigg Gasfield (Mure, 1987a, b and c; Conort, 1986).

Whereas Deegan and Scull (1977), Rochow (1981) and Milton et al. (1990) equated the Balder Formation with the lignitic Beauly Formation of the Moray Firth Basin, both Knox et al. (1981) and Morton (1982) considered it to be younger, and correlated the Sele Formation with the late Thanetian Moray Group (Figure 62). Stewart (1987) regarded both the Sele and Balder formations (his sequence 9) to be younger than the Beauly Formation, and indicated their seismic onlap on to the Moray Group delta slope. Mudge and Copestake (1992) equate the Sele Formation with Stewart's (1987) sequences 7 and 8, and with units D and E of Knox et al. (1981). According to Knox and Morton (1988), the Paleocene–Eocene boundary may correspond to a level in the upper part of the Sele Formation.

HORDALAND GROUP

The Hordaland Group overlies the Rogaland Group, and consists of Eocene, Oligocene and early Miocene marine clay-

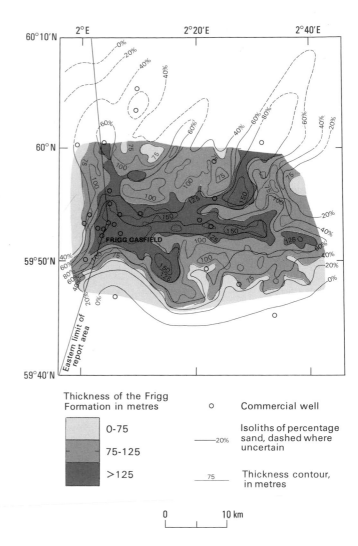

Figure 67 Thickness of the Frigg Formation in the Frigg Gasfield area, with isoliths of percentage sand in the formation. Slightly modified after Conort (1986). See Figure 61 for location of the Frigg Gasfield.

stones with some thin carbonate beds and local sandstones. The Hordaland Group is widely distributed over most of the North Sea, but the Frigg Formation is the only formal subdivision in the UK sector. In the Norwegian sector, coeval deposits include sand-rich, shallow-marine and deltaic strata.

The lower Eocene (Ypresian) Frigg Formation is up to 400 m thick, and is confined to part of the central and southern Viking Graben (Figure 66). An equivalent, mound-shaped seismic sequence has been mapped in the East Shetland Basin (Héritier et al., 1979; Condon, 1988), and coeval prodelta deposits accumulated in the South Viking Graben (Stewart, 1987). The Frigg Formation forms the reservoir in the Frigg Gasfield and its satellite fields, which are mainly located in the Norwegian sector (Figure 61). In the Frigg area, the formation mainly consists of unconsolidated, fine-grained, massive sandstones which are organised into amalgamated sets up to 100 m thick, and sandstones with laminations, ripples and convolute bedding. Also present are breccias, and laminated mudstones up to 3 m thick (Mure, 1987b, c and d; McGovney and Radovich, 1985; Nordgard Bolas, 1987). Core evidence, consisting of Bouma sequences, load casts and scoured bases of beds, and seismic facies which indicate overlapping mound-shaped reflectors, have generally been interpreted to indicate a channelised, submarine-fan environment (Héritier et al., 1981; Conort, 1986; Mure,

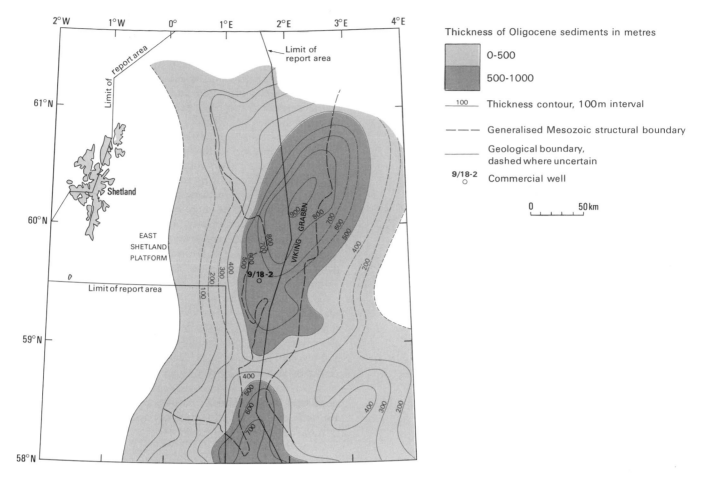

Figure 70 Generalised thickness of Oligocene deposits in the northern North Sea. After Kockel (1988).

tic of Paleocene and Eocene deposits. This faunal change may reflect a transition from a restricted-basin setting to more-oxygenated, shallower-water conditions, possibly as a result of infilling of the basin (Berggren and Gradstein, 1981). However, Ziegler (1982) postulated that Oligocene sedimentation and subsidence rates probably kept in balance, and inferred a mid-Oligocene, glacially induced lowstand of sea level. It has been speculated that the faunal change is related to a global oxygenation event associated with Eocene cooling, and a major change in deep-water circulation in the oceans (Berggren and Gradstein, 1981; Buchardt, 1978).

In the transgressive phase following the mid-Oligocene lowstand of sea level, a major shelf-deltaic foreset unit up to 500 m thick prograded from the East Shetland Platform into the central part of the northern North Sea Basin (Ziegler, 1982). In the Norwegian sector, above the central and southern parts of the Viking Graben, up to 200 m of fine- to medium-grained sandstones of late Oligocene age have been called the Skade Formation by Isaksen and Tonstad (1989). These sandstones are thought to have accumulated in an open-marine environment as a response to a relative fall in sea level (Isaksen and Tonstad, 1989).

On the East Shetland Platform, Oligocene strata are dominantly sandstones for which biostratigraphical analysis indicates a late Oligocene age. The sands are generally unconsolidated and glauconitic, with interbedded clay and lignites.

In well 9/18-2 in the Central Viking Graben (Figure 70), the Oligocene–Miocene boundary has been established by analysis of otoliths, the ear bones of fish; the well has a more complete sequence of otoliths than has been described elsewhere in north-west Europe (Gaemers, 1990). The top of the Hordaland Group lies within the Miocene succession.

NORDLAND GROUP

Deegan and Scull (1977) placed the boundary between the Hordaland Group and the overlying Miocene to Holocene Nordland Group at a transition into more massive and blocky clays. This contact is usually marked by a change in wireline-log response, which represents an unconformity of mid-Miocene age (Figure 62). Knox et al. (1988) placed the base of the Nordland Group in the Central Viking Graben at a change from Oligocene and lower Miocene sands to a lower to upper-middle Miocene unit of glauconitic clays and sands; the top of the latter unit is a mid-Miocene unconformity which forms a prominent seismic marker. Prograded seismic units overlying this unconformity indicate a pronounced mid-Miocene sea-level change of about 400 m (Gramann and Kockel, 1988; Kockel, 1988). Sandstones that commonly overlie this mid-Miocene unconformity are equivalent to the Utsira Formation in the Norwegian sector (Knox et al., 1988; Isaksen and Tonstad, 1989), which ranges up to late Miocene in age, and consists mainly of very fine- to fine-grained, glauconitic sandstones with interbeds of mudstone. These deposits are up to about 400 m thick, and are thought to have accumulated in a shallow, marine-shelf environment (Isaksen and Tonstad, 1989).

Nielsen et al. (1986) indicated two Miocene depocentres in the northern North Sea Basin, in which up to about 500 and 600 m of sediments accumulated respectively (Figure 71). One lies in the East Shetland Basin, and the other is situated along the eastern flank of the southern and central parts of the Viking Graben. Miocene deposits over the western part of the East Shetland Basin and the Central Viking Graben area are dominantly sandy (Héritier et al., 1979), but to the

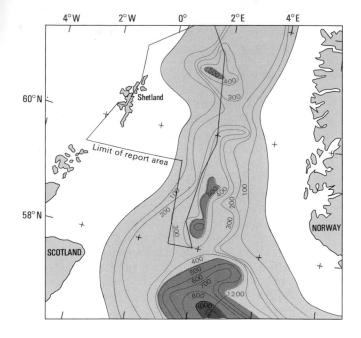

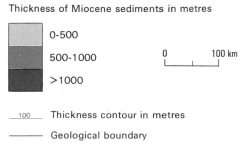

Thickness of Miocene sediments in metres

▨ 0-500

▨ 500-1000

■ >1000

0   100 km

<u>100</u>   Thickness contour in metres

———   Geological boundary

Figure 71 Generalised thickness of Miocene deposits in the northern and central North Sea. After Nielsen et al. (1986).

north and south the predominant lithologies are mudstones and shelly clays with interbedded sands. From mid-Miocene times onwards, warm-water microfaunas indicate a progressive shallowing of the northern North Sea Basin. This shallowing trend probably reflects rapid infilling of a relatively slowly subsiding basin by deltaic complexes which prograded eastward from the East Shetland Platform into the Viking Graben (Ziegler, 1982).

Lack of sampling in the shallow parts of commercial wells means that Pliocene deposits are rarely differentiated; however, they appear to be variable in lithology. North of 61°N they are claystones with some sands and sandy clays. In the central part of the report area the Pliocene sediments are predominantly argillaceous sands, locally with 10 to 30 m-thick, upward-coarsening cycles. South of about 59°N, in the Witch Ground area, the Pliocene deposits are claystones. Several boreholes have identified shelly gravel up to 30 m thick of possible Pliocene age; cored sections reveal these to be commonly coquinas, which on shallow-seismic sections appear as reefs or banks up to 30 m high and about 3 km across.

In the Norwegian northern North Sea, Rokoengen and Rønningsland (1983) identified a regional mid-Pliocene seismic unconformity which separates generally westward-tilted early Pliocene and older deposits from more horizontally layered beds. A lowstand of sea level was inferred to account for this mid-Pliocene erosion surface. Mid-Pliocene erosion is also indicated in the Moray Firth Basin by the local absence of early Pliocene sediments (Andrews et al., 1990).

8 Quaternary

The Quaternary Period, which comprises the Pleistocene and Holocene epochs, has been a time of dramatic changes in climate, and has included periods of severe erosion by glacial processes, rapid changes in sea level, and very high rates of sedimentation. At the end of Tertiary times, Shetland was an area of net erosion, while deposition occurred within the relatively slowly subsiding Viking Graben. There were prograding deltaic complexes on the eastern edge of the Shetland Platform, a pattern that continued into the early Pleistocene. However, decreasing temperature eventually led to the development of ice caps on the mountainous areas of Scotland and Scandinavia, and to a lesser extent on Shetland itself. The glaciers emanating from these centres caused both erosion and deposition on a large scale, particularly during the later part of the Pleistocene.

Early studies suggested that during the 'main glaciation of Shetland', the islands were first overridden by Scandinavian ice approaching from the north-east, before a local ice cap had become established from which ice flowed radially (Peach and Horne, 1879). Relatively recent studies (Mykura, 1976; Flinn, 1977) have suggested that the direct effects of Scandinavian ice were more limited. Ice from the east was deflected around Shetland or may have crossed only the northernmost and southernmost parts of the island chain. Any Scandinavian ice that overran the main part of Shetland did so before the late Weichselian glaciation.

Flinn (1970) suggested that ice flow on Fair Isle, was in a south-easterly direction, although Mykura (1976) stated that westward ice-movement had removed all traces of earlier glaciations. It would seem that Fair Isle was first glaciated by ice from the east, and later by ice from the north-west (Flinn, 1978) bringing erratics from the south-western side of Shetland.

Erratics have been the only evidence that ice from Scandinavia crossed Shetland. Although several exotic boulders have been found on Shetland and Fair Isle, only one is thought have been deposited naturally; the others have been reckoned to be the ballast of wrecked ships (Finlay, 1926b; Flinn, 1977). The one exception is a large, well-rounded boulder of tøngsbergite from the Oslo region of Norway (Finlay, 1926a) recorded at Dalsetter (Figure 72); this provides clear evidence that ice extended from Norway. In the southern part of Shetland, blocks derived from the east can be found along the upland axis and farther west, indicating westward ice flow from an area to the east of Shetland, possibly Scandinavia. Flinn (1978) attributed the movement of these boulders to Scandinavian ice crossing parts of the islands either at an early stage of the last glaciation or during an earlier glaciation.

Deposits older than Weichselian (Figure 73) have been recorded at two localities on Shetland. At Fugla Ness (Figure 72), up to 1.4 m of peat occur between two layers of boulder clay (Chapelhow, 1965), and at Sel Ayre there are 0.45 m of peat below 7.5 m of sand and gravel, capped by boulder clay. Pollen analyses suggest that the peat at Fugla Ness may date from an interglacial (Birks and Peglar, 1979). C^{14} ages ranging from 40 000 to 34 800 years BP for these deposits (Page, 1972; Mykura and Phemister, 1976) may be best considered as an infinite age of greater than 30 000 years BP.

The limits of the Shetland ice cap have not been established from land studies, although Flinn (1983) suggested that there was a late Weichselian ice margin at the north coast of Unst and immediately north of the coast of Yell; such an ice limit is supported by offshore evidence (Long and Skinner, 1985). Weakly developed morainic features attributed to the latest Weichselian Loch Lomond Stadial occur in a few valleys, sufficient to suggest that ice returned briefly to the islands at this time (Institute of Geological Sciences, 1982).

The Quaternary deposits found on Shetland and Fair Isle are particularly thin, and only rarely exceed 10 m in thickness. A similarly thin coverage generally extends eastwards from Shetland across the East Shetland Platform to approximately 0° 20'E (Figure 72; BGS Halibut Bank Quaternary Geology sheet). However, thicker Quaternary deposits occur locally closer to the coast, both to the north-east and south-west of Shetland (Figure 72). These occurrences overlie sedimentary basins, and reflect the greater erodibility of Mesozoic sediments compared with the harder basement and Devonian rocks.

The Quaternary deposits thicken above the Viking Graben (Figure 72), and at 61°N their base is more than 300 m below sea level (Figure 74). Farther north, the base of the Quaternary is even deeper. At about 60°N there is a col, the East Shetland Ridge, between the main North Sea Quaternary basin and the northern North Sea Quaternary basin (Figure 74). Both basins reach their maximum thicknesses outside the report area, but more than 300 m of Quaternary sediments occur at both the southern and northern limits of the area (Figure 72). This figure suggests a subsidence rate of up to 0.18 m/ka for the Viking Graben during the Quaternary.

Stratigraphies established by BGS for the offshore Quaternary (BGS Quaternary Geology sheets) form the basis for this account (Figure 73 and 75); in the south, the stratigraphy is that of the central North Sea, which equates with the northern North Sea succession as shown in Figure 73.

LOWER PLEISTOCENE

In the northern North Sea, the late Pliocene was a time of erosion in the west, and deposition in a shallow sea to the east. The boundary between Tertiary and Quaternary deposits is indistinct above the Viking Graben, for it appears conformable on seismic-reflection records. However, to the west, seismic records show that Quaternary sediments onlap rocks from Precambrian to Tertiary in age. East of the report area in the Norwegian Trench, the base of the Quaternary forms a prominent reflector, commonly exhibiting significant erosion of the underlying Pliocene sediments (Rokoengen and Rønningsland, 1983).

East of Shetland, BGS borehole 81/16 (Figure 72) revealed very early Pleistocene sediments similar to brackish-water Praetiglian deposits in The Netherlands (BGS Halibut Bank Quaternary Geology sheet). In studies of the Pliocene–Pleistocene boundary, the presence of the foraminifera *Cibicides lobatulus grossa* (cf. *Cibicides grossa*) ten Dam and Reinhold, and *Florilus boueanus* (D'Orbigny) has been taken to indicate a Pliocene age (King, 1983). These foraminifera were consistantly identified below 165 m in BGS borehole

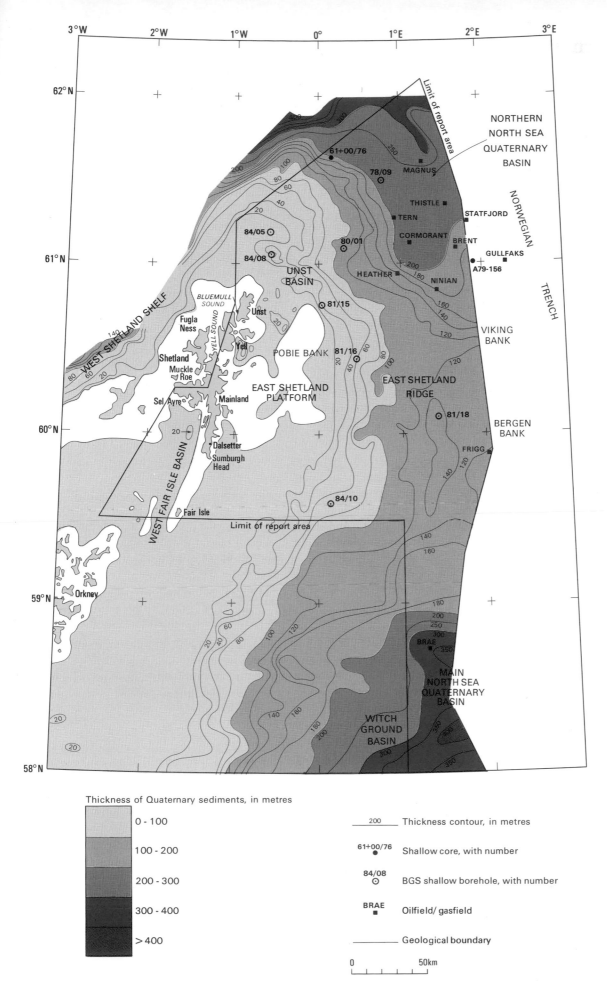

Figure 72 Quaternary isopach map of the northern North Sea based on BGS samples, seismic data and released wells.

75

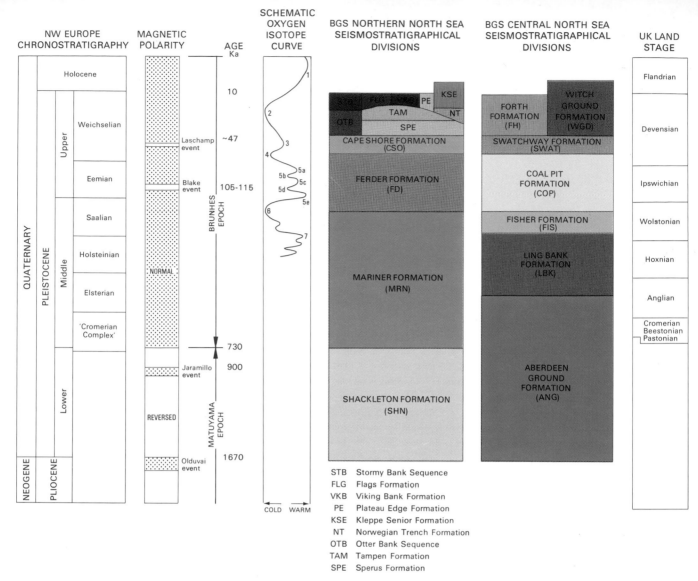

| NW EUROPE CHRONOSTRATIGRAPHY | | | MAGNETIC POLARITY | AGE Ka | SCHEMATIC OXYGEN ISOTOPE CURVE | BGS NORTHERN NORTH SEA SEISMOSTRATIGRAPHICAL DIVISIONS | BGS CENTRAL NORTH SEA SEISMOSTRATIGRAPHICAL DIVISIONS | UK LAND STAGE |

STB Stormy Bank Sequence
FLG Flags Formation
VKB Viking Bank Formation
PE   Plateau Edge Formation
KSE Kleppe Senior Formation
NT   Norwegian Trench Formation
OTB Otter Bank Sequence
TAM Tampen Formation
SPE Sperus Formation

Figure 73 Stratigraphical column illustrating the Quaternary formations and sequences of the northern North Sea. Palaeomagnetic, age and oxygen-isotope information after Imbrie et al. (1984), Levi et al. (1990), and Shackleton and Opdyke (1976).

81/18 above the graben. A few specimens were identified in the lowest samples from a borehole at the Ninian Oilfield (Figure 72), where the Pliocene–Pleistocene boundary is thought to lie just below the base of the borehole at 150 m below sea bed.

Shackleton Formation

The sediments at and just above the Pliocene–Pleistocene boundary are predominantly sandy, with increasing clay content occurring both upwards and northwards, reflecting increasing water depth and distance from sediment sources respectively. Acoustically, these sediments are represented by a unit containing subparallel reflectors which decrease in abundance southwards. This seismostratigraphical unit has been termed the Shackleton Formation (Rise et al., 1984), which equates with all but the highest part of the Aberdeen Ground Formation to the south of the East Shetland Ridge (Figures 73 and 76). The Shackleton Formation crops out locally on the East Shetland Platform (Figure 75), and is 96 m thick in borehole 81/18; it thins westward to only 26 m at borehole 81/15, and 42 m at borehole 81/16 (Figure 72).

Sediments of the Shackleton Formation have been identified in several BGS boreholes, and also in site investigation bore-

holes both within the report area and in the adjacent Norwegian sector at the Statfjord and Gullfaks oilfields (Feyling-Hansen, 1980; 1982; Feyling-Hansen and Knudsen, 1986). Palaeomagnetic analyses of sediments in BGS boreholes 78/09, 80/01 and 81/18 (Figures 72 and 73) identified reversed magnetic polarity zones that are correlated with the Matuyama epoch (Stoker et al., 1983; Skinner and Gregory, 1983). A normal polarity zone tentatively correlated with the Jaramillo event was recorded in borehole 78/09 (Stoker et al., 1983).

BGS borehole 84/10 in the south (Figure 72) contains 30 m of lower Pleistocene sandy sediments which probably equate with the Shackleton Formation. The dinoflagellate-cyst assemblage at this site has been compared to that of the Smith's Knoll and Winterton Shoal formations of the southern North Sea, which have been placed at, or below, the late Pliocene to earliest Pleistocene Olduvai magnetic event (Figure 73) by Cameron et al., (1984), although such assemblages are likely to be diachronous.

Samples taken from the Shackleton Formation suggest that it was deposited in a predominantly nonglacial environment. The formation can be subdivided into two members, each of which is 48 m thick in borehole 81/18. The lower member comprises well-sorted, fine-grained sands with some silt or clay; it occurs either as layers less than 2 cm thick, or more

76

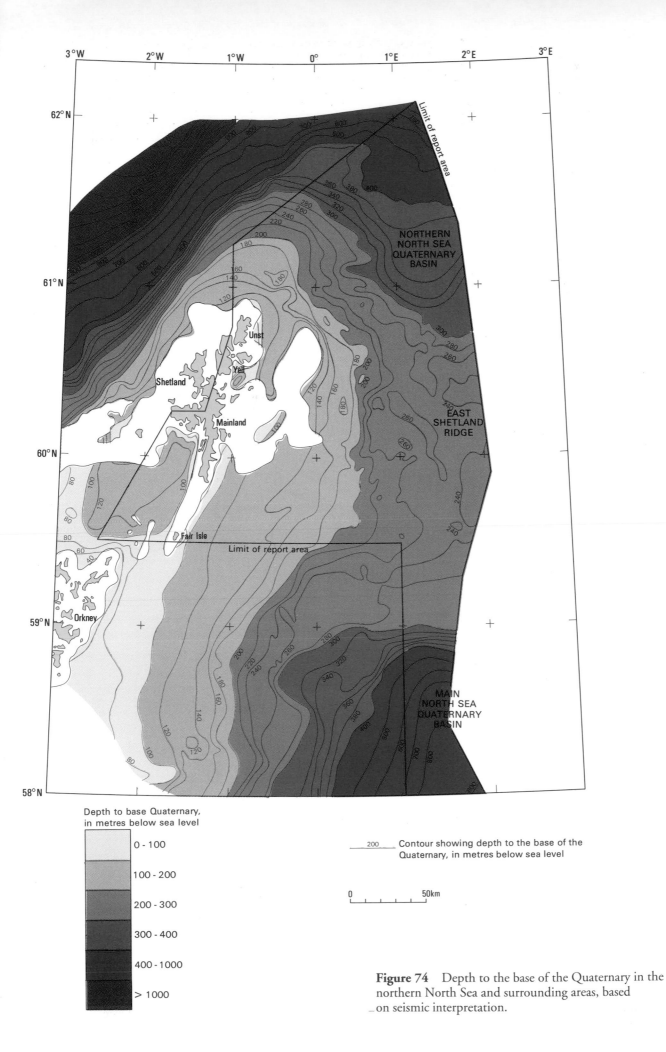

Figure 74 Depth to the base of the Quaternary in the northern North Sea and surrounding areas, based on seismic interpretation.

Depth to base Quaternary, in metres below sea level

- 0 - 100
- 100 - 200
- 200 - 300
- 300 - 400
- 400 - 1000
- > 1000

200 — Contour showing depth to the base of the Quaternary, in metres below sea level

0   50km

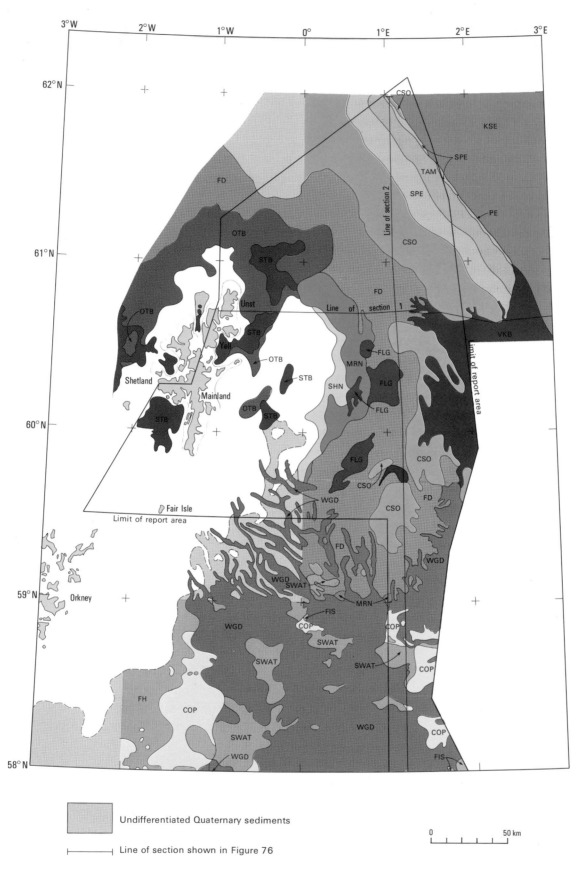

Figure 75 Outcrop map of Quaternary formations and sequences in and around the northern North Sea. For key see Figure 73. Note that the line of Section 1 extends to 4° E.

commonly as clay-rich sands. The dominant foraminifera are *Elphidium clavatum* Cushman, *Cassidulina teretis* Tappan and *Elphidiella hannai* Cushman.

The boundary between the upper and lower members is characteristically marked by abundant gravel and/or shell fragments, as well as derived foraminifera of Oligocene, Eocene, and Late Cretaceous age (BGS Halibut Bank Quaternary Geology sheet; Løfaldi, 1973). This suggests that the boundary represents a time of rapid erosion of the adjacent land, which may have included the western half of the

East Shetland Platform. A seismic reflector corresponding to this boundary can be traced over much of the eastern part of the East Shetland Platform (BGS Halibut Bank Quaternary Geology sheet). This mid-formation boundary may equate with a period of upland glaciation during the early Pleistocene, when there was a short-term increase in erosion.

The upper member consists of hard, sandy clay with fragmented shells and rare, well-rounded, small pebbles. It has an undrained shear strength of about 1 MPa (BGS Halibut Bank Quaternary Geology sheet). As with the lower member, the dominant foraminifera are *E. clavatum* with *C. teretis* and *E. hannai*. However, *Buccella vicksburgensis* (Cushman and Ellisor) is consistently present, in contrast to its absence in the lower member.

MIDDLE PLEISTOCENE, EEMIAN AND LOWER WEICHSELIAN

The upper surface of the Shackleton Formation is generally smooth in the northern part of the area (Figures 76 and 77), and is locally difficult to distinguish acoustically from the overlying Mariner Formation (BGS Miller Quaternary Geology sheet). However, there is increasing unevenness towards the south; initially there are isolated channels, but these increase in size and abundance southwards. There was also greater erosion at this level on the East Shetland Platform, where middle Pleistocene sediments extend to the west of the Shackleton Formation locally (Figure 75).

Mariner Formation

The Mariner Formation has an acoustic appearance comprising abundant subparallel reflectors with some structureless zones, particularly towards the base. The formation thickens towards the north and east (Figure 76), but is largely absent beneath the Norwegian Trench due to postdepositional erosion (Rise et al., 1984). It thins in the north-west, and may pass laterally into the upper part of the Morrison sequence identified on the West Shetland shelf and slope (BGS Miller Quaternary Geology sheet). It is 83 m thick at BGS borehole 78/09, 40 m at the Tern Oilfield, 47 m at the Ninian Oilfield, and 36 m in borehole 81/18 (Figure 72). The formation crops out on the East Shetland Platform (Figure 75).

Micropalaeontological and palaeomagnetic results from borehole 78/09 and boreholes at the Tern Oilfield suggest that the formation is of Cromerian Complex to Saalian age, although Holsteinian deposits are absent due to postdepositional erosion (Skinner and Gregory, 1983; BGS Cormorant Quaternary Geology sheet). The lithologies represent environments that vary from glaciomarine to marine interglacial. The base of the formation comprises a very sandy clay with abundant sand lenses, and contains gravel and occasional shell fragments; this is a diamicton deposited during glacial activity. The gravel content increases westwards, and to a lesser extent southwards towards the East Shetland Ridge (Figure 72). South of this ridge, sediments believed to be equivalent to the Mariner Formation comprise the upper part of the Aberdeen Ground Formation, as well as the Ling Bank and Fisher formations (Figures 73 and 75); these are sandy muds with some gravel and occasional sandy layers. Above the basal gravelly sediments, the Mariner Formation comprises silty clay with sand and silt layers, again with increasing grain size towards the East Shetland Platform and East Shetland Ridge (BGS Halibut Bank and Cormorant Quaternary Geology sheets).

The Mariner Formation is 83 m thick in BGS borehole 78/09 (Figure 72), where it can be divided into two members

(BGS Cormorant Quaternary Geology sheet; Skinner and Gregory, 1983). The lower, heavily overconsolidated member is of Cromerian Complex to Elsterian age. Within this member, beds deposited in relatively favourable conditions for foraminifera overlie thin sediments representing a colder episode. The upper member has lower shear strengths, and it is thought that it was laid down in cold conditions during Elsterian to Saalian times. The sediments adjacent to the boundary between the two members contain a foraminiferal spectrum suggestive of water shallower than 20 m, and the geotechnical parameters indicate that this part of the sequence may have dried above sea level (Skinner and Gregory, 1983).

The top of the Mariner Formation is represented on seismic records by a strong, uneven reflector (Figure 76) attributed to Saalian erosion; its irregularities increase in size and abundance to the south. This erosion level is one of the best defined and most extensive features in the Quaternary succession of the report area, and may indicate that the Saalian glaciation was one of the most significant erosional events in the northern North Sea.

Ferder Formation and equivalent sediments

Overlying the Mariner Formation is the Ferder Formation, which crops out in a crescent to the north and east of Shetland (Figure 75), and is equivalent to the Coal Pit Formation to the south of the East Shetland Ridge. The Ferder Formation generally thickens away from the islands, and may reach 80 m in thickness, particularly where it fills deep channels cut into the underlying surface. The basal sediments comprise stiff, sandy clays with occasional gravel, notably in the west. These basal sediments thin northwards and eastwards to be replaced or overlain by interlaminated silts, clays and sands. There is a bed of hard, gravelly, sandy clay with silty sand partings at the top of the formation. Micropalaeontological and palaeomagnetic evidence suggests that the middle, interlaminated sequence dates from Eemian times (Figure 73).

The Eemian Stage began about 125 000 years ago, when climatic conditions improved subsequent to the Saalian glacial episode. Sediments of Eemian age have been reported in the Ferder Formation both in BGS borehole 78/09 (Skinner and Gregory, 1983) and at the Statfjord Oilfield (Figure 72; Feyling-Hansen, 1980). Sediments in borehole 78/09, from 15 to 73 m beneath sea bed, contain deep-water foraminifera, and have an interval of magnetic reversal correlated with the Blake event (BGS Cormorant Quaternary Geology sheet). Similar magnetically reversed sediments attributed to the Blake event are present within the Ferder Formation in boreholes 80/01 and 81/18 (Stoker et al., 1983).

In a borehole at the Statfjord Oilfield, sediments between 37 and 56 m sub-sea bed were deposited during a warm period, but only the lower half of the sequence is correlated with the Eemian. A single sample contains high numbers of boreal foraminifera (Feyling-Hansen, 1980); it was obtained from a thin, sandy layer within the otherwise clayey sequence, suggesting that true interglacial sediments are very thin. Such thin deposits could easily not have been sampled in other boreholes, or could have been eroded by glacial activity. An oxygen isotope stage 5e age for this interglacial deposit is supported by amino-acid racemisation measurements (Sejrup et al., 1989).

Sediments from the Gullfaks Oilfield have been correlated with the Eemian in borehole 78/09 (Feyling-Hansen and Knudsen, 1986), and similar ameliorative episodes have been noted in boreholes at the Cormorant Oilfield (Lord, 1980; Figure 72) and the Troll Oilfield in the Norwegian sector, the

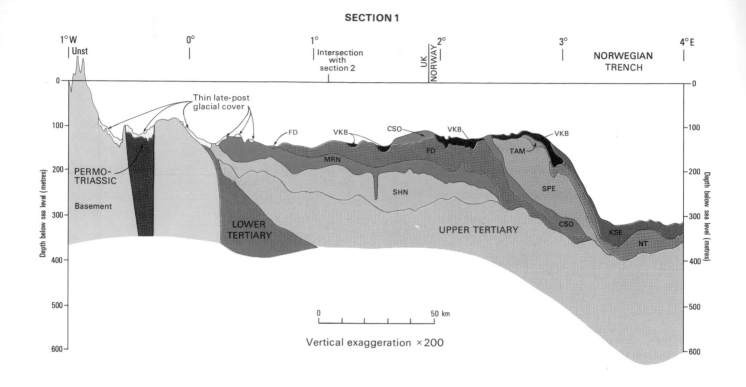

SECTION 1

1°W | Unst ... 0° ... 1° | Intersection with section 2 ... 2° | UK/NORWAY ... 3° ... 4°E | NORWEGIAN TRENCH

PERMO-TRIASSIC

Basement

Thin late-post glacial cover

FD · VKB · CSO · VKB · VKB · FD · TAM · MRN · SHN · SPE · CSO · KSE · NT

LOWER TERTIARY

UPPER TERTIARY

0 — 50 km

Vertical exaggeration ×200

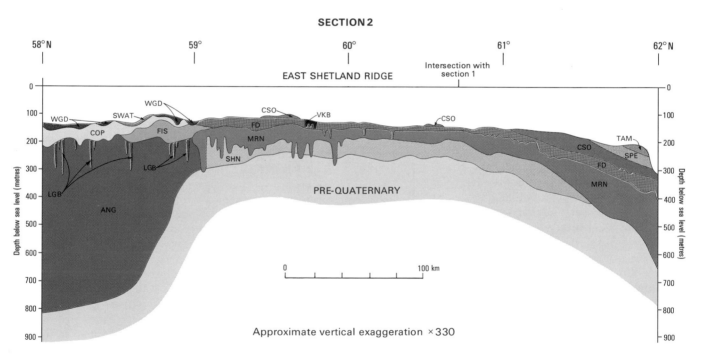

SECTION 2

58°N ... 59° ... 60° ... Intersection with section 1 ... 61° ... 62°N

EAST SHETLAND RIDGE

WGD · SWAT · WGD · CSO · VKB · CSO · COP · FIS · FD · MRN · TAM · SHN · CSO · SPE · LGB · FD · LGB · ANG · MRN

PRE-QUATERNARY

0 — 100 km

Approximate vertical exaggeration ×330

Figure 76 Cross-sections showing the relationships of Quaternary sediments in the northern North Sea. For key see Figure 73. For locations see Figure 75.

latter being correlated to oxygen isotope stage 5e by amino-acid racemisation results (Sejrup et al., 1989).

Sediments with an interglacial fauna noted in the Ferder Formation in borehole 84/08 (Figure 72) at 12 to 15 m depth may date from Eemian times (BGS Miller Quaternary Geology sheet). These sediments predominantly comprise silty clay with lenses and thin layers of sand. They are either normally or over-consolidated, with undrained shear strengths of 100 to 800 kPa, although where they are at outcrop (Figure 75), the uppermost 2 or 3 m may be of reduced strength due to stress relief at the sea bed.

The relatively warm conditions of Eemian times deteriorated in a cyclical manner into the early Weichselian glacial period (Figure 73), as evidenced by both lithological and faunal changes. The upper part of the Ferder Formation comprises hard, gravelly, sandy clay with silty sand partings. Acoustically, it generally appears structureless, although subparallel reflectors occur. The upper surface is marked by a very strong reflector which commonly crops out at sea bed as a topographic rise (BGS Halibut Bank Quaternary Geology sheet). Channels up to 30 m deep have been cut into the upper part of the formation; and these increase in abundance southwards. There are also many intraformational channels within the upper sediments of the formation, particularly south of 60° 20'N. One of the most dramatic is the Bressay Bank Channel, which is over 200 m deep, and has been eroded into Tertiary sediments (BGS Bressay Bank Quaternary Geology sheet).

The lithological content and seismic appearance of the upper part of the Ferder Formation are interpreted to be the products of early Weichselian glaciomarine and subglacial environments. The area was possibly overrun by ice sheets from both Scandinavia and Shetland, which may have met. Assuming that they have a subglacial origin, the size and distribution of channels suggest that the early Weichselian glacial advance was extensive.

MIDDLE WEICHSELIAN

Cape Shore Formation and equivalent sediments

At the end of early Weichselian times, climatic warming caused deglaciation and marine transgression, resulting in the formation of the surface that gives rise to a strong, horizontal to subhorizontal reflector evident at the top of the Ferder Formation (BGS Cormorant and Halibut Bank Quaternary Geology sheets). This transgression locally removed all of the Ferder Formation deposits on the southern part of the East Shetland Ridge. The basal sediments of the Cape Shore Formation overlie this surface, and contain much reworked material, as is evident from the microfauna in BGS borehole 81/18 and in boreholes at the Frigg Gasfield (Figure 72; BGS Halibut Bank Quaternary Geology sheet; Løfaldi, 1973). The southern occurrences of the Cape Shore Formation are predominantly sandy with rare pebbles, and with an increasing clay content northwards. The Cape Shore Formation may equate with parts of the Coal Pit and Swatchway formations recorded in the Witch Ground Basin (Figure 73).

The Cape Shore Formation, which crops out over a significant portion of the report area (Figure 75), is firmly dated as mid-Weichselian. Several radiocarbon dates have also been derived from this formation; Milling (1975) published a date of 31 150 ± 200 years BP for sediments from around the Brent Oilfield, and BGS vibrocore sample 61+00/76 (Figure 72) has yielded an infinite age of more than 28 000 years BP. Just inside the Norwegian sector, sample A79-156 has given ages close to 30 000 years BP for three samples within a metre of the sea bed (Rise and Rokoengen, 1984; Sejrup et al., 1989). Palaeomagnetic and oxygen isotope results from borehole 78/09 (Figure 72) also suggest a mid-Weichselian age. A magnetically reversed zone initially correlated with an upper leaf of the Blake event (Skinner and Gregory, 1983) has been attributed subsequently to the Laschamp event (BGS Cormorant Quaternary Geology sheet).

The foraminiferal assemblage is dominated by *E. clavatum*, *Cassidulina reniforme* Norvang and *Protelphidium orbiculare* (Brady), which suggested arctic or boreo-arctic conditions of moderate water depth to Løfaldi (1973). Similar assemblages identified at the Statfjord and Gullfaks oilfields (Feyling-Hansen, 1980; Feyling-Hansen and Knudsen, 1986) have been correlated with deep-ocean oxygen isotope stage 3 (Figure 73).

UPPER WEICHSELIAN TO HOLOCENE

The most recent time of severe, widespread glacial conditions, the late Weichselian, began at about 25 000 years BP, reaching its acme at around 18 000 years ago before rapid deglaciation left only mountain glaciers in mainland Scotland by 12 000 years BP. There was a brief return to glacial conditions during the Loch Lomond Stadial (Younger Dryas) at 11 000 to 10 000 years ago, before the rapid warming to the present interglacial. Upper Weichselian deposits within the report area are of disparate distribution, and comprise many different seismostratigraphical units (Figure 73).

Late Weichselian ice on Shetland may have expanded eastwards across the Pobie Bank, depositing small patches of reddish brown till. On northern Shetland, the glacial cover may not have extended beyond the northern coastlines of Yell and Unst (Flinn, 1983). However, glacial tongues possibly extended northwards (Figure 78) from Yell Sound and Blue Mull Sound (Long and Skinner, 1985), terminating in a marine environment and depositing the submarine morainal forms of the Otter Bank sequence (BGS Miller Quaternary Geology sheet). Farther south, ice moved southwards and south-eastwards to carve out the basin west of Sumburgh Head, and to engrave striae on Fair Isle, possibly terminating along a line where stony clays of high undrained shear strength are found (BGS Fair Isle Sea Bed Sediments and Quaternary Geology sheet). South-east of this line, the Quaternary is predominantly formed of sands and gravels; possibly the area was an outwash plain, with the shallow beginnings of a late-glacial channel system leading to the Witch Ground Basin (Figure 78).

During the peak of late Weichselian glaciation, there was a eustatic fall in sea level, and the sea floor of the report area probably rose due to the isostatic effect of being within the forebulge region of the Scandinavian, Scottish and Shetland ice caps (Eden et al., 1977). The sea bed became exposed, and was subjected to periglacial conditions. The high shear strengths noted close to the sea bed, and their reduction with depth, have been attributed to desiccation due to permafrost. Such characteristics have been recorded at the Brae (Aurora, 1983), Heather (Durning et al., 1979) and Magnus oilfields (Semple and Rigden, 1983). Microfabric studies also support the former presence of permafrost (Derbyshire et al., 1985). Although a similar profile was obtained at the Thistle Oilfield (Figure 72), it was attributed by Young et al., (1978) to ice loading, rather than desiccation.

Recent reconstructions of the Scandinavian ice sheet have suggested a thin ice-sheet margin (Nesje and Sejrup, 1988), with ice from Scotland/Shetland not meeting that from Scandinavia (e.g. Cameron et al., 1987; Sejrup et al., 1987). The earliest evidence for glacial retreat in the region is from the Norwegian Trench, where late Weichselian glaciomarine deposits indicate that the southern margin of the Scandinavian ice sheet began to retreat at about 15 000 years BP (Lehman et al., 1991).

Sperus and Tampen formations, and equivalent sediments

The Sperus and Tampen formations occur in the north-eastern corner of the report area (Figures 75 and 76). The lower unit, the Sperus Formation, is up to 40 m thick within the report area, and is identified as a seismically well-bedded series of parallel or subparallel reflectors. Its base is marked by a prominent, continuous, seismic reflector, and its top coincides with a change in seismic signature to the less well-bedded texture of the overlying Tampen Formation (BGS Cormorant Quaternary Geology sheet). The Sperus Formation comprises firm to very stiff, sandy, silty clay with shells and pebbles throughout. It is interpreted as a glaciomarine deposit, and is generally softened within 2 m of the sea bed, probably due to stress relief.

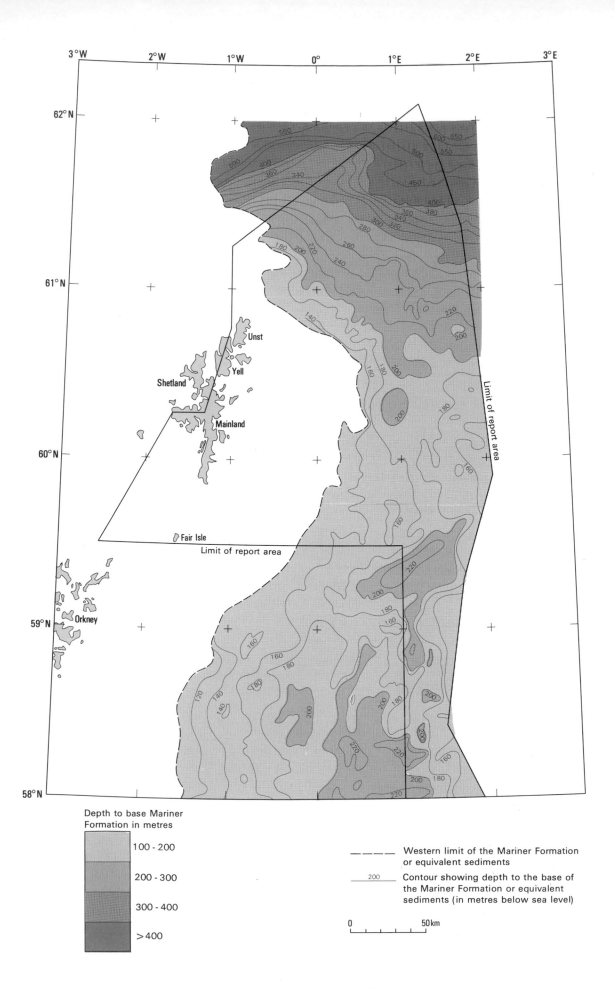

Figure 77 Contour map showing the depth below sea level to the base of the Mariner Formation, or approximately coeval units. This is commonly the depth to the base of the lowest glacial deposits.

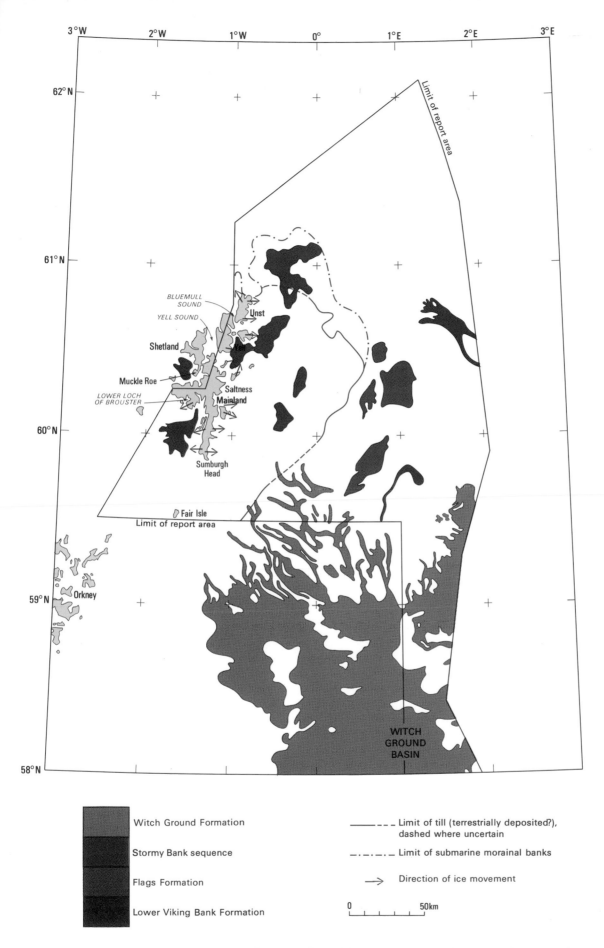

Figure 78 Map showing the distribution of acoustically well-layered, late-glacial deposits, with suggested limits of late Weichselian terrestrial and submarine tills.

The Sperus Formation is thought to have been deposited in a shallowing glaciomarine environment during the climatic deterioration that occurred from mid- to late Weichselian times, before the northern part of the North Sea Plateau became exposed, either during deposition of the Tampen Formation or shortly afterwards. Overconsolidation of the uppermost sediments at the Magnus Oilfield is therefore probably due to desiccation rather than loading by ice (Semple and Rigden, 1983). The subsequent marine transgression may have caused the planated surface evident at the present-day sea bed.

The Tampen Formation generally has a structureless seismic appearance, with some discontinuous reflectors and point-source reflections. This formation forms a positive topographic feature, the Tampen Ridge, on the edge of the North Sea Plateau (Figure 76), and consists of up to 50 m of firm to very stiff, grey to black, sandy and silty clays. Sand partings are common, and gravel lenses are also present, as are pebbles that are commonly angular, some with glacial striae. Radiocarbon dates from shells in the Norwegian sector give a maximum age of 18 860 ± 260 years BP for the Tampen Formation (Rokoengen et al., 1982). The topographic expression of the formation suggests that it is a moraine, possibly a lateral moraine, which was deposited by northward-flowing ice that was largely constrained within the Norwegian Trench during late Weichselian times.

A till-like deposit, the Norwegian Trench Formation (Figure 76), was laid down beneath the ice that formed the moraine at the margin of the Norwegian Trench. The feather edge of this latter deposit occurs in the north-easternmost corner of the report area. Its seismic appearance is largely structureless, with poor, discontinuous reflectors and abundant point-source reflections. This formation and the Tampen Formation are lateral equivalents formed in differing glacial environments. Carlsen et al. (1986) showed that the levels of both ice and water within the Norwegian Trench may have varied considerably through the late Weichselian, resulting in several episodes of deposition and erosion on the side walls of the trench. They suggested that between 16 000 and 13 000 years ago, sea level may have been as low as 190 m below present in this part of the North Sea.

Some sediments north of Shetland have been termed the Otter Bank sequence (BGS Miller Quaternary Geology sheet), and correlated with the Sperus and Tampen formations (Figure 73). They are a mounded to sheet-like unit comprising stiff to hard diamicts with overlying firm glaciomarine muddy and gravelly sands. The mounded deposits form ridges and are believed to represent a succession of submarine end-moraine deposits (BGS Miller Quaternary Geology sheet). Muddy gravelly sand of the Otter Bank sequence has been sampled in BGS borehole 84/05 (Figure 72).

Viking Bank and Plateau Edge formations

On the western side of the Viking Bank lie late Weichselian sediments termed the Viking Bank Formation (Figures 72 and 75), which comprises two units. The lower consists predominantly of clays with abundant thin layers (less than 10 cm) of sands and sandy gravels, and is restricted to a few depressions leading westwards from sea-bed highs. It fills channels up to 30 m deep, and has the acoustic appearance of a subhorizontal, multilayered sequence. The more extensive upper unit of locally very well-sorted sands occurs on topographic rises. On sparker records, the upper unit appears as ridges forming positive bathymetric features of acoustically transparent sediments. The ridges are approximately 5 m high, 5 km wide and up to 20 km in length; boomer records

reveal that they have weak internal reflectors, many as a series of cross-bedded units (BGS Halibut Bank Quaternary Geology sheet). Grains from both facies are commonly very angular, and may be wind faceted.

The topography and lithology of this formation suggest that it was deposited in shallow water, with possible aeolian contributions. The lower, clay-dominated unit may have been deposited as prodelta and delta-front sediments, derived from the Bergen and Viking Bank highs to the south-east and east, washed in by rivers draining ice overtopping the Norwegian Trench, whereas the upper sandy unit may have formed as shallow, mobile, barrier islands (BGS Halibut Bank Quaternary Geology sheet). Radiocarbon dating from the Norwegian sector suggests a late Weichselian to early Holocene age for this formation; the lower, channel-filling unit is older than 11 350 ± 120 years BP, and the uppermost part of the sand unit has yielded dates of 10 420 ± 80 and 8 530 ± 110 years BP (Rise and Rokoengen, 1984).

A beach deposit up to 40 m thick, known as the Plateau Edge Formation, was deposited outside the report area on the western side of the Norwegian Trench (Figures 72 and 75) during a period of exposure and marine transgression. However, only a thin layer was deposited on the North Sea Plateau. This is probably the result of the steeply dipping sea bed on the side of the Norwegian Trench, which would require a large rise in sea level to cause any significant lateral shift in the position of the coastline, whereas on the more gently sloping sea floor of the North Sea Plateau, even a very small rise in sea level would have caused a dramatic change in the location of the coastline. The beach deposit has been radiocarbon dated to between 12 500 and 10 800 years BP (Rokoengen et al., 1982).

Flags and Witch Ground formations, and equivalent sediments

Elsewhere in the report area, late Weichselian sediments are generally represented by acoustically well-layered sediments. On seismic profiles, these multilayered seismostratigraphical units show layering in their lowermost parts that is parallel to an uneven basal surface, with undulations up to 5 m in height and 150 m in width; these characteristics pass up into subhorizontal layering at the top of the sequence. Such acoustically distinctive sediments are up to 25 m thick, and largely comprise clays and silts, although on the north-eastern edge of the Witch Ground Basin, acoustically similar sediments in shallower water are muddy sands, possibly representing nearer-shore deposition. Acoustic turbidity is common due the presence of gas at shallow levels within the sediments.

At the southern end of the report area, the unit is known as the Witch Ground Formation, and the sediments occur either on the edge of the Witch Ground Basin, or within depressions leading towards it (Figure 78). In the central part of the report area, there are several enclosed basins infilled with up to 25 m of multilayered deposits that are termed the Flags Formation (Figure 78).

Sediments mapped as the Stormy Bank sequence some 30 km north-east of Unst (Figures 75 and 78) appear to be seismically and lithologically comparable to the Flags and Witch Ground formations. They have been similarly interpreted as being deposited during the waning stages of late Weichselian ice (BGS Miller Quaternary Geology sheet). Seismically similar sediments up to 20 m thick are recorded to the west of Sumburgh Head (Figure 78).

Late glacial to early Holocene sediments also occur just below sea bed in the Norwegian Trench, and so occur in the north-easternmost corner of the report area (Figures 73 and

75), overlying the Norwegian Trench Formation. They are lithologically, chronologically and acoustically similar to the Flags and Witch Ground formations, and are known as the Kleppe Senior Formation (Rise et al., 1984).

Large, rounded boulders up to 1.5 m in diameter, sometimes with glacial striae, have been recorded at the sea bed in the north-east of the report area. They are not derived from the underlying sediment, but appear to have been dropped by icebergs at the end of Weichselian times (Løken, 1976). They include boulders derived from the Oslo Graben.

Based on evidence collected from both within the report area and the western part of the Witch Ground Basin, it is possible to understand the environmental changes represented by these acoustically distinctive units. Their commonly uneven base is due to scouring by sea-ice keels, which also disturbed the sediment (Stoker and Long, 1984). Scouring ceased when the sea-ice keels no longer touched the sea bed, so that the acoustically layered nature of later sediments has been preserved (Long et al., 1986a). This 'lift off' may have been due to increasing water depth and/or a reduction in the size of sea-ice keels; both explanations suggest climatic warming, a conclusion supported by micropalaeontological evidence (Long et al., 1986a). These shallow seas were affected by seasonal sea ice until about 13 000 years ago, when temperatures rose rapidly, although sea ice returned briefly during the Loch Lomond Stadial (Long et al., 1986a).

Surface depressions up to 200 m wide and 8 m deep, known as pockmarks, have been recorded in the Witch Ground Basin, in the largest Flags Formation basins, and in the Norwegian Trench (Figure 78, and see Figure 81). These are gas-escape features, the gas having a thermogenic and/or biogenic origin (Hovland and Judd, 1988). Buried forms occur within the Witch Ground Formation, and statistical evidence suggests that there may have been a short period of above average pockmark eruption frequency around 13 000 years ago, coincident with a rapid rise in marine temperatures (Long, 1992).

Deglaciation

The deglaciation history of Shetland is largely unknown, but the earliest date on postglacial material is 12 090 ± 900 years BP (Hoppe, 1971). An earlier date of 15 080 ± 850 years BP from sediments 3.5 m below sea bed in the Lower Loch of Brouster (Figure 78) may be contaminated by old carbon, and may therefore be too old (Engstrand, 1967). It is fair to assume that by about 12 000 years BP, after the ice had melted, gyttja started to accumulate in lochs, and the deposition of organic material, first in this form and later as peat, has continued since. There was however a short period before 10 000 years BP, which coincided with the Loch Lomond Stadial on the Scottish mainland, when gravelly and varved clays were deposited. A few weakly developed morainic features in a few valleys may suggest that glacier ice returned briefly to the islands during this period (Institute of Geological Sciences, 1982).

The coastline of Shetland bears witness to Holocene submergence of the land (Flinn, 1964). Hoppe (1965) recorded a series of radiocarbon dates from submerged peats, the oldest of which implies that sea level was at least 9 m below present-day high water at 6670 ± 100 years BP, and was submerged sometime after 5455 ± 170 years BP. A radiocarbon date on an intertidal peat at Saltness (Figure 78) was interpreted by Flinn (in Harkness and Wilson, 1979) as implying that sea level reached approximately its present level after about 4000 years BP. Submergence records can be found within historic times; in the seventeenth and eighteenth centuries, the sea was fordable between the Mainland and Muckle Roe, but now a bridge is necessary to reach the island. Also Dixon (1936) noted that walls and buildings known to be above high water four generations earlier were below low water. This modern submergence of the landscape suggests that postglacial isostatic readjustment is continuing.

Submergence began earlier elsewhere within the report area. The beach gravels identified on the western margin of the Norwegian Trench (Plateau Edge Formation) are thought to belong to a Late Weichselian shoreline 130 to 160 m below present sea level (Dekko and Rokoengen, 1978; Rokoengen et al., 1982). The sea bed may have remained exposed in places on the Viking Bank into early Holocene times, and there is archaeological evidence that man may have lived in such areas of relatively flat coastal land (Long et al., 1986b).

9 Sea-bed sediments

The sea floor in the report area is covered by a thin layer of unconsolidated terrigenous and biogenic sediment which generally does not exceed a few decimetres in thickness. The cover is absent locally, exposing either bedrock, Pleistocene sediments, or a coarse-grained, lag deposit. Most of the terrigenous material is derived from underlying Quaternary and early Holocene deposits, whereas the bulk of the biogenic material has accumulated during the Holocene.

Sand-grade sediment is predominant (Figure 79). Gravel mainly occurs on the Orkney–Shetland Platform and on isolated bathymetric highs east of Shetland. Mud is mostly restricted to broad bathymetric lows far offshore, to enclosed deeps, and to the voes, or inlets, around Shetland. The sediment colour tends to be yellowish in water shallower than 70 to 90 m, indicating an oxidising environment; below this depth, the colour changes to a greyish or greenish hue, indicating an increasingly reducing environment with increasing water depth (Beg, 1990).

The coastline of Shetland has a drowned appearance (Flinn, 1964), and the sea floor generally descends steeply seawards from the coast, before becoming almost flat in water depths of about 80 m (Flinn, 1964; 1969). This break in slope forms a distinctive feature which can be traced around Shetland, mainly within 1.6 km of the shoreline off headlands. Beyond, there are three topographic provinces within the report area (Figure 80): the Orkney–Shetland Platform in the west, a large depression containing enclosed basins in the central portion, and a gradual rise in the east which culminates in the Tampen Ridge (Flinn, 1973).

The Orkney–Shetland Platform has positive relief, and is characterised by an irregular topography with local rock outcrop. Bathymetric lows on the platform, such as that south of Fetlar, coincide with Mesozoic sedimentary basins, whereas pronounced topographic highs, such as Pobie Bank, are formed of hard and resistant metamorphic rocks. By comparison, the sea bed east of the Orkney–Shetland Platform is relatively smooth and of low relief. Water depths increase gradually from about 100 m in the west to a maximum of 160 m in the central part of the northern North Sea. The sea bed is hummocky, with large-scale undulations of between about 20 and 30 m. Gradients are generally of the order of 1:100 to 1:500, with maximum gradients of about 1:60. North of 61°N, the sea bed is mostly very flat, and slopes gently northwards from about 150 m to about 200 m, although there is a rise in the east towards the Tampen Ridge. To the east of the ridge, the sea floor shelves relatively steeply into the Norwegian Trench, with gradients of about 1:50.

In the northern North Sea, an extensive, coarse, lag deposit was formed prior to, and during, the rapid early Holocene transgression (Rise and Rokoengen, 1984; Bent, 1986). This deposit and other sea-bed sediments have been reworked during the Holocene, and the present sediment distribution reflects either modern hydraulic conditions or the last active sedimentological processes (Rise and Rokoengen, 1984). The modern sedimentary environment around Shetland consists of an inner-shelf zone with modern and reworked sand deposits influenced by wave and longshore tidal currents, and an outer-shelf zone with palimpsest and relict sediments reworked by oceanic and storm-induced currents (Beg, 1990).

The substantial biogenic component is the only clearly identifiable Holocene input to the sea-bed sediments in the northern part of the North Sea (Owens, 1981). Carbonate production on the deeper parts of the shelf probably began during the early Holocene, and has since decreased as the water depth has increased. Present conditions for carbonate production were probably established 6000 years ago (Farrow et al., 1984). The sea floor around Orkney, Fair Isle and Shetland is a major area of high-latitude carbonate production, with large bodies of coarse-grained, mobile, shell sand, nourished through bioerosion and maceration of a prolific flora and fauna (Farrow et al., 1984).

Studies suggest that, in general, the rate of sedimentation in the northern North Sea is very low. Rise and Rokoengen (1984) concluded that there has been very little net sedimentation during the Holocene, and Jansen and Hensey (1981) reported no significant sedimentation after 8400 years ago. Johnson and Elkins (1979) estimated that depositional rates are of the order of 5 to 6 cm per thousand years in topographic depressions, with slower rates on elevated sea floors. However, near Shetland and Fair Isle, sedimentation rates are locally much greater; an average rate of 31 cm per thousand years is estimated for the carbonate production zone northeast of Orkney (Farrow et al., 1984). In the nearshore around Shetland, submerged peats with radiocarbon dates ranging from 5500 to 7000 years BP are overlain by up to 2 m of gravel and shell sands (Hoppe, 1965).

HYDROGRAPHY

The prevailing hydraulic processes are a combination of tidal currents, oceanic currents, and oscillatory, wave-induced currents (Figure 81). These are the major influences on sediment distribution (Kenyon and Stride, 1970; Rise and Rokoengen, 1984; Beg, 1990), and also influence the composition of the sediment. For example, the distribution and dispersal paths of heavy minerals around Shetland are consistent with the present hydraulic regime (Beg, 1990). The significance of bottom currents is such that, even in relatively deep water, erosion of sea-bed sediments can cause scouring problems in the vicinity of production platforms and pipelines (Dahlberg, 1983).

Measurements of tidal-current velocities mainly relate to surface currents, which are greater than those at the sea bed, but are nevertheless useful indicators of likely bed-load transport paths (Kenyon and Stride, 1970). Maximum surface tidal streams vary from 0.25 to 0.5 m/s over most of the area, and are in excess of 1.0 m/s on the Orkney–Shetland Platform (Pantin, 1991). However, around Shetland and Fair Isle, much higher rates are achieved; there are violent tidal races off Sumburgh Head, and tidal currents attain a velocity of between 3.3 and 3.9 m/s in Yell Sound, and 2.8 m/s off Fair Isle (Hydrographic Department, 1975). Net near-surface tidal flow both between Orkney and Shetland and north of Shetland is to the east and south-east, whereas off the southeast coast of Shetland the flow is to the north and north-east (Kenyon and Stride, 1970; Beg, 1990).

Predominantly south-easterly flowing oceanic currents south of Shetland are caused by the influx of mixed oceanic and coastal water into the North Sea through the gap be-

Figure 79
Simplified
sea-bed sediment
map of the
northern North
Sea and adjacent
areas.

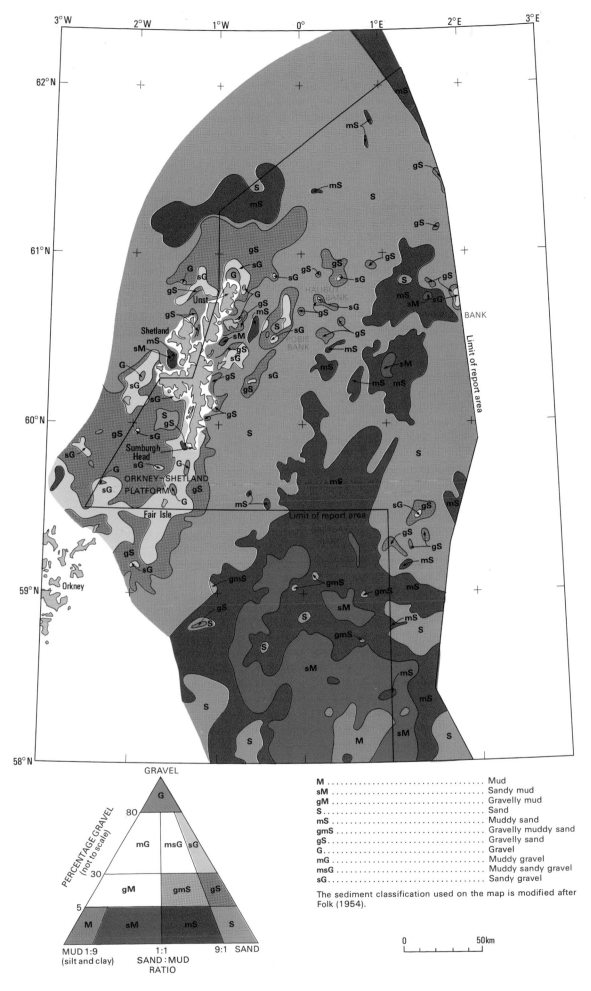

M	....	Mud
sM	....	Sandy mud
gM	....	Gravelly mud
S	....	Sand
mS	....	Muddy sand
gmS	....	Gravelly muddy sand
gS	....	Gravelly sand
G	....	Gravel
mG	....	Muddy gravel
msG	....	Muddy sandy gravel
sG	....	Sandy gravel

The sediment classification used on the map is modified after
Folk (1954).

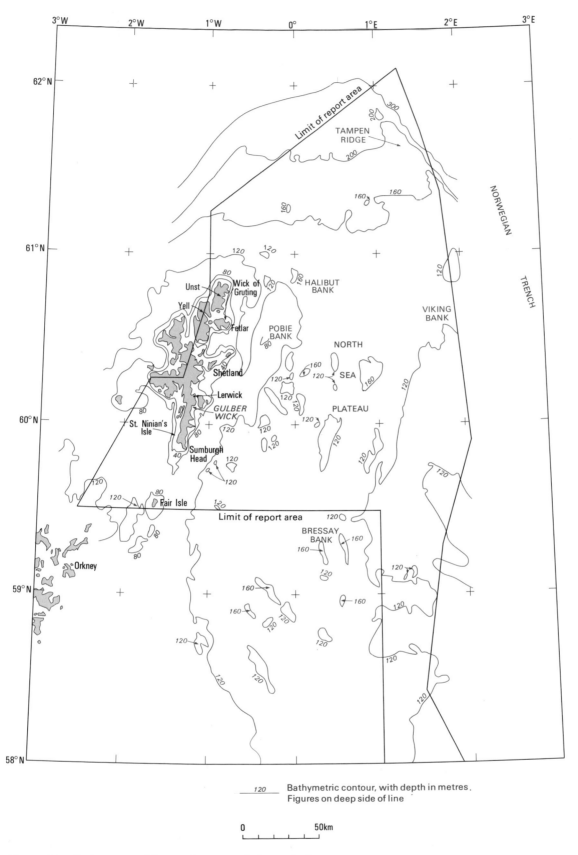

Figure 80 Bathymetry of the northern North Sea and adjacent areas.

tween Orkney and Shetland. Between Shetland and the eastern margin of the report area, these currents are mostly variable and wind driven, although eddies up to 20 km in diameter are caused by the mixing of water masses. North of Shetland, saline, Atlantic water flows eastwards across the outer shelf and upper slope below 200 m depth, then turns southwards near the Tampen Ridge to flow along the western side of the Norwegian Trench (Reid et al., 1988). Few direct measurements of these subsurface currents are available, and those which exist tend to be for short periods of time only. Residual currents in the south have estimated velocities of between 0.1 and 0.2 m/s, and the deep-water current in the north is estimated to flow at between 0.15 and 0.32 m/s (Lee, 1980).

The area is subject to frequent severe gales and storms, which result in both wind-driven surface currents, and oscillatory currents at the sea bed. The extreme 50-year wave height (crest to trough) is estimated to vary from 30 m in the north and west, to 28 m in the south (Draper, 1980). These large values indicate the potential for storm-induced oscillatory currents as agents of sediment transport, even in relatively deep water, especially when acting in conjunction with tidal or oceanic currents.

SEDIMENT DISTRIBUTION

The distribution of the sea-bed sediments within the area (Figure 79; BGS Sea Bed Sediment sheets) results from a combination of hydraulic conditions, bathymetry, and sediment supply. Sediments classified as either sand or muddy sand cover about 65 and 20 per cent of the sea floor respectively. The remainder is covered mostly by gravelly sand, with minor amounts of sandy gravel, and small patches of gravel and sandy mud.

Gravelly sand and sandy gravel occur extensively to the north of Shetland, on the Orkney–Shetland Platform, and on upstanding areas east of Shetland. Water depths in these areas are generally shallower than 110 m, peak surface tidal currents are greater than 0.75 m/s, and there are frequent, strong, wave-induced oscillatory currents. These factors are characteristic of a high-energy environment, and have resulted in the erosion and transportation of sediments. Quaternary deposits are mostly very thin or absent, resulting in large areas of patchy rock outcrop. The sediments generally contain a high proportion of biogenic carbonate material (Figure 82), although in nearshore areas with very strong bottom currents, the gravel fraction can have a lithic component in excess of 75 per cent.

Gravelly sand and sandy gravel (Figure 79) also form relatively small, irregularly shaped, isolated patches on Bressay Bank, Viking Bank and Halibut Bank. Water depths here range from 110 m to over 140 m, and subtle differences in topography, rather than absolute water depth, appear to determine gravel content.

Sand deposits occur within a very wide range of water depths, from sea level on beaches around Shetland to over 300 m on the outer continental shelf. They exhibit significant regional variations in grain size, sorting, and carbonate content. These variations reflect a spectrum of environments from relatively high energy around Orkney and Shetland where there are sources of carbonate material, to low energy farther offshore where there is relatively little sediment input.

Sand occurs extensively in a zone to the east of the Orkney–Shetland Platform. Here, water depths range from about 100 to 140 m. The sand that overlies bedrock in the west, and Pleistocene deposits to the east, is moderately to poorly sorted, with a mean grain size varying from coarse to fine. There is a general eastward improvement in sorting, and a concomitant decrease in mean grain size. Carbonate content varies from 10 per cent to over 80 per cent.

To the east of Shetland, the sand zone is between 40 and 60 km wide in water depths ranging from about 100 m to over 120 m. The sand overlies either Pleistocene deposits or a coarser-grained, early Holocene lag. The carbonate content varies from less than 1 per cent up to 10 per cent, and the mud content is generally greater than in the zone to the west. The sand is mainly fine grained and well sorted, becoming moderately sorted northwards.

Large areas of sand are also found on the eastern side of the report area north of 61°N, in water depths that range from about 100 m to over 300 m (Figures 79 and 80). These sands are moderately to well sorted, and are mainly fine grained; their carbonate content varies from about 10 to 40 per cent.

Muddy sand mainly occurs as very large, irregularly shaped patches up to 50 km across in water depths between 120 and 160 m. Some of these patches include sandy mud locally. There are also a number of smaller, isolated areas of muddy sediment, notably within local bathymetric deeps and in the voes of Shetland. The narrow band of muddy sand in the extreme north-east of the report area is the western edge of an extensive mud-rich deposit which covers the western flank and floor of the Norwegian Trench (Rise and Rokoengen, 1984), where a low-energy environment in deep water has allowed the deposition of fine-grained sediment.

CARBONATE DISTRIBUTION

The carbonate content of the whole sediment varies from almost 100 per cent on the Orkney–Shetland Platform to less than 1 per cent in the east between 59°N and 60°N (Figure 82). Similarly large variations occur within the individual gravel, sand and mud components of the sediment, and in all cases there are very strong regional trends to their distributions (BGS Sea Bed Sediment sheets).

The very high concentrations of biogenic carbonate around Shetland, and between Orkney and Shetland, are a result of modern carbonate production (Farrow et al., 1984). Bivalves, barnacles, bryozoans and serpulids living on rocky substrates are the main sources of the carbonate, which consists dominantly of low-magnesian calcite. This is rapidly broken down by the boring and grazing of epifauna, and by the mechanical action of strong bottom currents. The debris is transported by tidal and storm-induced bottom currents, and becomes mixed with exhumed infaunal debris. This results in the widespread distribution of mobile, carbonate-rich, coarse-grained sands that are subjected to physical breakdown, re-working, and sorting by tidal currents. This produces medium- to fine-grained shell sands both in deeper water and in areas of weaker bottom currents. Average carbonate accumulation rates on the open shelf around Orkney are estimated to be of the order of 125 g/m²/year, and are considerably higher locally (Farrow et al., 1984). It is likely that similar rates of accumulation also occur in the vicinity of Shetland and Fair Isle.

Carbonate content generally decreases eastwards away from these source areas, although there are local exceptions. To the south of 60°N, the carbonate content decreases rapidly eastwards to less than 10 per cent east of Fair Isle, and to less than 1 per cent east of 1°E. A low carbonate content is typical of large areas of the northern North Sea (Pantin, 1991), reflecting the combination of low in-situ carbonate production, and the lack of transport of carbonate from source areas to the west. By contrast, in the far north on the outer continental shelf, carbonate content varies from 10 to 20 per cent, indicating that the increasingly oceanic conditions here may be more favourable for carbonate production. In between, there is a zone of relatively high carbonate content, typically between 20 and 40 per cent, extending north-eastwards from Shetland. There are several possible sites of enhanced carbonate production here, notably Pobie Bank, Halibut Bank and the Tampen Ridge (Figure 82). However, the trend of this occurrence suggests that there may also be north-eastward dispersal of carbonate material from the vicinity of Shetland, or from the West Shetland Platform.

89

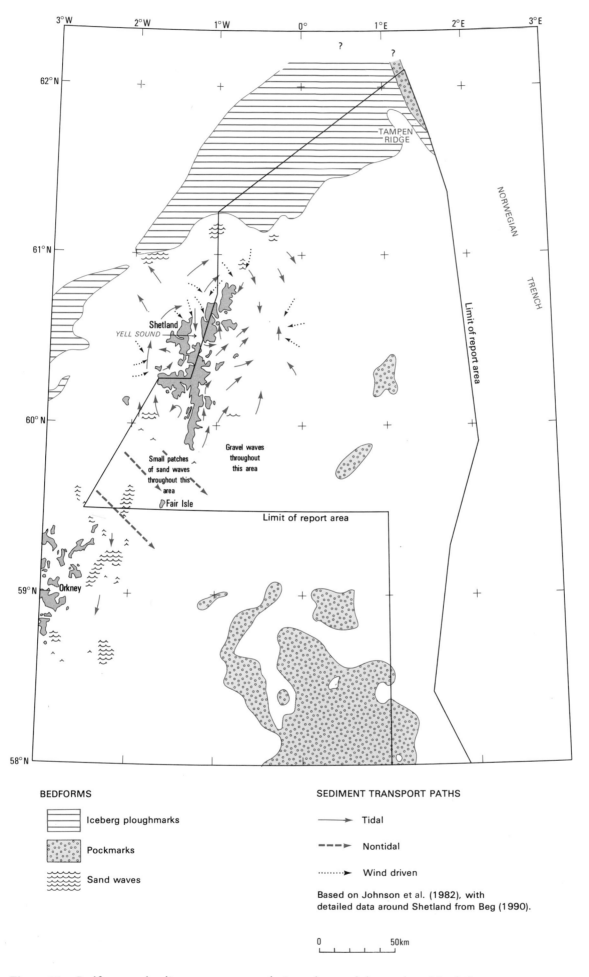

BEDFORMS

(horizontal lines pattern)	Iceberg ploughmarks
(dotted pattern)	Pockmarks
(wave pattern)	Sand waves

SEDIMENT TRANSPORT PATHS

→ Tidal

– – – ► Nontidal

········► Wind driven

Based on Johnson et al. (1982), with
detailed data around Shetland from Beg (1990).

0   50km

Figure 81   Bedforms and sediment-transport paths in and around the northern North Sea.

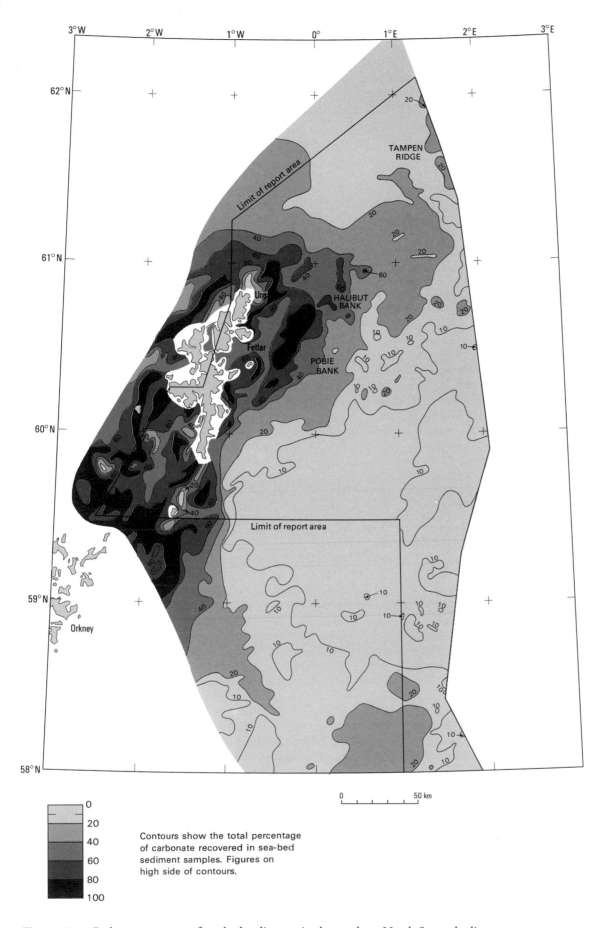

Figure 82 Carbonate content of sea-bed sediments in the northern North Sea and adjacent areas.

91

On the UK Continental Shelf, the gravel fraction of gravelly sands and sandy gravels generally contains a mixture of lithic and biogenic material (Pantin, 1991). In contrast, the gravel fraction within sands and muddy sands, which can be up to 5 per cent of the total sample, consists predominantly of biogenic material. However, in the north near to the shelf-break, there is a marked increase in the proportion of lithic gravel relative to carbonate gravel in the sands. This change is characteristic of the entire shelfbreak west and north of Scotland (Pantin, 1991). Areas of more muddy sediments tend to have a more variable proportion of lithic and carbonate gravel compared to sandy sediments, although there is a noticeable decrease in the carbonate component of the gravel fraction within the large area of muddy sand south of 60°N.

The distribution of carbonate in the sand fraction is very similar to the total carbonate distribution. The highest concentrations, exceeding 75 per cent of the sand fraction, occur between Orkney and Shetland and to the east and north of Shetland. The areas of highest mud carbonate, exceeding 60 per cent of the mud fraction, are located east and north of Shetland, where they occur as very local concentrations.

Synsedimentary carbonate cementation, caused by the oxidation of methane within the sediment, occurs in some muddy areas (Farrow and Fyfe, 1988). Carbonate-cemented concretions have been collected by fishermen from around Shetland (Sabine, 1970), and one such concretion recovered south of Fetlar (Figure 82) was described as being composed of pelleted mud cemented with aragonite, and of Recent origin (Farrow and Fyfe, 1988). Cementation of muddy sediments has also been reported in central areas of the northern North Sea, many in association with pockmarks (Hovland and Judd, 1988).

BEDFORMS AND SEDIMENT TRANSPORT

Sand waves in the area (Figure 81) have been mapped using sidescan sonar and echo-sounder data; they are defined as mesoscale features by Pantin (1991) because they have a width between about 0.6 m and 500 m. Smaller-scale features such as sand ripples have been observed (BGS Cormorant Sea Bed Sediment sheet), and probably occur over much of the sea floor.

Sand waves and megaripples occur between Orkney and Shetland (Figure 81; Flinn, 1973), and gravel waves occur south-east of Shetland (BGS Fair Isle Sea Bed Sediment and Quaternary Geology sheet), although the latter are probably relict. The bedforms occur both in trains and as individual features with maximum crest heights of between 3.5 and 7.3 m (Flinn, 1973). East and north-east of Shetland, there are longitudinal sand patches with a general north–south trend (Kenyon and Stride, 1970; Beg, 1990).

The orientation of bedforms, together with estimates of the prevailing bottom-current velocities, has been used to identify sediment transport paths (Kenyon and Stride, 1970). The main path lies between Orkney and Shetland, with overall sediment movement to the south-east (Figure 81). North-east of Shetland, the transport direction is to the south and south-east, whereas to the south-east of Shetland it is to the north and north-east (Figure 81). This latter path is similar to that inferred from the dispersal patterns of heavy minerals within the sediments (Beg, 1990). The directions of the transport paths east of Shetland imply that a bed-load convergence zone exists there.

Both in the north and along the western slope of the Norwegian Trench (Figure 81), there is an extensive area of partially infilled iceberg ploughmarks on the outer shelf and upper slope (Pantin, 1991). The ploughmarks are of late Pleistocene age, and were caused by floating ice grounding on the edge of the continental shelf. The furrows may be straight, curved or sinuous, and are usually several hundreds of metres in length; they may also be cross-cutting. They are typically 20 m in width and 2 m deep, and are flanked by low ridges rising about 2 m above the sea floor. The troughs usually contain fine-grained, sandy sediment collected since their formation, whereas the adjacent ridges are formed of coarser-grained material with little or no sediment cover.

Pockmarks occur in densities of up to 20 per km² in several zones of fine-grained, muddy sediments (Figure 81), possibly including the area of fine-grained sediments to the east of the Tampen Ridge (Hovland and Judd, 1988). Pockmarks are shallow, ovoid depressions in the sea floor, typically 50 m in diameter and 2 m deep, with internal slopes of about 1°. They probably result from the escape of gas into the water column (Hovland and Judd, 1988). This process lifts soft, fine-grained sediment into suspension; it is then redeposited away from its source because of weak bottom currents. Active pockmarks have been observed in the northern North Sea; some contain rich benthic communities that are sustained by escaping methane (Hovland and Judd, 1988). Gas emissions may also occur beyond areas of fine-grained sediments, but coarser-grained sediments are less mobile and do not produce features recognisable on sidescan sonar records.

GEOCHEMISTRY AND HEAVY MINERALS

Trace-metal concentrations within the sediments are generally of the order of a few parts per million, with locally higher values of up to several tens of parts per million east of Shetland (Basford and Eleftheriou, 1988).

The highest values of chlorophyllous pigments and particulate organic matter are found in bathymetric deeps, where they occur in association with fine-grained sediments. In some areas, the concentrations suggest deposition of material imported from the surrounding sea floor by residual currents (Basford and Eleftheriou, 1988). Concentrations of organochlorines are relatively low; there is a trend of increasing values from west to east, with the highest concentrations in sediments containing high amounts of silt, clay and organic material (Basford and Eleftheriou, 1988). Relatively high petrogenic methane concentrations (greater than 100 parts per billion) occur in sediments in the south-east of the area (Faber and Stahl, 1984).

Concentrations of heavy minerals around Shetland (Beg, 1990) are generally less than 0.1 per cent, but near to onshore basic or ultrabasic rock sources, there are magnetite and chromite concentrations of up to 5 per cent off Fetlar and immediately east of Unst (Figure 80). Farther offshore, relatively high concentrations of heavy minerals have been found locally in water depths between 80 and 100 m; these are thought to coincide with relict shorelines. The overall distribution of heavy minerals suggests that the heaviest components are being transported northwards by tidal currents in the nearshore, while the finer-grained and lighter particles are being transported offshore, mainly by wind-induced currents (Beg, 1990).

10 Economic geology

HYDROCARBONS

Spurred on initially by the Groningen gas find in The Netherlands, and later by the Permian, Cretaceous and Tertiary finds in the southern and central North Sea, the oil industry began its gradual northwards progression into the deeper, more hostile waters of the northern North Sea in 1970. Seismic surveys shot in the northern North Sea led to the identification of a major regional unconformity at depth, burying a presumed pre-Cretaceous topography showing large-amplitude structural highs. Interpretations regarding the age of sediments underlying the unconformity ranged from Devonian or older, to Jurassic (Brennand et al., 1990).

In 1971, Shell/Esso drilled one of the large structural highs in its Third Round block 211/29, to test their hypothesis that the sequence below the unconformity was Mesozoic. As a secondary objective, the well was designed to test the potential of the Tertiary interval above the unconformity. The well discovered oil-bearing Middle Jurassic sands some 6 m from prognosis, at a site that later became the Brent Oilfield. The Paleocene interval, so productive farther south in the central North Sea, was not oil-bearing. Drilling in the 282 blocks awarded in the Fourth Round of licensing later in 1971 resulted in the discovery of many more oilfields in the East Shetland Basin and Viking Graben; subsequent drilling activity has significantly increased the number of discoveries.

Over 800 exploration and appraisal wells have been drilled in the UK sector of the northern North Sea. The rate of sinking of new wells increased significantly after 1971 (Figure 83), and has since averaged 45 per year from 1973 to 1990. Twenty eight fields have come into production during this time, producing a total of over 5500 million barrels of oil by the end of 1990 (Department of Energy, 1991), and making the northern North Sea the most important oil-producing area on the UK Continental Shelf (Figure 84). A further six oilfields are undergoing development drilling. These fields under development, together with those already in production, had original recoverable reserves of approximately 12 000 million barrels (Department of Energy, 1991), and are therefore potentially capable of producing over 6000 million barrels more of oil (Figure 85). A further 49 'significant discoveries' had also been made by end 1990, 17 of which have been named, and at least 5 were undergoing appraisal drilling in 1990 (Department of Energy, 1991). A 'significant discovery' indicates a measure of flow rates rather than the potential commerciality of a find (Department of Energy, 1991). Large quantities of gas have also been found, both as gas caps to oil reservoirs, and in gasfields such as Frigg. The positions of the major fields, and many of the significant discoveries, are shown in Figure 86.

The fields discovered to date in the northern North Sea include at least 20 'giant' oilfields. A 'giant' field is usually defined as one capable of producing 100 million barrels or more of oil, although a 500 million barrel figure is needed to qualify for giant status in the Middle East, North Africa and Asiatic Russia. Several oilfields in the northern North Sea, namely Beryl, Brent, Magnus, Ninian, and Statfjord, therefore qualify as giants (Figure 85), even by comparison with Middle Eastern fields.

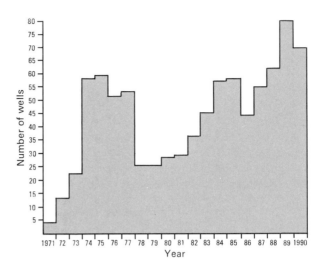

Figure 83 Rate of commencement of exploration and appraisal wells in the northern North Sea. After Department of Energy (1989; 1991) .

Geological factors

In order for an oilfield to form, several important geological criteria have to be met. A structural and/or stratigraphical trap, capped by an impermeable seal, is required to allow accumulation of the hydrocarbons. A porous and permeable reservoir is essential to contain the fluids and allow them to be effectively drained when the reservoir is drilled. There must also have been generation of hydrocarbons from local, deeply buried shales or other source rocks, and these hydrocarbons must have migrated up into the structurally highest part of the trap. Furthermore, the trap has also got to be in existence, and capped by the impermeable seal, before migration of the hydrocarbons, otherwise they will be lost.

RESERVOIRS

The main reservoir horizon in the northern North Sea is the Middle Jurassic Brent Group in the East Shetland Basin, and the partially coeval Sleipner and Hugin formations in the central and southern parts of the Viking Graben (Figures 13 and 32). Oil is also found in strata ranging in age from Devonian to Eocene.

Devonian strata, similar to those that provide a reservoir at the West Brae Oilfield, have generally low porosities, with an average of 7.6 per cent at the Buchan Oilfield in the outer Moray Firth (Downie, 1988), and corresponding low permeabilities. However, commonly extensive fracture systems allow significant local accumulations, and well 16/7-18 in the West Brae Oilfield flowed 3698 barrels of 37.7° API oil per day in drill-stem tests.

Triassic sands, which are found across most of the basinal areas, do not generally form a significant reservoir, although oil is produced from Triassic sands in the Beryl and Crawford oilfields. Oil is also found in Triassic rocks at isolated locations where the succession has been uplifted sufficiently to place them in the depth zone more usually occupied by Jurassic strata.

The Triassic to Lower Jurassic sands of the Statfjord Formation form an important reservoir in the eastern part of

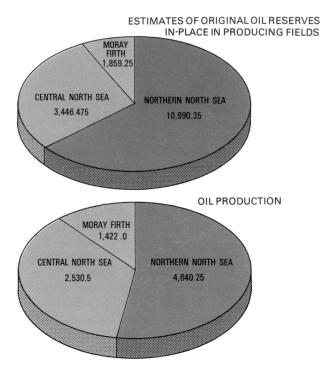

ESTIMATES OF ORIGINAL OIL RESERVES IN-PLACE IN PRODUCING FIELDS

MORAY FIRTH 1,859.25

CENTRAL NORTH SEA 3,446.475

NORTHERN NORTH SEA 10,990.35

OIL PRODUCTION

MORAY FIRTH 1,422.0

CENTRAL NORTH SEA 2,530.5

NORTHERN NORTH SEA 4,640.25

Figure 84 Pie charts indicating the relative importance of the northern North Sea as an oil-producing province in comparison with other parts of the UK Continental Shelf. Figures in millions of barrels. After Department of Energy (1989).

the East Shetland Basin, particularly at the Brent and Statfjord oilfields. This Statfjord Formation reservoir is separated from the overlying Brent Group reservoir by Lower Jurassic shales, and is itself subdivided by shaly intervals into different reservoir units (Johnson and Stewart, 1985).

Lower Jurassic sands within the Dunlin Group are less oil-prone than the Statfjord Formation. Pliensbachian Cook Formation sands contain hydrocarbons in places, particularly in Norwegian waters, but the succession is not generally considered to have reservoir potential.

The Middle Jurassic Brent Group is preserved across much of the basin, and is absent only from the crests of some tilted fault blocks. The stratigraphy can be simplistically considered in terms of a 'layer-cake' whose subdivisions correspond broadly to a simple reservoir zonation. More complex reservoir zonations are used where there are high well concentrations, allowing local variations in facies and geometry to be demonstrated (e.g. Johnson and Stewart, 1985; Livera, 1989).

The Broom Formation at the base of the Brent Group usually has the poorest reservoir qualities of the units in the group, and is commonly below the oil/water contact. The overlying Rannoch Formation sandstones contain and produce oil, but vertical permeability is severely limited in places by the low-angle, micaceous laminae and calcareous doggers that occur throughout this formation. Etive Formation sandstones above the Rannoch Formation are generally coarser grained and less micaceous, and therefore tend to have better reservoir qualities. Although the Etive Formation appears to have a generally sheet-like geometry, in detail, it has a complex variation of facies and bed geometries, and does not act as a simple reservoir. The overlying Ness Formation fluvial sands form an important part of the Brent Group reservoir, and display excellent reservoir qualities; Livera (1989) has noted porosities of 30 per cent and permeabilities of up to 4 Darcies in the Ness Formation of

the Brent Oilfield. Tarbert Formation sands at the top of the group also provide a hydrocarbon reservoir where they form a sheet of irregular thickness across parts of some oilfields (Stewart, 1988).

Upper Jurassic sands are best developed as oil reservoirs in the South Viking Graben, where they form the main producing interval in the Brae and Miller oilfields, and in the T-Block area. The latter is so-called because block 16/17 contains the Toni, Tiffany and Thelma oilfields. Upper Jurassic sands also form important reservoirs in the north of the East Shetland Basin, particularly at the Magnus Oilfield. Harris and Fowler (1987) have described the porosity characteristics of the Brae Formation submarine-fan deposits, noting porosity ranges of between 5 and 21 per cent, and have shown that the diagenetic history is largely dependent on variations in overpressuring regimes. Similar porosities, ranging up to 25 per cent, have been described from the Upper Jurassic sands of the Magnus Oilfield by De'Ath and Schuyleman (1981), who note that for only slight reductions in porosity in these sands, there is a dramatic decrease in permeability. De'Ath and Schuyleman (1981) also observed a distinct decrease of porosity and residual oil saturation with depth in the Magnus Oilfield reservoir.

Although Lower Cretaceous sands form an important reservoir in places in the northern North Sea, very few descriptions of these occurrences have been published. Gas con-

Oilfield	Operators estimate of original reserves (millions of barrels)	Oil produced to end 1990 (millions of barrels)	Main reservoir
Alwyn North	196.35	85.04	Middle Jurassic
Balmoral	66.75	50.96	Paleocene
Beryl	751.5	460.42	Middle Jurassic
Brae Central	52.5	6.1	Upper Jurassic
Brae South	300.0	202.79	Upper Jurassic
Brae North	157.5	57.9	Upper Jurassic
Brent	1808.25	1289.14	Middle Jurassic
Cormorant North	394.5	238.57	Middle Jurassic
Cormorant South	185.25	117.92	Middle Jurassic
Crawford	5.1	4.04	Triassic
Cyrus	11.4	1.98	Paleocene
Deveron	18.0	12.66	Middle Jurassic
Don	56.25	2.39	Middle Jurassic
Dunlin	368.25	297.61	Middle Jurassic
Eider	86.25	29.94	Middle Jurassic
Glamis	17.25	6.05	Upper Jurassic
Heather	105.0	90.04	Middle Jurassic
Hutton	197.25	130.94	Middle Jurassic
NW Hutton	144.75	99.53	Middle Jurassic
Linnhe	5.25	0.57	Middle Jurassic
Magnus	667.5	338.07	Upper Jurassic
Maureen	210.0	173.85	Paleocene
Murchison	342.0	219.5 (UK)	Middle Jurassic
Ness	29.25	16.9	Middle Jurassic
Ninian	1057.5	905.42	Middle Jurassic
Statfjord	3600.0	313.21 (UK)	Middle Jurassic
Tern	178.5	19.06	Middle Jurassic
Thistle	397.5	353.9	Middle Jurassic
Brae East	279.75 (condensate)	Under development	Upper Jurassic
Emerald	40.5	Under development	Middle Jurassic
Miller	301.5	Under development	Upper Jurassic
Osprey	62.25	Under development	Middle Jurassic
Staffa	6.3	Under development	Upper Jurassic
Tiffany	16.79	Under development	Upper Jurassic
Toni	39.75	Under development	Upper Jurassic
Frigg (Gasfield)	69.0*	67436**	Eocene

*   Billion cubic metres
**   Gas produced to end of 1990 in million cubic metres } UK share only

Figure 85 Fields in production or under development in the northern North Sea by the end of 1990, with original reserve and total production figures. From Department of Energy (1991).

Figure 86 Positions of the major fields, and many of the significant discoveries, in the report area.

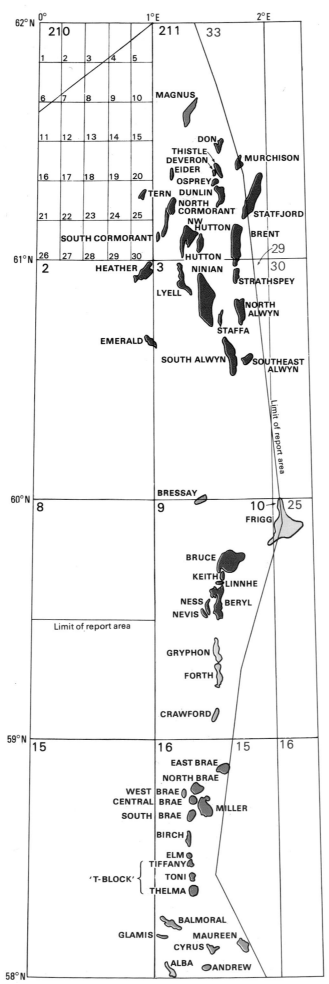

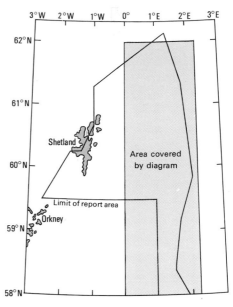

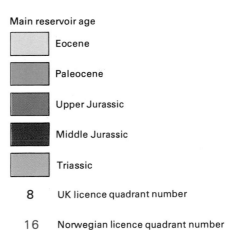

Main reservoir age

	Eocene
	Paleocene
	Upper Jurassic
	Middle Jurassic
	Triassic

8   UK licence quadrant number

16   Norwegian licence quadrant number

The licence areas are numbered by quadrant (eg 210) followed by the block number (eg 210/4), and wells are numbered in sequential order of drilling within that total block (eg 210/4-1 etc).

0   50km

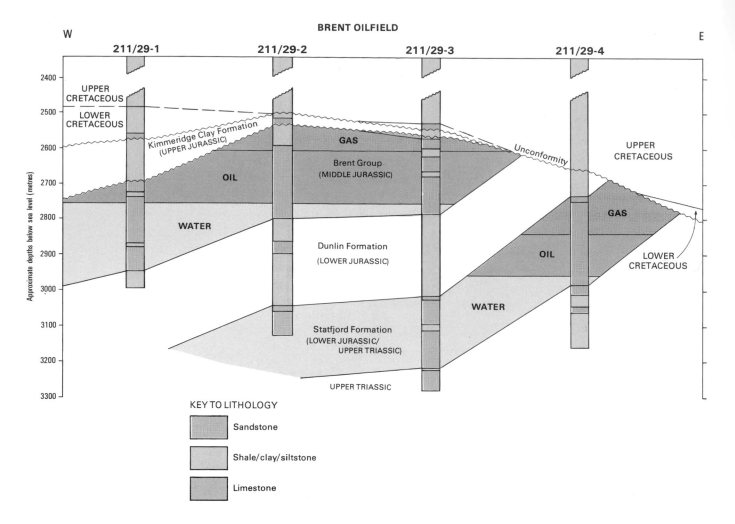

W BRENT OILFIELD E

211/29-1   211/29-2   211/29-3   211/29-4

Figure 87 Structural cross-section through the Brent Oilfield, showing tilting of the fault block and erosion of the reservoir intervals over the crest of the tilted block. After Bowen (1975). For oilfield location, see Figure 86.

densate has been found in Lower Cretaceous sands at the Bosun Oilfield in the very south of the Viking Graben. These sands extend westwards into the outer Moray Firth, where the reservoir has been described as a submarine-fan deposit (Andrews et al., 1990). Gas with condensate has also been found in Lower Cretaceous sands in the Agat Field in Norwegian waters near 62°N.

Paleocene sandstones contain oil in a number of fields in the South Viking Graben, for example at Andrew, Maureen and Balmoral. Although Paleocene sands on the East Shetland Platform also locally contain oil, as at the Bressay Oilfield, these oils tend to be heavy and biodegraded, and have not yet been commercially developed.

The Eocene interval is likely to form a major exploration target over the next few years, following the discovery of oil in Eocene sandstones in the Forth, Gryphon and Alba oilfields. Little has been published on these three newer Eocene discoveries, but Héritier et al. (1981) have reviewed the geology and field characteristics of the Frigg Gasfield, a lower Eocene submarine-fan sequence containing gas, that was discovered in 1971.

TRAPS

Most of the trapping mechanisms in the northern North Sea are of the structural/stratigraphic type, as for example at the Brent Oilfield (Figure 87) where sands occur along the crest of a tilted fault block. All of the Middle Jurassic fields in the East Shetland Basin and Beryl Embayment (Figure

13) are of this type. The basic tilt-block topography was probably initiated during Permian times, enhanced by minor structural movements during the Early and Mid-Jurassic, and more fully developed during the Late Jurassic. The erosion of Middle Jurassic sands over the crests of the tilted blocks occurred during the Late Jurassic, and may have been rapid. Yielding et al. (1992) have suggested that the islands created by up-tilting of the fault-block crests were short lived, and some may have been eroded by as much as 350 m.

The Upper Jurassic reservoirs of the South Viking Graben are also found in combined structural/stratigraphic traps; the sands and coarser-grained clastics occur on the downthrown sides of the major basin-margin faults, and pinch out to shales away from these faults (Figures 45 and 46). Hydrocarbons occupy the structurally highest zones of these fault-controlled fan deposits, with the basin-bounding faults and the sand pinchouts forming lateral traps. The other Upper Jurassic oilfield in the northern North Sea, Magnus, comprises an easterly dipping, combined structural/stratigraphic trap with a down-dip oil/water contact (Figure 88). All of these Middle and Upper Jurassic reservoirs are sealed by Upper Jurassic and/or Cretaceous shales.

Most of the major discoveries within the Tertiary succession in the northern North Sea are defined by relatively low-amplitude, domal features. These overlie either deeper, tilted blocks, as in the case of the Frigg Gasfield (Figure 89), or salt domes, as in the case of the Andrew structure. However, the internal

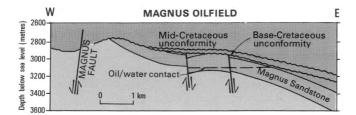

Figure 88 Structural cross-section through the Magnus Oilfield, showing the easterly dipping, combined structural/stratigraphic trap. After De'Ath and Schuyleman (1981). For oilfield location, see Figure 86.

geometry of the sandstone packages within these Tertiary fields is complex, and can provide an element of stratigraphic trapping (Johnson and Stewart, 1975; Parsley, 1990).

SOURCE ROCKS

The principal source rock of the northern North Sea is the Late Jurassic to earliest Cretaceous Kimmeridge Clay Formation. These organic-rich strata usually have total organic carbon values ranging from 2.1 to 10 per cent (Cornford, 1990), and commonly produce a very high gamma-ray log response, leading to their characterisation as 'hot shales'. These organic-rich, oil-prone shales probably became buried, to depths sufficient to generate oil, during Tertiary times (Goff, 1983; Cornford, 1990).

NONHYDROCARBON RESOURCES

There is no commercial exploitation of nonhydrocarbon resources within the area at present. On land (Beveridge et al., 1991; Mykura, 1976), copper in various forms has been found and mined on Fair Isle, and talc and kaolin occur within many of the basement rocks at the coast of Shetland (May and Phemister, 1968). It is likely that these extend offshore. Talc and magnesite are presently being extracted from altered ultrabasic rocks south of Lerwick (Figure 80), and talc was worked until very recently at Queyhouse on the northern edge of the Unst ophiolite. Also found on Shetland are chromite and platinum-group minerals.

Heavy minerals

Chromite is a common accessory mineral in the serpentinite of Unst and Fetlar (Figure 80), and was formerly mined on the island of Unst (Beveridge et al., 1991). Examination of heavy minerals from sea-bed samples (Beg, 1990) has shown high concentrations of chromite and magnetite to the north of Fetlar. Samples from the Wick of Gruting (Figure 80) show magnetite forming 10 to 20 per cent, and chromite about 15 per cent, of the heavy-mineral assemblage, which itself is generally more than 5 per cent of the sea-bed sediment. However, the economic value of such a deposit is limited since the sea-bed sediment is generally less than 0.5 m thick, although it lies in water less than 40 m deep. The area east of Unst has a more variable heavy-mineral assemblage; analyses reveal about 5 per cent magnetite, 3 per cent chromite, 5 per cent staurolite and 20 to 50 per cent garnet. The concentration of heavy minerals varies considerably, but samples close to the islands, and at 80 to 100 m water depth, generally contain the highest concentrations. The minerals are predominantly derived from the Unst ultramafics, and secondarily from reworked glacial sediments. Those at 80 to 100 m depth may be from a former beach deposit. There is a possibility of higher concentrations of chromite and magnetite in the subsurface (Beg, 1990), as the surface sediments are 'diluted' by substantial, modern, carbonate sands.

Sand and gravel

As Shetland is virtually devoid of fluvial or fluvioglacial deposits, beaches have provided an extremely important source of sand and gravel, some beaches have been irreparably damaged by sand extraction (Mather and Smith, 1974). The main sites of extraction have been St Ninian's Isle and Gulber wick (Figure 80; Mykura, 1976). The rapid fall of the sea floor away from the coast suggests that large offshore accumulations of sand and gravel are unlikely at dredgeable depths.

Carbonate

Extraction of carbonate-rich sands for agricultural purposes has occurred at several beaches around Shetland (Mather and Smith, 1974), and others are potential sources of carbonate

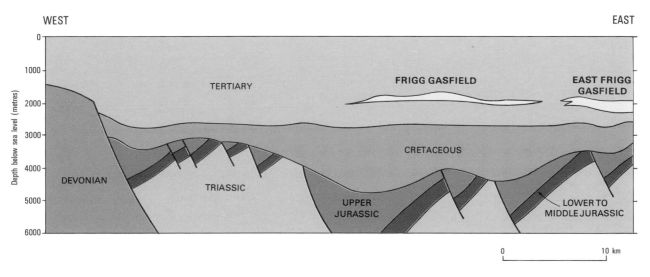

Figure 89 Structural setting of the Frigg Gasfield above deeper, tilted, fault blocks. After Parsley (1990). For gasfield location, see Figure 86.

for agriculture, or even for cement. However, their generally low volumes and inaccessibility prevent exploitation. Offshore, analyses reveal high carbonate contents for sea-bed samples, commonly in excess of 80 per cent on Pobie Bank, north and north-east of Unst, off Fetlar, and to the south-west of mainland Shetland (Figure 82; BGS Shetland Sea Bed Sediments sheet). Allen (1983) presented a rather different distribution for these carbonate deposits, most particularly off south-west Shetland. All deposits contain high proportions of bivalve debris; inshore occurrences tend to be fine-grained and contain much foraminiferal material, whereas those farther offshore are richer in barnacles (Allen, 1983). Allen (1983) suggested that 262×10^6 m^3 of carbonate occur east of Shetland, predominantly on the Pobie Bank.

References

Most of the references listed below are held in the Library of the British Geological Survey at Keyworth, Nottingham. Copies of the references can be purchased subject to the current copyright legislation.

References to BGS offshore maps are not given here, but an index map showing their distribution in the report area is presented inside the back cover.

ALHILALI, K A, and DAMUTH, J E. 1987. Slide block(?) of Jurassic sandstone and submarine channels in the basal Upper Cretaceous of the Viking Graben: Norwegian North Sea. *Marine and Petroleum Geology*, Vol. 4, 35–48.

ALLEN, J R L. 1979. Old Red Sandstone facies in external basins, with particular reference to southern Britain. 65–80 *in* The Devonian System. *Special Papers in Palaeontology*, Vol. 23.

ALLEN, N H. 1983. Recent temperate carbonate deposits on the continental shelf north and west of Scotland: distribution, sedimentology and reserves. Unpublished PhD thesis, University of Strathclyde.

ALLEN, P A, and MARSHALL, J E A. 1981. Depositional environments and palynology of the Devonian south-east Shetland basin. *Scottish Journal of Geology*, Vol. 17, 257–274.

ANDERTON, R. 1985. Sedimentation and tectonics in the Scottish Dalradian. *Scottish Journal of Geology*, Vol. 21, 407–436.

ANDREWS, I J, and six others. 1990. *United Kingdom offshore regional report: the geology of the Moray Firth*. (London: HMSO for the British Geological Survey.)

AURORA, R P. 1983. Lateral response of a group of large diameter piles — a case study of a North Sea Platform. *Proceedings of the Fifteenth Offshore Technology Conference, Houston*, Vol. 1, 519–524, Paper No. 4504.

AVERY, O E, BURTON, G D, and HEIRTZLER, J R. 1968. An aeromagnetic survey of the Norwegian Sea. *Journal of Geophysical Research*, Vol. 73, 4583–4600.

BADLEY, M E, EGEBERG, T, and NIPEN, O. 1984. Development of rift basins illustrated by the structural evolution of the Oseberg feature, Block 30/6, offshore Norway. *Journal of the Geological Society of London*, Vol. 141, 639–649.

— PRICE, J D, RAMBECH DAHL, C, and AGDESTEIN, T. 1988. The structural evolution of the northern Viking Graben and its bearing upon extensional modes of basin formation. *Journal of the Geological Society of London*, Vol. 145, 455–472.

BARRACLOUGH, R. 1987. The Magnus Sandstone: an example of a sand-rich submarine fan system from the North Sea. *British Sedimentology Research Group Annual Meeting, Aberdeen. Core Workshop Guide*, 3–4.

BARTON, P J. 1986. Comparison of deep reflection and refraction structures in the North Sea. 297–300 *in* Reflection seismology: a global perspective. BARAZANGI, M, and BROWN, L (editors). *American Geophysical Union Geodynamic Series*, Vol. 13.

— MATTHEWS, D H, HALL, J, and WARNER, M. 1984. Moho beneath the North Sea compared on normal incidence and wide-angle seismic records. *Nature, London*, Vol. 308, 55–56.

BASFORD, D, and ELEFTHERIOU, A. 1988. The benthonic environment of the North Sea (56° to 61°N). *Journal of the Marine Biological Association*, Vol. 68, 125–141.

BEACH, A. 1985. Some comments on sedimentary basin development in the northern North Sea. *Scottish Journal of Geology*, Vol. 21, 493–512.

— 1986. A deep seismic reflection profile across the northern North Sea. *Nature, London*, Vol. 323, 53–55.

— BIRD, T, and GIBBS, A. 1987. Extensional tectonics and crustal structure: deep seismic reflection data from the northern North Sea

Viking Graben. 467–476 *in* Continental extensional tectonics. COWARD, M P, DEWEY, J F, and HANCOCK, P L (editors). *Special Publication of the Geological Society of London*, No. 28.

BEG, M A. 1990. The distribution and dispersal of heavy minerals on the continental shelf around the Shetland Isles. Unpublished PhD thesis, University of Strathclyde.

BENT, A J A. 1986. Aspects of Pleistocene glaciomarine sequences in the North Sea. Unpublished PhD thesis, University of Edinburgh.

BERGGREN, W A, and GRADSTEIN, F M. 1981. Agglutinated benthonic foraminifera assemblages in the Palaeogene of the central North Sea: their biostratigraphic and depositional environmental significance. 282–285 in *Petroleum geology of the continental shelf of North-West Europe*. ILLING, L V, and HOBSON, G D (editors). (London: Heyden and Son.)

BEVERIDGE, R, BROWN, S, GALLAGHER, M J, and MERRITT, J W. 1991. Economic geology. 545–595 in *Geology of Scotland* (3rd edition). CRAIG, G Y (editor). (Bath: Geological Society Publishing House.)

BIRKS, H J B, and PEGLAR, S M. 1979. Interglacial pollen spectra from Sel Ayre, Shetland. *New Phytology*, Vol. 83, 559–575.

BLACK, M. 1980. On chalk, globigerina ooze and aragonite mud. 54–85 *in* Andros Island, chalk and oceanic oozes. Unpublished work of Maurice Black. JEANS, C V, and RAWSON, P F (editors). *Occasional Publication of the Yorkshire Geological Society*, No. 5.

BOTT, M H P. 1975. Structure and evolution of the North Scottish Shelf, the Faeroe Bank and the intervening region. 105–115 in *Petroleum and the continental shelf of North-West Europe*. WOODLAND, A W (editor). (London: Applied Science Publishers.)

— and BROWITT, C W A. 1975. Interpretation of geophysical observations between the Orkney and Shetland Islands. *Journal of the Geological Society of London*, Vol. 131, 353–371.

BOWEN, J M. 1975. The Brent Oilfield. 353–360 in *Petroleum and the continental shelf of North-West Europe*. WOODLAND, A W (editor). (London: Applied Science Publishers.)

BRENNAND, T P, VAN HOORN, B, and JAMES K H. 1990. Historical review of North Sea exploration. 1–33 in *Introduction to the petroleum geology of the North Sea*. GLENNIE, K W (editor). (London: Blackwell Scientific Publications.)

BROWN, P E. 1991. Caledonian and earlier magmatism. 229–295 in *Geology of Scotland* (3rd edition). CRAIG, G Y (editor). (Bath: Geological Society Publishing House.)

BROWN, S S, and RICHARDS, P C. 1989. Facies and development of the Mid-Jurassic Brent delta near the northern limit of its progradation, UK North Sea. 253–267 *in* Deltas: sites and traps for fossil fuels. WHATELEY, M K G, and PICKERING, K T (editors). *Special Publication of the Geological Society of London*, Vol. 41.

— and THOMSON, A R. 1987. Patterns in the deposition of the Brent Group (Middle Jurassic) UK North Sea. 899–914 in *Petroleum geology of North West Europe*. BROOKS, J, and GLENNIE, K W (editors). (London: Graham and Trotman.)

BUCHARDT, B. 1978. Oxygen isotope palaeotemperatures from the Tertiary Period in the North Sea area. *Nature, London*, Vol. 275, 121–123.

BUDDING, M C, and INGLIN, H F. 1981. A reservoir geological model of the Brent sands in Southern Cormorant.. 326–334 in *Petroleum geology of the continental shelf of North-West Europe*. ILLING, L V, and HOBSON, G D (editors). (London: Heyden and Son.)

BURNHILL, T J, and RAMSAY, W V. 1981. Mid-Cretaceous palaeontology and stratigraphy, central North Sea. 245–254 in *Petroleum geology of the continental shelf of North-West Europe*. ILLING, L V, and HOBSON, G D (editors). (London: Heyden and Son.)

BUZA, J W, and UNNEBERG, A. 1987. Geological and reservoir engineering aspects of the Statfjord Field. 23–38 in *North Sea oil and gas reservoirs*. (London: Graham and Trotman.)

CALLOMON, J H. 1975. Jurassic ammonites from the northern North Sea. *Norsk Geologisk Tiddskrift*, Vol. 55, 373–386.

CAMERON, T D J, BONNY, A P, GREGORY, D M, and HARLAND, R. 1984. Lower Pleistocene dinoflagellate cyst, foraminiferal and pollen assemblages in four boreholes in the southern North Sea. *Geological Magazine*, Vol. 121, 85–97.

— STOKER, M S, and LONG, D. 1987. The history of Quaternary sedimentation in the UK sector of the North Sea Basin. *Journal of the Geological Society of London*, Vol. 144, 43–58.

CANNON, S J C, GILES, M R, WHITTAKER, M F, PLEASE, P H, and MARTIN, S V. 1992. A regional reassessment of the Brent Group, UK sector, North Sea. *In* Geology of the Brent Group. MORTON, A C, HASZELDINE, R S, GILES, M R, and BROWN, S (editors). *Special Publication of the Geological Society of London,* No. 61.

CARLSEN, R, LØKEN, T, and ROALDSET, E. 1986. Late Weichselian transgression, erosion and sedimentation at Gullfaks, northern North Sea. 145–152 in North Atlantic palaeo-oceanography. SUMMERHAYES, C P, and SHACKLETON, N J (editors). *Special Publication of the Geological Society of London*, No. 21.

CHAPELHOW, R. 1965. On glaciation in North Roe, Shetland. *Geographical Journal*, Vol. 131, 60–70.

CHAUVIN, A L, and VALACHI, L Z. 1980. Sedimentology of the Brent and Statfjord formations of Statfjord Field. 1–17 in *The sedimentation of the North Sea reservoir rocks*. (Geilo: Norwegian Petroleum Society.)

CHRISTIANSEN, J B, and STRAND, J E. 1987. 15/5–1 Discovery. 265–272 in *Geology of the Norwegian oil and gas fields*. SPENCER, A M, and others (editors). (London: Graham and Trotman.)

CLEMMENSEN, L, JACOBSEN, V, and STEEL, R. 1980. Some aspects of Triassic sedimentation and basin development, east Greenland, North Sea. 1–21 in *The sedimentation of the North Sea reservoir rocks*. (Geilo: Norwegian Petroleum Society.)

CLOETINGH, S, LAMBECK, K, and McQUEEN, H. 1987. Apparent sea level fluctuations and a paleo-stress field for the North Sea region. 49–58 in *Petroleum geology of North West Europe*. BROOKS, J, and GLENNIE, K W (editors). (London: Graham and Trotman.)

CONDON, P J. 1988. Seismic stratigraphy and distribution of Palaeogene sediments west and east of Shetland. Unpublished PhD thesis, University of Edinburgh.

— JOLLEY, D W, and MORTON, A C. 1992. Eocene succession on the East Shetland Platform, North Sea. *Marine and Petroleum Geology*, Vol. 9, 633–647.

CONORT, A. 1986. Habitat of Tertiary hydrocarbons, south Viking Graben. 159–170 in *Habitat of hydrocarbons on the Norwegian continental shelf*. SPENCER, A M, and others (editors). (London: Graham and Trotman.)

CORNFORD, C. 1990. Source rocks and hydrocarbons of the North Sea. 294–361 in *Introduction to the petroleum geology of the North Sea* (3rd edition). GLENNIE, K W (editor). (Oxford: Blackwell Scientific Publications.)

COWARD, M P. 1990. The Precambrian, Caledonian and Variscan framework to NW Europe. 1–34 *in* Tectonic events responsible for Britain's oil and gas reserves. HARDMAN, R F P, and BROOKS, J (editors). *Special Publication of the Geological Society of London*, No. 55.

DAHLBERG, R. 1983. Observations of scour around offshore structures. *Canadian Geotechnical Journal*, Vol. 20, 617–628.

DAY, G A, and five others. 1981. Regional seismic structure maps of the North Sea. 76–84 in *Petroleum geology of the continental shelf of North-West Europe*. ILLING, L V, and HOBSON, G D (editors). (London: Heyden and Son.)

DE'ATH, N G, and SCHUYLEMAN, S F. 1981. The geology of the Magnus Oilfield. 342–351 in *Petroleum geology of the continental shelf of North-West Europe*. ILLING, L V, and HOBSON, G D (editors). (London: Heyden and Son.)

DEEGAN, C E, and SCULL, B J. 1977. A proposed standard lithostratigraphic nomenclature for the central and northern North Sea. *Report of the Institute of Geological Sciences*, No. 77/25; *Bulletin of the Norwegian Petroleum Directorate*, No. 1.

DEKKO, T, and ROKOENGEN, K. 1978. A submerged beach in the northern part of the North Sea. *Norsk Geologisk Tidsskrift*, Vol. 58, 233–236.

DEMAISON, G J, and MOORE, G T. 1980. Anoxic environments and oil source bed genesis. *Organic Geochemistry*, Vol. 2, 9–31.

DEPARTMENT OF ENERGY. 1989. *Development of the oil and gas resources of the United Kingdom*. (London: HMSO.)

— 1991. *Development of the oil and gas resources of the United Kingdom*. (London: HMSO.)

DERBYSHIRE, E, LOVE, M A, and EDGE, M J. 1985. Fabrics of probable segregated ground ice origin in some sediment cores from the North Sea Basin. 261–280 in *Soils and Quaternary landscape evolution*. BOARDMAN, J (editor). (Chichester: J Wiley and Sons.)

DEWEY, J F. 1982. Plate tectonics and the evolution of the British Isles. *Journal of the Geological Society of London*, Vol. 139, 371–412.

DIXON, E. 1936. The geology of Shetland. 104–120 in *Manson's guide to Shetland* MANSON, T M Y (editor). (Lerwick: Shetland News Office.)

DIXON, J E, FITTON, J G, and FROST, R T C. 1981. The tectonic significance of post-Carboniferous igneous activity in the North Sea Basin. 121–137 in *Petroleum geology of the continental shelf of North-West Europe*. ILLING, L V, and HOBSON, G D (editors). (London: Heyden and Son.)

DONATO, J A, and TULLY, M C. 1981. A regional interpretation of North Sea gravity data. 65–75 in *Petroleum geology of the continental shelf of North-West Europe*. ILLING, L V, and HOBSON, G D (editors). (London: Heyden and Son.)

— — 1982. A proposed granite batholith along the western flank of the North Sea Viking Graben. *Geophysical Journal of the Royal Astronomical Society*, Vol. 69, 187–195.

DONOVAN, R N. 1980. Lacustrine cycles, fish ecology and stratigraphic zonation in the Middle Devonian of Caithness. *Scottish Journal of Geology*, Vol. 16, 35–50.

DORÉ, A S, and GAGE, M S. 1987. Crustal alignments and sedimentary domains in the evolution of the North Sea, north-east Atlantic Margin and the Barents Shelf. 1131–1148 in *Petroleum geology of North West Europe*. BROOKS, J, and GLENNIE, K W (editors). (London: Graham and Trotman.)

DOWNIE, R A. 1988. Controls on the reservoir quality of the Devonian age Old Red Standstone of the Orcadian Basin Abstract. *British Sedimentological Research Group, Annual Meeting, Cambridge*. [Unpaginated.]

DRAPER, L. 1980. Wave climatology on the UK Continental Shelf. 353–368 in *The North-West European shelf seas: the sea bed and sea in motion — II. Physical and chemical oceanography, and physical resources*. BANNER, F T, COLLINS, M B, and MASSIE, K S (editors). (Amsterdam: Elsevier.)

DUINDAM, P, and VAN HOORN, B. 1987. Structural evolution of the West Shetland continental margin. 765–774 in *Petroleum geology of North West Europe*. BROOKS, J, and GLENNIE, K W (editors). (London: Graham and Trotman.)

DURNING, P J, RENNIE, I A, THOMPSON, J M, and RUCKSTUHL, R J. 1979. Installing a piled foundation in hard, overconsolidated North Sea clay for the Heather Platform. *Ground Engineering*, Vol. 12, 24–31.

EDEN, R A, HOLMES, R, and FANNIN, N G T. 1977. The Quaternary deposits of the central North Sea, 6. Depositional environment of offshore Quaternary deposits of the continental shelf around Scotland. *Report of the Institute of Geological Sciences*, No. 77/15.

ENGSTRAND, L G. 1967. Stockholm natural radiocarbon measurements VII. *Radiocarbon*, Vol. 9, 387–438.

ENJOLRAS, J M, GOUADAIN, J, MUTTI, E, and PIZON, J. 1986. New turbiditic model for the Lower Tertiary sands in the south Viking Graben. 171–180 in *Habitat of hydrocarbons on the Norwegian continental shelf.* SPENCER, A M, and others (editors). (London: Graham and Trotman.)

EVANS, D, CHESHER, J A, DEEGAN, C E, and FANNIN, N G T. 1981. The offshore geology of Scotland in relation to the IGS shallow drilling programme, 1970–1978. *Report of the Institute of Geological Sciences,* No. 81/12.

EYNON, G. 1981. Basin development and sedimentation in the Middle Jurassic of the northern North Sea. 96–204 in *Petroleum geology of the continental shelf of North-West Europe.* ILLING, L V, and HOBSON, G D (editors). (London: Heyden and Son.)

FABER, E, and STAHL, W. 1984. Geochemical surface exploration for hydrocarbons in the North Sea. *Bulletin of the American Association of Petroleum Geologists,* Vol. 68, 363–368.

FAERSETH, R B, and PEDERSTAD, K. 1988. Regional sedimentology and petroleum geology of marine, late Bathonian–Valanginian sandstone in the North Sea. *Marine and Petroleum Geology,* Vol. 5, 17–33.

FAGERLAND, N. 1983. Tectonic analysis of a Viking Graben border fault. *Bulletin of the American Association of Petroleum Geologists,* Vol. 67, 2125–2136.

FANNIN, N G T. 1989. Offshore investigations 1966–87. *British Geological Survey Technical Report,* WB/89/2.

FARRIMOND, P, EGLINGTON, G, BRASSELL, S C, and JENKYNS, H C. 1990. The Cenomanian/Turonian anoxic event in Europe: organic geochemical study. *Marine and Petroleum Geology,* Vol. 7, 75–89.

FARROW, G E, ALLEN, N H, and AKPAN, E B. 1984. Bioclastic carbonate sedimentation on a high-latitude, tide-dominated shelf: northeast Orkney Islands, Scotland. *Journal of Sedimentary Petrology,* Vol. 54, 373–393.

— and FYFE, J A. 1988. Bioerosion and carbonate mud production on high-latitude shelves. *Sedimentary Geology,* Vol. 60, 281–297.

FETTES, D J, and HARRIS, A L. 1986. The Caledonian geology of the Scottish Highlands. 303–334 in *Synthesis of the Caledonian rocks of Britain.* FETTES, D J, and HARRIS, A L (editors). (Dordrecht: Reidel Publishing Company.)

FEYLING-HANSEN, R W. 1980. Foraminiferal indication of Eemian interglacial in the northern North Sea. *Bulletin of the Geological Society of Denmark,* Vol. 29, 175–189.

— 1982. Foraminiferal zonation of a boring in Quaternary deposits of the northern North Sea. *Bulletin of the Geological Society of Denmark,* Vol. 31, 29–47.

— and KNUDSEN, K L. 1986. Three North Sea borings: correlation between three borings in Quaternary deposits of the northern North Sea. *Aarhus Universitet Geoskrifter,* Vol. 24, 125–143.

FICHLER, C, and HOSPERS, J. 1990. Gravity modelling in the Viking Graben area. 71–81 in *Evolution of the North Sea Rifts.* BLUNDELL, D J, and GIBBS, A D (editors). (Oxford: Oxford University Press.)

FINLAY, T M. 1926a. A Tøngsbergite boulder from the boulder-clay of Shetland. *Transactions of the Edinburgh Geological Society,* Vol. 12, 180.

— 1926b. The Old Red Sandstone of Shetland, Part I, south-eastern area. *Transactions of the Royal Society of Edinburgh,* Vol. 54, 553–572.

FISHER, M J, and MUDGE, D C. 1990. Triassic. 191–218 in *Introduction to the petroleum geology of the North Sea* (3rd edition). GLENNIE, K W (editor). (Oxford: Blackwell Scientific Publishers.)

FLINN, D. 1961. Continuation of the Great Glen Fault beyond the Moray Firth. *Nature, London,* Vol. 191, 589–591.

— 1964. Coastal and submarine features around the Shetland Islands. *Proceedings of the Geologists' Association,* Vol. 75, 321–339.

— 1969. A geological interpretation of the aeromagnetic maps of the continental shelf around Orkney and Shetland. *Geological Journal,* Vol. 6, 279–292.

— 1970. The glacial till of Fair Isle, Shetland. *Geological Magazine,* Vol. 107, 273–276.

— 1973. The topography of the seafloor around Orkney and Shetland and in the northern North Sea. *Journal of the Geological Society of London,* Vol. 129, 39–59.

— 1977. The erosion history of Shetland: a review. *Proceedings of the Geologists' Association,* Vol. 88, 129–146.

— 1978. The most recent glaciation of the Orkney–Shetland Channel and adjacent areas. *Scottish Journal of Geology,* Vol. 14, 109–123.

— 1983. Glacial meltwater channels in the northern isles of Shetland. *Scottish Journal of Geology,* Vol, 19, 311–320.

— 1985. The Caledonides of Shetland. 1159–1172 in *The Caledonide Orogen — Scandinavia and related areas.* GEE, D G, and STURT, B A (editors). (Chichester: J Wiley and Sons.)

— MAY, F, ROBERTS, J L, and TREAGUS, J E. 1972. A revision of the stratigraphic succession of the East Mainland of Shetland. *Scottish Journal of Geology,* Vol. 8, 335–343.

FOLK, R L. 1954. Sedimentary rock nomenclature. *Journal of Geology,* Vol. 62, 344–359.

FROST, R E. 1987. The evolution of the Viking Graben tilted fault-block structures: a compressional origin. 1009–1024 in *Petroleum geology of North West Europe.* BROOKS, J, and GLENNIE, K W (editors). (London: Graham and Trotman.)

— 1989. Discussion on the structural evolution of the northern Viking Graben and its bearing upon extensional modes of basin formation. *Journal of the Geological Society of London,* Vol. 146, 1035–1040.

FROST, R T C, FITCH, F J, and MILLER, J A. 1981. The age and nature of crystalline basement of the North Sea Basin. 43–57 in *Petroleum geology of the continental shelf of North-West Europe.* ILLING, L V, and HOBSON, G D (editors). (London: Heyden and Son.)

FROSTICK, L E, LINSEY, T K, and REID, I. 1992. Tectonic climatic control of Triassic sedimentation in the Beryl Basin, northern North Sea. *Journal of the Geological Society of London,* Vol. 149, 13–26.

FYFE, J A, ABBOTTS, I, and CROSBY, A. 1981. The subcrop of the mid-Mesozoic unconformity in the UK area. 236–244 in *Petroleum geology of the continental shelf of North-West Europe.* ILLING, L V, and HOBSON, G D (editors). (London: Heyden and Son.)

GABRIELSEN, R H. 1986. Structural elements in graben systems and their influence on hydrocarbon trap types. 55–60 in *Habitat of hydrocarbons on the Norwegian continental shelf.* SPENCER, A M, and others (editors). (London: Graham and Trotman.)

GAEMERS, P A M. 1990. The definition of the classical Palaeogene–Neogene boundary in the North Sea Basin by means of *Gadidae* otoliths *(Pisces). Tertiary Research,* Vol. 11, 97–144.

GALLOIS, R W. 1976. Coccolith blooms in the Kimmeridge Clay, and origin of North Sea oil. *Nature, London,* Vol. 259, 473–475.

GATLIFF, R W, and eleven others. 1994. *United Kingdom offshore regional report: the geology of the central North Sea.* (London: HMSO for the British Geological Survey.)

GIBBS, A D. 1984. Structural evolution of extensional basin margins. *Journal of the Geological Society of London,* Vol. 141, 609–620.

— 1987a. Linked tectonics of the northern North Sea basins. 163–171 in Sedimentary basins and basin-forming mechanisms. BEAUMONT, C, and TANKARD, A J (editors). *Memoir of the Canadian Society of Petroleum Geologists,* No. 12.

— 1987b. Deep seismic profiles in the northern North Sea. 1025–1028 in *Petroleum geology of North West Europe.* BROOKS, J, and GLENNIE, K W (editors). (London: Graham and Trotman.)

— 1987c. Development of extension and mixed-mode sedimentary basins. 19–33 in Continental extensional tectonics. COWARD, M P, DEWEY, J F, and HANCOCK, P L (editors). *Special Publication of the Geological Society of London,* No. 28.

GILTNER, J P. 1987. Application of extensional models to the northern Viking Graben. *Norsk Geologisk Tidsskrift*, Vol. 67, 339–352.

GLENNIE, K W. 1990a. Outline of North Sea history and structural framework. 34–77 in *Introduction to the petroleum geology of the North Sea* (3rd edition). GLENNIE, K W (editor). (Oxford: Blackwell Scientific Publications.)

— 1990b. Lower Permian — Rotliegend. 120–152 in *Introduction to the petroleum geology of the North Sea.* GLENNIE, K W (editor). (Oxford: Blackwell Scientific Publications.)

GOFF, J C. 1983. Hydrocarbon generation and migration from Jurassic source rocks in the East Shetland Basin and Viking Graben of the northern North Sea. *Journal of the Geological Society of London,* Vol. 140, 445–474.

GOWERS, M B. 1979. Folding and reverse faulting in the tensional regime. 10/1–27 in *Norwegian Sea Symposium.* (Oslo: Norwegian Petroleum Society.)

GRAMMAN, F, and KOCKEL. F. 1988. Palaeogeographical, lithological, palaeoecological and palaeoclimatic development of the Northwest European Tertiary Basin. 428–441 *in* the Northwest European Tertiary Basin. VINKEN, R (compiler). *Geologisches Jahrbuch,* Vol. 100A.

GRAUÉ E, and seven others. 1987. Advance and retreat of Brent Delta system, Norwegian North Sea. 915–937 in *Petroleum geology of North West Europe.* BROOKS, J, and GLENNIE, K W (editors). (London: Graham and Trotman.)

HAILWOOD, E A, and five others. 1979. Chronology and biostratigraphy of northeast Atlantic sediments. 1119–1141 in *Initial Reports of the Deep Sea Drilling Project*, Vol. 48. (Washington: United States Government Printing Office.)

HALLETT, D. 1981. Refinement of the geological model of the Thistle Field. 315–325 in *Petroleum geology of the continental shelf of North-West Europe.* ILLING, L V, and HOBSON, G D (editors). (London: Heyden and Son.)

HAMAR, G P, JAKOBSSON, K H, ORMAASEN, D E, and SKARPNES, O. 1980. Tectonic development of the North Sea north of the Central Highs. 1–11 in *The sedimentation of the North Sea reservoir rocks.* (Geilo: Norwegian Petroleum Society.)

— and HJELLE, K. 1984. Tectonic framework of the Møre Basin and the northern North Sea. 349–358 in *Petroleum geology of the North European Margin.* SPENCER, A M (editor). (London: Graham and Trotman.)

HAMILTON, P J, FALLICK, A E, MacINTYRE, R M, and ELLIOTT, S. 1987. Isotope tracing of the provenance and diagenesis of Lower Brent Group sands, North Sea. 939–950 in *Petroleum geology of North West Europe.* BROOKS, J, and GLENNIE, K W (editors). (London: Graham and Trotman.)

HANCOCK, J M. 1986. Cretaceous. 161–178 in *Introduction to the petroleum geology of the North Sea.* GLENNIE, K W (editor). (Oxford: Blackwell Scientific Publications.)

— 1990. Cretaceous. 255–272 in *Introduction to the petroleum geology of the North Sea* (3rd edition). GLENNIE, K W (editor). (Oxford: Blackwell Scientific Publications.)

— and KAUFFMAN, E G. 1979. The great transgressions of the Late Cretaceous. *Journal of the Geological Society of London,* Vol. 136, 175–186.

— and SCHOLLE, P A. 1975. Chalk of the North Sea. 413–427 in *Petroleum and the continental shelf of North-West Europe.* WOODLAND, A W (editor). (London: Applied Science Publishers.)

HANSLIEN, S. 1987. Balder. 193–202 in *Geology of the Norwegian oil and gas fields.* SPENCER, A M, and others (editors). (London: Graham and Trotman.)

HAQ, B U, HARDENBOL, J, and VAIL, P R. 1987. Chronology of fluctuating sea level since the Triassic. *Science, New York,* Vol. 235, 1156–1167.

HARDING, A W, HUMPHREY, T J, LATHAM, A, LUNSFORD, M K, and STRIDER, M H. 1990. Controls on Eocene submarine fan deposition in the Witch Ground Graben. 353–367 *in* Tectonic events responsible for Britain's oil and gas reserves. HARDMAN, R F P, and BROOKS, J (editors). *Special Publication of the Geological Society of London,* No. 55.

HARKNESS, D D, and WILSON, H W. 1979. Scottish Universities Research and Reactor Centre Radiocarbon Measurements III. *Radiocarbon*, Vol. 21, 203–256.

HARLAND, W B, and five others. 1990. *A geologic time scale 1989.* (Cambridge: Cambridge University Press.)

HARMS, J C, and McMICHAEL, W J. 1983. Sedimentology of the Brae Oilfield area, North Sea. *Journal of Petroleum Geology*, Vol. 5, 437–439.

— TACKENBERG, P, PICKLES, E, and POLLOCK, R E. 1981. The Brae Oilfield area. 352–357 in *Petroleum geology of the continental shelf of North-West Europe.* ILLING, L V, and HOBSON, G D (editors). (London: Heyden and Son.)

HARRIS, A L. 1983. The growth and structure of Scotland. 1–22 in *Geology of Scotland* (2nd edition). CRAIG, G Y (editor). (Edinburgh: Scottish Academic Press.)

HARRIS, J P, and FOWLER, R M. 1987. Enhanced prospectivity of the Mid-Late Jurassic sediments of the South Viking Graben, northern North Sea. 879–898 in *Petroleum geology of North West Europe.* BROOKS, J, and GLENNIE, K W (editors). (London: Graham and Trotman.)

HART, M B, and LEARY, P N. 1989. The stratigraphic and palaeogeographic setting of the late Cenomanian 'anoxic' event. *Journal of the Geological Society of London*, Vol. 146, 305–310.

HASZELDINE, R S, and RUSSELL, M J. 1987. The Late Carboniferous northern North Atlantic Ocean: implications for hydrocarbon exploration from Britain to the Arctic. 1163–1175 in *Petroleum geology of North West Europe.* BROOKS, J, and GLENNIE, K W (editors). (London: Graham and Trotman.)

HATTON, I R. 1986. Geometry of allochthonous Chalk Group members, Central Trough, North Sea. *Marine and Petroleum Geology*, Vol. 3, 79–98.

HAY, J T C. 1978. Structural development in the northern North Sea. *Journal of Petroleum Geology*, Vol. 1, 65–77.

HAZEU, G J A. 1981. 34/10 Delta structure, geological evaluation and appraisal. 13/1-36 in *Norwegian symposium on exploration.* (Oslo: Norwegian Petroleum Society.)

HELLAND-HANSEN, W, STEEL, R, NAKAYAMA, K, and KENDEL, C G ST C. 1989. Review and computer modelling of the Brent Group stratigraphy. 237–252 *in* Deltas: sites and traps for fossil fuels. WHATELEY, M K G, and PICKERING, K T (editors). *Special Publication of the Geological Society of London,* No. 41.

HÉRITIER, F E, LOSSEL, P, and WATHNE, E. 1979. Frigg Field — large submarine fan trap in Lower Eocene rocks of North Sea Viking Graben. *Bulletin of the American Association of Petroleum Geologists*, Vol. 63, 1999–2020.

— — — 1981. The Frigg gas field. 380–391 in *Petroleum geology of the continental shelf of North-West Europe.* ILLING, L V, and HOBSON, G D (editors). (London: Heyden and Son).

HITCHEN, K, and RITCHIE, J D. 1987. Geological review of the West Shetland area. 737–749 in *Petroleum geology of North West Europe.* BROOKS, J, and GLENNIE, K W (editors). (London: Graham and Trotman.)

HOLLOWAY, S, REAY, D M, DONATO, J A, and BEDDOE-STEPHENS, B. 1991. Distribution of granite and possible Devonian sediments in part of the East Shetland Platform, North Sea. *Journal of the Geological Society of London*, Vol. 148, 635–638.

HOPPE, G. 1965. Submarine peat in the Shetland Islands. *Geografiska Annaler*, Vol. 47A, 195–203.

— 1971. Nordvästeuropas inlandsisar under den sista istiden — några glimtar från ett forskningsprogram. *Svensk Naturvetenskap.* 31–40. [In Swedish.]

HOSPERS, J, and EDIRIWEERA, K K. 1991. Depth and configuration of the crystalline basement in the Viking Graben area, northern North Sea. *Journal of the Geological Society of London*, Vol. 148, 261–265.

HOVLAND, M, and JUDD, A G. 1988. *Seabed pockmarks and seepages.* (London: Graham and Trotman.)

HOWITT, F, ASTON, E R, and JAQUÉ, M. 1975. The occurrence of Jurassic volcanics in the North Sea. 379–387 in *Petroleum and the continental shelf of North-West Europe.* WOODLAND, A W (editor). (London: Applied Science Publishers.)

HYDROGRAPHIC DEPARTMENT. 1975. *North coast of Scotland Pilot.* (Taunton: Hydrographer of the Navy.)

IMBRIE, J, and eight others. 1984. The orbital theory of Pleistocene climate: support from a revised chronology of the marine W^{18}0 record. 269–305 in *Milankovitch and climate, Part 1.* BERGER, A L (editor). (Hingham, Massachusetts: Reidal.)

INSTITUTE OF GEOLOGICAL SCIENCES. 1982. Central Shetland. Scotland Sheet 128. Drift. 1:63 360. (Southampton: Ordnance Survey for Institute of Geological Sciences.)

ISAKSEN, D, and TONSTAD, K (editors). 1989. A revised Cretaceous and Tertiary lithostratigraphic nomenclature for the Norwegian North Sea. *Bulletin of the Norwegian Petroleum Directorate*, No. 5.

JACQUÉ, M, and THOUVENIN, J. 1975. Lower Tertiary tuffs and volcanic activity in the North Sea. 455–465 in *Petroleum and the continental shelf of North-West Europe.* WOODLAND, A W (editor). (London: Applied Science Publishers.)

JANSEN, J H, and HENSEY, A M. 1981. Interglacial and Holocene sedimentation in the northern North Sea: an example of Eemian deposits in the Tartan Field. 323–334 *in* Holocene marine sedimentation in the North Sea Basin. NIO, S -D, SCHÜTTENHELM, R T E, and WEERING, TJ C E VAN (editors). *Special Publication of the International Association of Sedimentologists*, No. 5.

JARVIS, G T, and MCKENZIE, D P. 1980. Sedimentary basin formation with finite extension rates. *Earth and Planetary Science Letters*, Vol. 48, 42–52.

JOHNS, C R, and ANDREWS, I J. 1985. The petroleum geology of the Unst Basin, North Sea. *Marine and Petroleum Geology*, Vol. 2, 361–372.

JOHNSON, H D, and STEWART, D J. 1985. Role of clastic sedimentology in the exploration and production of oil and gas in the North Sea. 249–310 *in* Sedimentology: recent developments and applied aspects. BRENCHLEY, P J, and WILLIAMS, B P J (editors). *Special Publication of the Geological Society of London*, No. 18.

JOHNSON, M R W. 1983. Dalradian. 77–104 in *Geology of Scotland* (2nd edition). CRAIG, G Y (editor). (Edinburgh: Scottish Academic Press.)

JOHNSON, R J. 1975. The base of the Cretaceous: a discussion. 389–402 in *Petroleum and the continental shelf of North-West Europe.* WOODLAND, A W (editor). (London: Applied Science Publishers.)

— and DINGWALL, R G. 1981. The Caledonides: their influence on the stratigraphy of the Northwest European continental shelf. 85–97 in *Petroleum geology of the continental shelf of North-West Europe.* ILLING, L V, and HOBSON, G D (editors). (London: Heyden and Son.)

JOHNSON, T C, and ELKINS, S R. 1979. Holocene deposits of the Northern North Sea: evidence for dynamic control of their mineral and chemical composition. *Geologie en Mijnbouw*, Vol. 58, 353–366.

JOHNSTONE, G S, and MYKURA, W. 1989. *British regional geology: the northern Highlands of Scotland.* (London: HMSO for British Geological Survey.)

KENNEDY, W J. 1980. Aspects of chalk sedimentation in the southern Norwegian offshore. 1–29 in *The sedimentation of the North Sea reservoir rocks.* (Geilo: Norwegian Petroleum Society.)

— 1987. Sedimentology of Late Cretaceous–Palaeocene chalk reservoirs, North Sea Central Graben. 469–481 in *Petroleum geology of North West Europe.* BROOKS, J, and GLENNIE, K W (editors). (London: Applied Science Publishers.)

KENT, P E. 1975. The tectonic development of Great Britain and the surrounding seas. 3–28 in *Petroleum and the continental shelf of North-West Europe.* WOODLAND, A W (editor). (London: Applied Science Publishers.)

KENYON, N H, and STRIDE, A H. 1970. The tidal-swept continental shelf sediments between the Shetland Isles and France. *Sedimentology*, Vol. 14, 159–173.

KESSLER, L G, and MOORHOUSE, K. 1984. Depositional processes and fluid mechanics of Upper Jurassic conglomerate accumulations, British North Sea. 383–397 *in* Sedimentology of gravels and conglomerates. KOSTER, E H, and STEEL, R (editors). *Memoir of the Canadian Society of Petroleum Geologists,* No. 10.

KING, C. 1983. Cainozoic micropalaeontological biostratigraphy of the North Sea. *Report of the Institute of Geological Sciences,* No. 82/7.

KIRK, R J. 1980. Statfjord Field: a North Sea giant. 95–116 *in* Giant oil and gas fields of the decade. HALBOUTY, M T (editor). *Memoir of the American Association of Petroleum Geologists*, No. 30.

KLEMPERER, S L. 1988. Crustal thinning and the nature of extension in the northern North Sea from deep seismic reflection profiling. *Tectonics*, Vol. 7, 803–821.

— and HURICH, C A. 1990. Lithospheric structure of the North Sea from deep seismic reflection profiling. 37–63 in *Evolution of the North Sea Rifts.* BLUNDELL, D J, and GIBBS, A D (editors). (Oxford: Oxford University Press.)

— and WHITE, N. 1989. Coaxial stretching or lithosperic simple shear in the North Sea? Evidence from deep seismic profiling and subsidence. 511–522 *in* Extensional tectonics and stratigraphy of the North Atlantic margins. TANKARD, A J, and BALKWILL, H R (editors). *Memoir of the American Association of Petroleum Geologists*, No. 46.

KNELLER, B C, and AFTALION, M. 1987. Isotopic and structural age of the Aberdeen Granite. *Journal of the Geological Society of London,* Vol. 144, 717–721.

KNOX, R W O'B, and MORTON, A C, 1983. Stratigraphical distribution of early Palaeocene pyroclastic deposits in the North Sea Basin. *Proceedings of the Yorkshire Geological Society*, Vol. 44, 355–363.

— — 1988. The record of early Tertiary North Atlantic volcanism in sediments of the North Sea Basin. 407–420 *in* Early Tertiary volcanism and the opening of the NE Atlantic. MORTON, A C, and PARSON, L M (editors). *Special Publication of the Geological Society of London*, No. 39.

— — and HARLAND, R. 1981. Stratigraphical relationships of Palaeocene sands in the UK sector of the central North Sea. 267–281 in *Petroleum geology of the continental shelf of North-West Europe.* ILLING, L V, and HOBSON, G D (editors). (London: Heyden and Son.)

— — NIELSEN, O B, and KING, C. 1988. The North Sea, central Viking Graben (Beryl–Frigg area, including Norwegian territories). 18–21 *in* The Northwest European Tertiary Basin. VINKEN, R (compiler). *Geologisches Jahrbuch*, Vol. 100A.

KOCKEL, F. 1988. The palaeogeographic maps. 423–427 *in* The Northwest European Tertiary Basin. VINKEN, R (compiler). *Geologisches Jahrbuch,* Vol. 100A.

LARSEN, V, and JAARVIK, L J. 1981. The geology of the Sleipner Field complex. 15/1-31 in *Norwegian symposium on exploration.* (Geilo: Norwegian Petroleum Society.)

LATIN, D M, DIXON, J E, and FITTON, J G. 1990. Rift-related magmatism in the North Sea Basin. 101–144 in *Evolution of the North Sea Rifts.* BLUNDELL, D J, and GIBBS, A D (editors). (Oxford: Oxford University Press.)

LEE, A J. 1980. North Sea: physical oceanography. 467–493 in *The North-West European shelf seas: the sea bed and sea in motion — II. Physical and chemical oceanography, and physical resources.* BANNER, F T, COLLINS, M B, and MASSIE, K S (editors). (Amsterdam: Elsevier.)

LEEDER, M R. 1983. Lithospheric stretching and North Sea Jurassic clastic sourcelands. *Nature, London,* Vol. 305, 510–514.

— BOLDY, S R, RAISWELL, R, and CAMERON, R. 1990. The Carboniferous of the Outer Moray Firth Basin, quadrants 14 and 15, central North Sea. *Marine and Petroleum Geology*, Vol. 7, 29–37.

LEHMAN, S J, and five others. 1991. Initiation of Fennoscandian ice-sheet retreat during the last glaciation. *Nature, London,* Vol. 349, 513–516.

LERVIK, K S, SPENCER, A M, and WARRINGTON, G, 1989. Outline of Triassic stratigraphy and structure in the central and northern North Sea. 173–189 in *Correlation in hydrocarbon exploration.* COLLINSON, J D (editor). (London: Graham and Trotman.)

LEVI, S, and five others. 1990. Late Pleistocene geomagnetic excursion in Icelandic lavas: confirmation of the Laschamp excursion. *Earth and Planetary Science Letters,* Vol. 96, 443–457.

LILLENG, T. 1980. Lower Tertiary (Danian–lower Eocene) reservoir sand developments between 59°30'N and 61°30'N of the northern North Sea. 1–22 in *Sedimentation of North Sea reservoir rocks.* (Oslo: Norwegian Petroleum Society.)

LIVERA, S E. 1989. Facies associations and sand body geometries in the Ness Formation of the Brent Group, Brent Field. 269–286 *in* Deltas: sites and traps for fossil fuels. WHATELEY, M K G and PICKERING, K J, (editors). *Special Publication of the Geological Society of London,* No. 41.

LØFALDI, M. 1973. Foraminferal biostratigraphy of late Quaternary deposits from the Frigg Field and Booster Station. Rate of sedimentation and depositional environment. *NTNF's Kontinentalsokkelkontor Publication,* No. 18, 1–82.

LØKEN, T. 1976. Geology of superficial sediments in the northern North Sea. 501–514 *in* Proceedings of the Behaviour of Offshore Structures Conference (BOSS '76), Trondheim. *The Norwegian Institute of Technology,* Vol. 1, 501–514.

LONG, D. 1992. Late glacial gas escape in the central North Sea. *Journal of Continental Shelf Research,* Vol. 12. 1097–1110.

— and five others. 1986a. Late Quaternary palaeontology, sedimentology and geochemistry of a vibrocore from the Witch Ground Basin, central North Sea. *Marine Geology,* Vol. 73, 109–123.

— and SKINNER, A C. 1985. Glacial meltwater channels in the northern isles of Shetland: a comment. *Scottish Journal of Geology,* Vol. 21, 222–224.

— WICKHAM-JONES, C R, and RUCKLEY, N A. 1986b. A flint artifact from the northern North Sea. 55–62 *in* Studies in the Upper Palaeolithic of Britain and Northwest Europe. ROE, D A (editor). *British Archaeological Reports, International Series,* Vol. 296.

LORD, A R. 1980. Interpretation of the Lateglacial marine environment of NW Europe by means of foraminiferida. 103–114 in *Studies in the Lateglacial of North-West Europe.* LOWE, J J, GRAY, J M, and ROBINSON, R E (editors). (Oxford: Pergamon Press.)

LOTT, G K, THOMAS, J E, RIDING, J B, DAVEY, R J, and BUTLER, N. 1989. Late Ryazanian black shales in the southern North Sea Basin and their lithostratigraphical significance. *Proceedings of the Yorkshire Geological Society,* Vol. 47, 321–324.

MARSDEN, G, YIELDING, G, ROBERTS, A M, and KUSZNIR, N J. 1990. Application of a flexural cantilever simple-shear/pure-shear model of continental lithosphere extension to the formation of the northern North Sea Basin. 240–261 in *Evolution of the North Sea Rifts.* BLUNDELL, D J, and GIBBS, A D (editors). (Oxford: Oxford University Press.)

MARSHALL, J E A. 1988. Devonian miospores from Papa Stour, Shetland. *Transactions of the Royal Society of Edinburgh: Earth Sciences,* Vol. 13–18.

— 1991. Palynology of the Stonehaven Group, Scotland: evidence for a Mid Silurian age and its geological implication. *Geological Magazine,* Vol. 128, 283–286.

MATHER, A S, and SMITH, J S. 1974. *Beaches of Shetland.* (Aberdeen: University of Aberdeen.)

MAY, F, and PHEMISTER, J. 1968. Kaolin deposits in the Shetland Islands, UK. *Report of the XXIII International Geological Congress, Prague,* Vol. 14, 23–29.

McGEARY, S. 1987. Nontypical BIRPS on the margin of the northern North Sea: the SHET survey. *Geophysical Journal of the Royal Astronomical Society,* Vol. 89, 231–238.

— CHEADLE, M J, WARNER, M R, and BLUNDELL, D J. 1987. Crustal structure of the continental shelf around Britain derived from BIRPS deep seismic profiling. 33–44 in *Petroleum geology of North West Europe.* BROOKS, J, and GLENNIE, K W (editors). (London: Graham and Trotman.)

McGOVNEY, J E, and RADOVICH, B J. 1985. Seismic stratigraphy and facies of the Frigg fan complex. *Memoir of the American Association of Petroleum Geologists,* No. 39, 139–154.

McKENZIE, D P. 1978. Some remarks on the development of sedimentary basins. *Earth and Planetary Science Letters,* Vol. 40, 25–32.

McQUILLIN, R, DONATO, J A, and TULSTRUPP, J. 1982. Development of basins in the Inner Moray Firth and the North Sea by crustal extension and dextral displacement of the Great Glen Fault. *Earth and Planetary Science Letters,* Vol. 60, 127–139.

MELVIN, J. 1985. Walls Formation, Western Shetland: distal alluvial plain deposits within a tectonically active Devonian basin. *Scottish Journal of Geology,* Vol. 21, 23–40.

MILLING, M E. 1975. Geological appraisal of foundation conditions, northern North Sea. *Proceedings of Oceanology International, Brighton, 1975,* 310–319.

MILTON, N J, BERTRAM, G T, and VANN, I R. 1990. Early Palaeogene tectonics and sedimentation in the central North Sea. 339–351 *in* Tectonic events responsible for Britain's oil and gas reserves. HARDMAN, R F P, and BROOKS, J (editors). *Special Publication of the Geological Society of London,* No. 55.

MORTON, A C. 1982. Lower Tertiary sand development in the Viking Graben, North Sea. *Bulletin of the American Association of Petroleum Geologists,* Vol. 66, 1542–1559.

— 1983. Lower Tertiary sand development in the Viking Graben, North Sea: reply. *Bulletin of the American Association of Petroleum Geologists,* Vol. 67, 2151.

— 1985. A new approach to provenance studies: electron microprobe analysis of detrital garnets from Middle Jurassic sandstones of the northern North Sea. *Sedimentology,* Vol. 32, 553–566.

— and HUMPHREYS, B. 1983. The petrology of the Middle Jurassic sandstones from the Murchison Field, North Sea. *Journal of Petroleum Geology,* Vol. 5, 245–260.

MORTON, W H, and BLACK, R. 1975. Crustal attenuation in Afar. 55–65 *in* Afar Depression of Ethiopia. PILGER, A, and ROSLER, A (editors). *Report of the Inter-Union Commission on Geodynamics Scientific Report,* No. 14. (Stuttgart: Schweizerbart'sche Verlagsbuchlandlung.)

MUDGE, D C, and BLISS, G M. 1983. Stratigraphy and sedimentation of the Palaeocene sands in the northern North Sea. 95–111 *in* Petroleum geochemistry and exploration of Europe. BROOKS, J (editor). *Special Publication of the Geological Society of London,* No. 12.

— and COPESTAKE, P. 1992. A revised Lower Palaeogene lithostratigraphy for the Outer Moray Firth, North Sea. *Marine and Petroleum Geology,* Vol. 9, 53–69.

MURE, E. 1987a. Heimdal. 229–234 in *Geology of the Norwegian oil and gas fields.* SPENCER, A M, and others (editors). (London: Graham and Trotman.)

— 1987b. Frigg. 203–213 in *Geology of the Norwegian oil and gas fields.* SPENCER, A M, and others (editors). (London: Graham and Trotman.)

— 1987c. Øst Frigg-Alpha and Beta. 215–222 in *Geology of the Norwegian oil and gas fields.* SPENCER, A M, and others (editors). (London: Graham and Trotman.)

— 1987d. Nord-øst Frigg. 223–228 in *Geology of the Norwegian oil and gas fields.* SPENCER, A M, and others (editors). (London: Graham and Trotman.)

MYKURA, W. 1975. Possible large-scale sinistral displacement along the Great Glen Fault in Scotland. *Geological Magazine,* Vol. 112, 91–94.

— 1976. *British regional geology: Orkney and Shetland.* (Edinburgh: HMSO for Institute of Geological Sciences.)

– 1983. Old Red Sandstone. 205–251 in *Geology of Scotland* (2nd edition). CRAIG, G Y (editor). (Edinburgh: Scottish Academic Press.)

— and PHEMISTER, J. 1976. The geology of western Shetland. *Memoir of the Geological Survey of Great Britain.*

NELSON, P H H, and LAMY, J-M. 1987. The Møre/West Shetlands area: a review. 775–784 in *Petroleum geology of North West Europe.* BROOKS, J, and GLENNIE, K W (editors). (London: Graham and Trotman.)

NESJE, A, and SEJRUP, H P. 1988. Late Weichselian/Devensian ice sheets in the North Sea and adjacent land areas. *Boreas*, Vol. 17, 371–384.

NEWTON, R B. 1916. On a fossiliferous limestone from the North Sea. *Quarterly Journal of the Geological Society of London*, Vol. 72, 7–22.

NIELSEN, B O, SØRENSEN, S, THIEDE, J, and SKARB, O. 1986. Cenozoic differential subsidence of the North Sea. *Bulletin of the American Association of Petroleum Geologists*, Vol. 70, 276–298.

NORDGARD BOLAS, H M. 1987. Odin. 235–242 in *Geology of the Norwegian oil and gas fields.* SPENCER, A M, and others (editors). (London: Graham and Trotman.)

NORTON, M G, McCLAY, K R, and WAY, N A. 1987. Tectonic evolution of Devonian basins in northern Scotland and southern Norway. *Norsk Geofisk Tidsskrift*, Vol. 67, 323–338.

NYBAKKEN, S, and BÄCKSTRØM, S A. 1989. Shetland Group: stratigraphic subdivision and regional correlation in the Norwegian North Sea. 253–269 in *Correlation in hydrocarbon exploration.* COLLINSON, J D (editor). (London: Graham and Trotman.)

ORMAASEN, O E, HAMAR, G P, JAKOBSSON, K H, and SKARPNES, O. 1980. Permo-Triassic correlations in the North Sea north of the Central Highs. 1–15 in *The sedimentation of the North Sea reservoir rocks.* (Geilo: Norwegian Petroleum Society.)

OSTVEDT, O J. 1987. Sleipnerøst. 243–252 in *Geology of the Norwegian oil and gas fields.* SPENCER, A M, and others (editors). (London: Graham and Trotman.)

OWENS, R. 1981. Holocene sedimentation in the north-western North Sea. 303–322 in *Holocene marine sedimentation in the North Sea Basin.* NIO, S -D, SCHÜTTENHELM, R T E, and WEERING, TJ C E VAN (editors). *Special Publication of the International Association of Sedimentologists*, Vol. 5.

PAGE, N R. 1972. On the age of the Hoxnian interglacial. *Geological Journal*, Vol. 8, 129–142.

PANTIN, H M. 1991. The sea-bed sediments around the United Kingdom: their bathymetric and physical environment, grain size, mineral composition and associated bedforms. *British Geological Survey Research Report*, SB/90/1.

PARKER, J R. 1975. Lower Tertiary sand development in the central North Sea. 447–453 in *Petroleum and the continental shelf of North-West Europe.* WOODLAND, A W (editor). (London: Applied Science Publishers.)

PARNELL, J. 1988. Significance of lacustrine cherts for the environment of source rock deposition in the Orcadian Basin, Scotland. 205–217 in *Lacustrine petroleum source rocks.* FLEET, A J, KELTS, K, and TALBOT, M R (editors). *Special Publication of the Geological Society of London*, No. 40.

PARRY, C C, WHITLEY, P K J, and SIMPSON, R D H. 1981. Intergration of palynological and sedimentological methods in facies analysis of the Brent Formation. 205–215 in *Petroleum geology of the continental shelf of North-West Europe.* ILLING, L V, and HOBSON, G D (editors). (London: Heyden and Son.)

PARSLEY, A J. 1990. North Sea hydrocarbon plays. 362–388 in *Introduction to the petroleum geology of the North Sea* (3rd edition). GLENNIE, K W (editor). (Oxford: Blackwell Scientific Publications.)

PATERSON, I B, and HALL, I H S. 1986. Lithostratigraphy of the Late Devonian and Early Carboniferous rocks in the Midland Valley of Scotland. *Report of the British Geological Survey*, Vol. 18, No. 3.

PEACH, B N, and HORNE, J 1879.. The glaciation of the Shetland Isles. *Quarterly Journal of the Geological Society of London*, Vol. 35, 778–811.

PEGRUM, R M, and LJONES, T E. 1984. 15/9 Gamma Field offshore Norway, new trap type for the North Sea Basin with regional structural implications. *Bulletin of the American Association of Petroleum Geologists*, Vol. 68, 874–902.

— and SPENCER, A M. 1990. Hydrocarbon plays in the northern North Sea. 441–470 in Classic petroleum provinces. BROOKS, J (editor). *Special Publication of the Geological Society of London*, No. 50.

PERCH-NIELSEN, K, ULLEBERG, K, and EVENSEN, J A. 1979. Comments on 'The terminal Cretaceous event: a geological problem with an oceanic solution' (Gartner and Keary, 1978). 106–111 in *Proceedings of the Cretaceous–Tertiary boundary symposium, Copenhagen, 1979.* (Copenhagen: University of Copenhagen.)

PIASECKI, M A J, and VAN BREEMAN, O. 1983. Field and isotopic evidence for a c. 750 Ma tectonothermal event in Moine rocks in the Central Highland region of the Scottish Caledonides. *Transactions of the Royal Society of Edinburgh: Earth Sciences,* Vol. 73, 119–134.

RANAWEERA, H K A. 1987. Sleipner Vest. 253–264 in *Geology of the Norwegian oil and gas fields.* SPENCER, A M, and others (editors). (London: Graham and Trotman.)

RATHBONE, P A, and HARRIS, A L. 1980. Moine and Lewisian near the Great Glen Fault in Easter Ross. *Scottish Journal of Geology*, Vol. 16, 51–64.

RAWSON, P F, and RILEY, L A. 1982. Latest Jurassic–Early Cretaceous events and the 'Late Cimmerian Unconformity' in the North Sea area. *Bulletin of the American Association of Petroleum Geologists*, Vol. 66, 2628–2648.

READ, W A, 1987. The interplay of sedimentation, volcanicity and tectonics in the Passage Group (Arnsbergian E2 to Westphalian A) in the Midland Valley of Scotland. 143–152 in The role of tectonics in Devonian and Carboniferous sedimentation in the British Isles. ARTHURTON, R S, GUTTERIDGE, P, and NOLAN, S C (editors). *Occasional Publication of the Yorkshire Geological Society*, No. 6.

REID, P C, TAYLOR, A H, and STEPHENS, J A. 1988. The hydrography and hydrographic balances of the North Sea. 3–19 in *Pollution of the North Sea, an assessment.* SOLOMONS, W, BAYNE, B L, DUURSMA, E K, and FORSTNER, U (editors). (Berlin: Springer-Verlag.)

RICHARDS, P C. 1989. Lower and Middle Jurassic sedimentology of the Beryl Embayment, and implications for the evolution of the northern North Sea. Unpublished PhD thesis, University of Strathclyde.

— 1990a. Devonian. 78–89 in *Introduction to the petroleum geology of the North Sea* (3rd edition). GLENNIE, K W (editor). (Oxford: Blackwell Scientific Publications.)

— 1990b. The Early to Mid-Jurassic evolution of the northern North Sea. 191–205 in Tectonic events responsible for Britain's oil and gas reserves. HARDMAN, R F P, and BROOKS, J (editors). *Special Publication of the Geological Society of London*, No. 55.

— 1991a. Evolution of Lower Jurassic coastal plain and fan delta sediments in the Beryl Embayment, North Sea. *Journal of the Geological Society of London*, Vol. 148, 1037–1047.

— 1991b. An estuarine facies model for the Middle Jurassic Sleipner Formation: Beryl Embayment, North Sea. *Journal of the Geological Society of London*, Vol. 48, 459–471.

— and BROWN, S S. 1986. Shoreface storm deposits in the Rannoch Formation (Middle Jurassic), North West Hutton Oilfield. *Scottish Journal of Geology*, Vol. 22, 367–375.

— — DEAN, J M, and ANDERTON, R. 1988. A new palaeogeographic reconstruction for the Middle Jurassic of the northern North Sea. *Journal of the Geological Society of London*, Vol. 145, 883–886.

— — — — 1990. A new palaeogeographic reconstruction for the Middle Jurassic of the northern North Sea: reply to discussion. *Journal of the Geological Society of London*, Vol. 147, 1085–1090.

RILEY, L A, ROBERTS, M J, and CONNELL, E R. 1989. The application of palynology in the interpretation of Brae Formation stratigraphy and reservoir geology in the South Brae Field area, British North Sea. 339–356 in *Correlation in hydrocarbon exploration.* COLLINSON, J D (editor). (London: Graham and Trotman.)

RISE, L, and ROKOENGEN, K. 1984. Superficial sediments in the Norwegian sector of the North Sea between 60°30' and 62°N. *Marine Geology*, Vol. 58, 287–317.

— — SKINNER, A C, and LONG, D. 1984. *Nordlige Nordsjø. Kvartaergeologisk kart mellom 60°30''og 62°N, og øst for 1°'* (Northern North Sea. Quaternary geology map between 60°30' and 62°N, and east of 1°E). 1:500 000. (Trondheim: Institutt for kontinentalsokkelundersøkelser (IKU), Norway.)

RITCHIE, J D, HITCHEN, K, and MITCHELL, J G. 1987. The offshore continuation of the Moine Thrust north of Shetland as deduced from basement isotopic ages. *Scottish Journal of Geology*, Vol. 23, 163–173.

— SWALLOW, J L, MITCHELL, J G, and MORTON, A C. 1988. Jurassic ages from intrusives and extrusives within the Forties Igneous Province. *Scottish Journal of Geology*, Vol. 24, 81–88.

ROBERTS, A M, YIELDING, G, and BADLEY, M E. 1990. A kinematic model for the orthogonal opening of the late Jurassic North Sea rift system, Denmark–Mid Norway. 180–199 in *Evolution of the North Sea Rifts.* BLUNDELL, D J, and GIBBS, A D (editors). (Oxford: Oxford University Press.)

ROCHOW, K A, 1981. Seismic stratigraphy of the North Sea 'Palaeocene' deposits. 255–266 in *Petroleum geology of the continental shelf of North-West Europe.* ILLING, L V, and HOBSON, G D (editors). (London: Heyden and Son.)

RØE, S-L, and STEEL, R J. 1985. Sedimentation, sea-level rise and tectonics at the Triassic–Jurassic boundary (Statfjord Formation), Tampen Spur, northern North Sea. *Journal of Petroleum Geology*, Vol. 8, 163–186.

ROGERS, D A, MARSHALL, J E A, and ASTIN, T R. 1989. Devonian and later movements on the Great Glen Fault system, Scotland. *Journal of the Geological Society of London*, Vol. 146, 369–372.

— and ASTIN, T R. 1991. Stratigraphy and rhythmicity in lacustrine deposits. 199–221 in Lacustrine facies analysis. ANADON, P, CABRERA, L I, and KELTS, K (editors). *Special Publication of the International Association of Sedimentologists*, No. 13.

ROGERS, G, DEMPSTER, T J, BLUCK, B J, and TANNER, P W G. 1989. A high precision U-Pb age for the Ben Vuirich granite: implications for the evolution of the Scottish Dalradian Supergroup. *Journal of the Geological Society of London*, Vol. 146, 789–798.

ROKOENGEN, K, LØFALDI, M, RISE, L, LØKEN, T, and CARLSEN, R. 1982. Description and dating of a submerged beach in the northern North Sea. *Marine Geology*, Vol. 50, M21–M28.

— and RØNNINGSLAND, T M. 1983. Shallow bedrock geology and Quaternary thickness in the Norwegian sector of the North Sea between 60°30'N and 62°N. *Norsk Geologisk Tidsskrift*, Vol. 63, 83–102.

RØNNING, K, JOHNSTON, C D, JOHNSTAD, S E, and SONGSTAD, P. 1986. Geology of the Hild Field. 199–206 in *Habitat of hydrocarbons on the Norwegian continental shelf.* SPENCER, A M, and others (editors). (London: Graham and Trotman.)

– 1987. Hild. 287–294 in *Geology of the Norwegian oil and gas fields.* SPENCER, A M, and others (editors). (London: Graham and Trotman.)

— and STEEL, R J. 1987. Depositional sequences within a 'transgressive' reservoir sandstone unit: the Middle Jurassic Tarbert Formation, Hild area, northern North Sea. 169–176 in *North Sea oil and gas reservoirs.* (London: Graham and Trotman.)

ROWLEY, D B, and SAHAGIAN, D. 1986. Depth-dependent stretching: a different approach. *Geology*, Vol. 14, 32–35.

RYSETH, A. 1989. Correlation of depositional patterns in the Ness Formation, Oseberg area. 313–326 in *Correlation in hydrocarbon exploration.* COLLINSON, J D (editor). (London: Graham and Trotman.)

SABINE, P A. 1970. A bowl-like object of aragonite-limestone from Shetland waters. *Proceedings of the Geologists' Association*, Vol. 81, 539–548.

SARG, J F, and SKJOLD, L J. 1981. Stratigraphic traps in Paleocene sands in the Balder area, North Sea. *Memoir of the American Association of Petroleum Geologists*, No. 32, 197–206.

SEJRUP, H P, and nine others. 1987. Quaternary stratigraphy of the Fladen area, central North Sea: a multidisciplinary study. *Journal of Quaternary Science*, Vol. 2, 35–58.

— NAGY, J, and BRIGHAM-GRETTE, J. 1989. Foraminiferal stratigraphy and amino acid geochronology of Quaternary sediments in the Norwegian Channel, northern North Sea. *Norsk Geologisk Tidsskrift*, Vol 69, 111–124.

SEMPLE, R M, and RIGDEN, W J. 1983. Site investigation for Magnus. *Proceedings of the Fifteenth Offshore Technology Conference, Houston*, Vol. 1, 205–216.

SHACKLETON, N J, and OPDYKE, N D. 1976. Oxygen isotope and palaeomagnetic stratigraphy of Pacific core 228–239, Late Pliocene to Late Holocene. *Geological Society of America Memoirs*, Vol. 145, 449–464.

SKARPNES, O, HAMAR, G P, JAKOBSON, K H, and ORMAASEN, D E. 1980. Regional Jurassic setting of the North Sea north of the central highs. 13/1-8 in *The sedimentation of the North Sea reservoir rocks.* (Geilo: Norwegian Petroleum Society.)

SKINNER, A C, and GREGORY, D M. 1983. Quaternary stratigraphy in the northern North Sea. *Boreas*, Vol. 12, 145–152.

SOLLI, M. 1976. En seismisk skorpeundersokelse Norge–Shetland. Unpublished PhD thesis, University of Bergen. [In Norwegian.]

SPEKSNIJDER, A. 1987. The structural configuration of Cormorant Block IV in context of the northern Viking Graben structural framework. *Geologie en Mijnbouw*, Vol. 65, 357–379.

STEEL, R, and RYSETH, A. 1990. The Triassic–Early Jurassic succession in the northern North Sea: megasequence stratigraphy and intra-Triassic tectonics. 139–168 *in* Tectonic events responsible for Britain's oil and gas reserves. HARDMAN, R F P, and BROOKS, J (editors). *Special Publication of the Geological Society of London* , No. 55.

STEWART, D J. 1988. The history of oil exploration in the northern North Sea. *Geology Today*, Vol. 4 , 130–137.

STEWART, I J. 1987. A revised stratigraphic interpretation of the Early Palaeogene of the central North Sea. 557–576 in *Petroleum geology of North West Europe.* BROOKS, J, and GLENNIE, K W (editors). (London: Graham and Trotman.)

STOKER, M S, SKINNER, A C, FYFE, J A, and LONG, D. 1983. Palaeomagnetic evidence for early Pleistocene in the central and northern North Sea. *Nature, London,* Vol. 304, 332–334.

— and LONG, D. 1984. A relict ice-scoured erosion surface in the central North Sea. *Marine Geology*, Vol. 61, 85–93.

STOKER, S J, and BROWN, S S. 1986. Coarse clastic sediments of the Brae Field and adjacent areas, North Sea: a core workshop. *British Geological Survey Marine Report*, No. 86/8.

STOW, D A V. 1984a. Sedimentology of the Brae Oilfield area: a reply. *Journal of Petroleum Geology*, Vol. 6, 103–104.

– 1984b. Upper Jurassic overlapping-fans slope-apron system: Brae Oilfield, North Sea. *Geo-Marine Letters*, Vol. 3, 217–222.

— and ATKIN, B. 1987. Sediment facies and geochemistry of Upper Jurassic mudrocks in the central North Sea area. 797–808 in *Petroleum geology of North West Europe.* BROOKS, J, and GLENNIE, K W (editors). (London: Graham and Trotman.)

SUESS, E. 1906. *Face of the Earth (Das Antlitz der Erde).* Translated by SOLLAS, H B C. (Oxford: Clarendon Press.)

SWALLOW, J L. 1986. The seismic expression of a low angle detachment (sole fault) from the Beryl Embayment, Central Viking Graben. *Scottish Journal of Geology*, Vol. 22, 315–324.

TARLING, D H. 1985. Palaeomagnetic studies of the Orcadian Basin. *Scottish Journal of Geology*, Vol. 21, 261–273.

TAYLOR, J C M. 1990. Upper Permian–Zechstein. 130–190 in *Introduction to the petroleum geology of the North Sea* (3rd edition). GLENNIE, K W (editor). (Oxford: Blackwell Scientific Publications.)

THIRLWALL, M F. 1989. Movement on proposed terrane boundaries in northern Britain: constraints from Ordovician–Devonian igneous rocks. *Journal of the Geological Society of London*, Vol. 146, 373–376.

THORNE, J A, and WATTS, A B. 1989. Quantitative analysis of North Sea subsidence *Bulletin of the American Association of Petroleum Geologists*, Vol. 73, 88–116.

THRELFALL, W F. 1981. Structural framework of the central and northern North Sea. 98–103 in *Petroleum geology of the continental shelf of North- West Europe*. ILLING, L V, and HOBSON, G D (editors). (London: Heyden and Son.)

TURNER, C C, COHEN, J M, CONNELL, E R, and COOPER, D M. 1987. A depositional model for the South Brae Oilfield. 853–864 in *Petroleum geology of North West Europe*. BROOKS, J, and GLENNIE, K W (editors). (London: Graham and Trotman.)

TURNER, P, TARLING, D H, ARCHER, R, and DONOVAN, R N, 1976. A palaeomagnetic argument concerning post-Devonian displacement along the Great Glen Fault. *Geological Magazine*, Vol. 113, 365–370.

TYLOR, A. 1869. On the formation of deltas; and on the evidence and cause of great changes in sea level during the glacial period. *Quarterly Journal of the Geological Society of London*, Vol. 25, 7–12.

TYSON, V, WILSON, R C L, and DOWNIE, C. 1979. A stratified water column environmental model for the type Kimmeridge Clay. *Nature, London,* Vol. 277, 377–380.

VAIL, P R, and TODD, R G. 1981. Northern North Sea Jurassic unconformities, chronostratigraphy and sea-level changes from seismic stratigraphy. 216–235 in *Petroleum geology of the continental shelf of North-West Europe*. ILLING, L V, and HOBSON, G D (editors). (London: Heyden and Son.)

VOLLSET, J, and DORÉ, A G (editors). 1984. A revised Triassic and Jurassic lithostratigraphic nomenclature for the Norwegian North Sea. *Bulletin of the Norwegian Petroleum Directorate*, No. 3.

WATSON, J. 1985. Northern Scotland as an Atlantic–North Sea divide. *Journal of the Geological Society of London*, Vol. 142, 221–243.

WERNICKE, B. 1981. Low-angle normal faults in the Basin and Range Province: tectonics in an extending orogen. *Nature, London*, Vol. 291, 645–648.

WHEATLEY, T J, BIGGINS, D, BUCKINGHAM, J, and HOLLOWAY, N H. 1987. The geology and exploration of the Transitional Shelf, an area to the west of the Viking Graben. 979–989 in *Petroleum geology of North West Europe*. BROOKS, J, and GLENNIE, K W (editors). (London: Graham and Trotman.)

WHITE, N. 1990. Does the uniform stretching model work in the North Sea? 217–239 in *Evolution of the North Sea Rifts*. BLUNDELL, D J, and GIBBS, A D (editors). (Oxford: Oxford University Press.)

WHITEMAN, A J, REES, G, NAYLOR, D, and PEGRUM, R M. 1975. North Sea troughs and plate tectonics. 137–162 *in* Petroleum

geology and geology of the North Sea and NE Atlantic continental margin. WHITEMAN, A J, ROBERTS, D, and SELLEVOLL, M A (editors). *Norges Geologiske Undersokelse*, Vol. 316.

WILLIAMS, J. 1983. Lower Tertiary sand development in Viking Graben, North Sea: Discussion. *Bulletin of the American Association of Petroleum Geologists*, Vol. 67, 2150.

WOODHALL, D, and KNOX, R W O'B. 1979. Mesozoic volcanism in the northern North Sea and adjacent areas. *Bulletin of the Geological Survey of Great Britain*, No. 70, 34–56.

WOOLLAM, R, and RIDING, J B. 1983. Dinoflagellate cyst zonation of the English Jurassic. *Report of the Institute of Geological Sciences*, No. 83/2.

YIELDING, G, BADLEY, M E, and ROBERTS, A M. 1992. The structural evolution of the Brent Province. *In* Geology of the Brent Group. MORTON, A C, HASZELDINE, R S, GILES, M R, and BROWN, S (editors). *Special Publication of the Geological Society of London,* No. 61.

YOUNG, A C, SULLIVAN, R A, and RYBICKI, C A. 1978. Pile design and installation features of the Thistle Platform. *Proceedings of European Offshore Petroleum Conference and Exhibition, London, October 1978.* 101–110.

ZERVOS, F. 1987. A compilation and regional interpretation of the northern North Sea gravity map. 477–493 *in* Continental extensional tectonics. COWARD, M P, DEWEY, J F, and HANCOCK, P L (editors). *Special Publication of the Geological Society of London,* No. 28.

ZIEGLER, P A. 1975. North Sea basin history in the tectonic framework of North-western Europe. 131–149 in *Petroleum and the continental shelf of North-West Europe*. WOODLAND, A W (editor). (London: Applied Science Publishers.)

— 1978. North-western Europe: tectonics and basin development. *Geologie en Mijnbouw*, Vol. 57, 509–626.

— 1982. *Geological atlas of Western and Central Europe.* (Amsterdam: Elsevier for Shell Internationale Petroleum, Maatschappij BV.)

— 1983. Crustal thinning and subsidence in the North Sea. *Nature, London,* Vol. 304, 561.

— 1988a. Evolution of the Arctic–North Atlantic and the western Tethys. *Memoir of the American Association of Petroleum Geologists*, No. 43.

— 1988b. Post-Hercynian plate reconstruction in the Tethys and Arctic–North Atlantic domains. 711–755 in *Triassic–Jurassic rifting: continental breakup and the origin of the Atlantic Ocean and passive margins, Part B*. MANSPEIZER, W (editor). (Amsterdam: Elsevier.)

— 1990. *Geological atlas of Western and Central Europe.* (Amsterdam: Drukketij VERWEIJ BV, MIJDRECHT for Shell Internationale Petroleum, Maatschappij, BV.)

— and VAN HOORN, B. 1989. Evaluation of North Sea rift system. 471–500 *in* Extensional tectonics and stratigraphy of the North Atlantic margins. TANKARD, A J, and BALKWILL, H R (editors). *Memoir of the American Association of Petroleum Geologists*, No. 46.

INDEX

BRITISH GEOLOGICAL SURVEY

Keyworth, Nottingham NG12 5GG
(0602) 363100

Murchison House, West Mains Road, Edinburgh EH9 3LA
031-667 1000

London Information Office, Natural History Museum
Earth Galleries, Exhibition Road, London SW7 2DE
071 589 4090

The full range of Survey publications is available through the
Sales Desks at Keyworth and at Murchison House,
Edinburgh, and in the BGS London Information Office in
the Natural History Museum Earth Galleries. The adjacent
bookshop stocks the more popular books for sale over the
counter. Most BGS books and reports are listed in HMSO's
Sectional List 45, and can be bought from HMSO and
through HMSO agents and retailers. Maps are listed in the
BGS Map Catalogue, and can be bought from BGS approved
stockists and agents as well as direct from BGS.

*The British Geological Survey carries out the geological survey of
Great Britain and Northern Ireland (the latter as an agency
service for the government of Northern Ireland), and of the
surrounding continental shelf, as well as its basic research
projects. It also undertakes programmes of British technical aid
in geology in developing countries as arranged by the Overseas
Development Administration.*

*The British Geological Survey is a component body of the
Natural Environment Research Council.*

HMSO publications are available from:

HMSO Publications Centre
(Mail, fax and telephone orders only)
PO Box 276, London, SW8 5DT
Telephone orders 071-873 9090
General enquiries 071-873 0011
(queuing system in operation for both numbers)
Fax orders 071-873 8200

HMSO Bookshops
49 High Holborn, London, WC1V 6HB
(counter service only)
071-873 0011 Fax 071-873 8200
258 Broad Street, Birmingham, B1 2HE
021-643 3740 Fax 021-643 6510
33 Wine Street, Bristol, BS1 2BQ
0272 264306 Fax 0272 294515
9-21 Princess Street, Manchester, M60 8AS
061-834 7201 Fax 061-833 0634
16 Arthur Street, Belfast, BT1 4GD
0232 238451 Fax 0232 235401
71 Lothian Road, Edinburgh, EH3 9AZ
031-228 4181 Fax 031-229 2734

HMSO's Accredited Agents
(see Yellow Pages)

and through good booksellers